MONOGRAPHS ON THE PHYSICS AND CHEMISTRY OF MATERIALS

General Editors

WILLIS JACKSON   H. FRÖHLICH   N. F. MOTT
E. C. BULLARD

MONOGRAPHS ON THE
PHYSICS AND CHEMISTRY OF MATERIALS

This series is intended to summarize recent results in academic or long-range research in materials and allied subjects, in a form that should be useful to physicists in universities and in Government and industrial laboratories

PHYSICAL PRINCIPLES AND APPLICATIONS OF JUNCTION TRANSISTORS

BY

J. H. SIMPSON

AND

R. S. RICHARDS

National Research Council of Canada

OXFORD
AT THE CLARENDON PRESS
1962

Oxford University Press, Amen House, London E.C.4

GLASGOW   NEW YORK   TORONTO   MELBOURNE   WELLINGTON
BOMBAY   CALCUTTA   MADRAS   KARACHI   LAHORE   DACCA
CAPE TOWN   SALISBURY   NAIROBI   IBADAN   ACCRA
KUALA LUMPUR   HONG KONG

PRINTED IN GREAT BRITAIN

PREFACE

THIS book is based on a course of lectures given to electrical engineers working towards a McGill University master's degree. It is intended for students who have a background of mathematics and physics equivalent to that obtained in an engineering course.

The principles of solid state physics which are especially applicable to the transistor are outlined in the first two chapters of the book. These chapters, which are necessarily condensed and restricted in subject-matter, are intended to give the reader sufficient knowledge to understand the main features of transistor operation. This knowledge is applied to the p-n junction in Chapter IV and to the development of equivalent circuits for the transistor in Chapters V, VI, and VII. Further applications are found in Chapters IX and X where the subjects of transistor biasing and noise are discussed. These chapters illustrate our conviction that a clear understanding of transistor properties can only be gained from a knowledge of the physics of the device. The remaining chapters (III and VIII) in this first part of the book also demonstrate the application of the physical theory to the techniques of transistor construction.

In the second part of the book typical circuit applications of the transistor are described. Many of these will seem familiar to readers who have experience in vacuum-tube circuit design but we have tried to avoid drawing on such experience directly. We have therefore introduced complete definitions of circuit types (e.g. the various classes of push-pull circuit) where necessary. However, we have not hesitated to include references to papers on vacuum-tube circuit design when these have obvious applications to transistor circuits, or to compare vacuum tubes and transistors for certain uses.

In this circuit section we have given, for a few common types of circuit, rather more detailed design information than is available in most books. The common procedure is to present the basic principles and to assume that the student will develop his own design methods from them. However, in practice, this hope is not generally realized; the student's approach often becomes one of trial and error which, because the transistor is quite a complicated device, may lead to considerable frustration. We hope that this will be avoided in the cases that we have described and that the reader will be encouraged to take a similar approach to other circuits for which the steps of a design procedure are outlined.

It should be made clear that these detailed design methods do not obviate the need for a final experimental adjustment of operating conditions. This adjustment is, however, a relatively simple matter if a design procedure based on average device properties has been used.

Another aspect of this second part that requires a brief explanation is the emphasis on the practical application of negative feedback. In the writers' opinion a working knowledge of this subject is essential even in the most elementary continuous signal transistor circuits. We have therefore tried to supply enough information for the design of feedback amplifiers and have discussed the stability problem briefly. This discussion is based on elementary principles rather than on complex variable analysis but several references to more advanced methods are given.

In the remainder of the circuit section we have tried to maintain a balance between steady-state applications and switching. The reader's opinion of the extent to which we have been successful will depend on his own viewpoint and on future trends in transistor electronics. The authors' feeling is that the present arrangement is satisfactory but that somewhat greater emphasis on switching may be desirable in a few years.

A final remark about the large number of appendixes is in order. Most of these are devoted to detailed analyses of physical processes or circuit problems which should be included for completeness but would obscure the main body of the text with too much detail. In addition, many of them are referred to at several places in the text and are more readily located if they are at the back of the book. The latter argument also applies to references which are grouped, according to chapters, immediately following the appendixes.

In preparing material for such diverse topics as noise characteristics, biasing, the properties of feedback amplifiers, high-frequency gain controls and switching circuits, the writers found that information available to them was incomplete and it was necessary to check several points experimentally. The results obtained are mentioned as we proceed.

In our discussions of transistor properties we have used device and circuit information supplied by the following manufacturers, to whom we express our thanks: Texas Instruments Inc. for permission to use the data on the 2N369 contained in Appendix XI, for Fig. 6.6, and for the circuits of Figs. 16.16 and 16.18; General Electric Company (U.S.A.) for the characteristic of the 2N167 in Fig. 7.16; Bendix Corpn. for the characteristic of the 2N235A in Fig. 8.26; Radio Corporation of America for the 2N104 noise characteristic of Fig. 10.4; and Delco Division of General Motors Corporation for the heat sink curves of Fig. 12.1. We also wish to thank the Editor of the *Physical Review* for permission to use Figs. 8.12 and 8.14.

Finally we express our special thanks to Professor Fröhlich who arranged for publication of the book and gave much helpful advice concerning the manuscript, and to A. R. Morse and Dr. J. Rolfe for reading the manuscript and making numerous suggestions leading to improvement of both form and content.

J. H. S.
R. S. R.

Radio and Electrical Engineering Division
National Research Council
Ottawa, Canada

October 1960

CONTENTS

CONTENTS

THE ELECTRICAL PROPERTIES
OF SEMICONDUCTORS

1.1. Introduction

THE field of electronics has in recent years been completely transformed by devices which depend on the control of electron flow in solids. The event that opened this era of 'solid-state electronics' was the invention of the point-contact transistor by Bardeen and Brattain in 1948 [1]. The study of this device revealed the principle of transistor action and led to the invention of the junction transistor, about a year later, by Shockley [2]. The extraordinary technological growth that has taken place since that time has established the junction transistor as a device of major engineering and economic importance. In this book we shall try to explain how the properties that have led to this development arise and shall describe circuit techniques that illustrate the usefulness and versatility of the transistor.

The existence of the transistor in its normal form depends upon one very important characteristic of the flow of electricity in solids—the fact that electronic conduction can take place in two distinctly different ways. These are usually referred to as conduction by electrons and positive holes respectively. The properties of these two types of current carrier are responsible not only for those advantages that transistors have over vacuum tubes but also for many disadvantages that plague the transistor-circuit engineer. In order to understand why these disadvantages exist, and the methods of compensating for them, and indeed, to understand why the transistor operates at all, it is essential to have a certain basic knowledge of the physics of semiconductors. It is the purpose of this chapter to summarize this knowledge as briefly as possible and to show how it is applied to semiconductors used in the manufacture of transistors.

A thorough understanding of the physics of conducting solids requires a knowledge of two important branches of modern physics, quantum mechanics and statistical mechanics. From the point of view of the construction and application of transistors, however, it is not necessary to delve deeply into these subjects, provided one is willing to accept certain results which are plausible in the light of our knowledge concerning isolated atoms and gases. For the discussion of the electronic properties of solids with which we shall be concerned, the so-called Energy-band Theory of Solids has proved very useful. This has been described with varying degrees of rigour in a large number of books and papers. We now outline the salient facts briefly.

1.2. Energy-band theory of solids

The existence of discrete energy levels corresponding to stationary states of electrons in atoms is well known. In the Bohr model of the atom, the energy of such a state is the total energy (potential plus kinetic) that an electron has when it is moving in a certain orbit about the nucleus. A series of orbits is possible, spaced at definite distances from the nucleus, and electrons can only exist between orbits during the very short time that they are jumping (with the absorption or emission of energy) from one energy state to another. Only a relatively small number of these energy states will be occupied by electrons, starting with the lowest and proceeding in the direction of increasing energy. The higher energy states will be empty except in a non-equilibrium condition when an electron is excited to a higher state by some external influence.

A series of such energy states in an isolated atom is sketched in Fig. 1.1 a. The shaded portion at the top of the figure is an energy continuum and represents the condition of ionization or complete removal of an electron from the atom since the electron may then have any of a continuous series of energies corresponding to different velocities of motion away from the atom.

When atoms are brought together to form a solid crystal the interaction between them causes the discrete energy states which exist in the isolated atoms to be broadened into bands as shown in Fig. 1.1 *b*. Each energy band contains a number of energy states of the order of the number of atoms in the crystal and only one electron can occupy each state. In a perfect crystal no energy states exist between the bands and no electrons can have energies in these regions. The widths (on the energy scale) of the bands and of the gaps between them are independent of the number of atoms and hence of crystal size. If the size is increased the density of states in each band must therefore

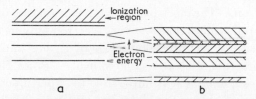

Fɪɢ. 1.1. Electron energy-levels in: (*a*) an isolated atom, (*b*) a solid. The shaded portion on the left represents an energy (ionization) continuum. Those on the right represent bands of closely spaced discrete levels.

increase in proportion. Since the number of atoms per c.c. is about 10^{23} and the width of a band is a few electron volts the states are very close together on the energy scale.

If the effect of temperature could be ignored, energy bands would be filled with electrons up to a certain level while above this they would be empty. Just as in an atom there exist empty 'excited' states above those occupied by electrons, so in solids there exist bands above the uppermost band that contains electrons. Some of these bands may overlap as shown in Fig. 1.1 *b*.

1.2.1. *Metals and insulators*

The electrical properties are decided, in most solids, by conditions in the uppermost band containing electrons and in the empty band immediately above it. If the former is partially full of electrons there are empty states immediately above the occupied levels. Application of an electric field will impart additional kinetic energy to electrons in the uppermost levels and they will then occupy states of slightly higher energy. The existence of many empty levels immediately above those normally occupied by electrons thus makes it possible for a large current to flow under the influence of the applied field. The material is then a good conductor and is, in fact, a metal.

A very different state of affairs exists if the top band containing electrons is completely full and if the energy gap between this full band and the empty band above it is large. Application of an electrical field cannot then produce a net flow of current through the material because no new energy states are available to the electrons. The electrons do have motion but the fact that the band is full implies that for every electron moving in a certain direction with a certain velocity there is one moving in the opposite direction with the same velocity. Since there are no empty states available it is impossible to superimpose a drift in the direction of an applied field and the material (in the pure state) is an insulator at ordinary temperatures. At very high temperatures, because of the thermal motion in the crystal, some of the electrons in the full band may receive sufficient energy to put them into the empty band above. They are then free to move under the influence of an applied field because there are many empty states, having energies very close to each other, in this band. Because electrons in the empty band can thus contribute to the flow of current through the crystal, this band is often called the conduction band. The lower band is called the full or valence band since the electrons in it are those that determine the chemical properties of the material, i.e. the valence electrons.

The removal of an electron from the valence band to the conduction band leaves an empty state, which will be near the top of the valence band since electrons tend to occupy the lowest possible states. This is shown schematically on the energy diagram of Fig. 1.2 *a*. A two-dimensional diagram of the bond structure of a simple insulating crystal (diamond) is shown in Fig. 1.2 *b*. Here the atomic cores (i.e. atoms minus valence electrons) are shown as shaded circles each having a charge $+4q$, where q is the magnitude of the electronic charge. Each atom contributes four valence electrons to the four bonds connected to it. These bonds are shown as electronic charge clouds, shaded by light dots, each normally having a charge of $-2q$. (These charge clouds may be considered to indicate the limits within which the electrons concerned would normally move. Electrons in adjacent charge clouds can interchange positions so that no one electron is confined to a certain atom, but such an interchange does not affect the sum of the energies of the electrons.) The empty state in the valence band of Fig. 1.2 a corresponds

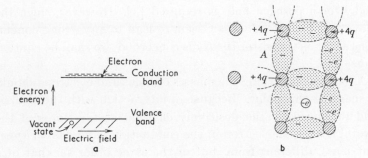

FIG. 1.2. (a) Simple energy-level diagram of a perfect insulator. (b) Two-dimensional diagram of the valence-bond structure in a perfect insulator (diamond).

to the fact that an electron is missing from bond A. The conduction-band electron is shown in Fig. 1.2 b as a free charge $(-q)$ in the lower part of the figure.

A particularly simple model for the behaviour of the empty state has been described in the literature [3]. In this model the empty state can move through the crystal because of successive jumps of valence electrons into the vacancy. When an electric field is applied, as shown in Fig. 1.2 a, the chance that an electron will jump into the vacancy from the right is greater than the chance that it will come from another direction, so that there is a drift of the vacancy to the right. It therefore behaves as if it had a positive charge. The other properties of this vacant state are such that, in discussing the electrical properties of the crystal, it may be treated as a real particle having an energy in the valence band. Since it arises because of a vacancy in the valence band this particle is called a positive hole.

The above description of the positive hole implies that electrons in a normally full band cannot move unless a vacant state exists in it. This is not strictly in accord with the energy-band theory since, as mentioned above, that theory requires that the electrons be in motion with velocities in a full band coordinated in such a way that for every electron moving in a certain direction with a certain velocity there is another moving in the opposite direction with the same velocity. When this fact is taken into account a more sophisticated development of the model for a positive hole is required [4]. However, since the above simple model does not seem to lead to any wrong conclusions as far as transistor theory is concerned, we shall be content to use it.

A remark concerning the masses of holes and electrons should be made at this point. Because of interaction with the electric field produced by the positively charged atomic cores of the crystal lattice, an electron in the conduction band has an apparent mass, different from, but of the same order as, that of a free electron, and dependent on its direction of motion. For our purpose it is sufficient to note that the mass averaged over all crystal directions, which is called the effective mass m_e, is a fraction of the mass of the free electron. An analogous though somewhat more complicated situation exists for a positive hole whose effective mass is designated m_h. Experimentally determined values of the effective masses of electrons and holes in germanium and silicon have been discussed by Kittel [4, 5].

As noted above, the minimum energy of the system shown in Fig. 1.2 a is obtained when, on an electron-energy diagram, the electron is at the bottom of the conduction band and the positive hole is at the top of the valence band. Thus, in an electron-energy diagram, the positive hole should be treated as a bubble. To push the hole downwards or the electron upwards requires the application of energy. The diagram of Fig. 1.2 a could also be inverted to give a positive-hole energy diagram. The positions of valence and conduction bands would then be reversed so that the electrons would act as bubbles and the positive holes as particles.

1.2.2. *Intrinsic semiconductors*

Another type of material is defined which differs from an insulator only in the fact that the energy gap between the valence and conduction bands is smaller. At very low temperatures a material of this type is an insulator. At a higher temperature, because the energy gap is relatively small, some electrons are excited by thermal agitation from the valence band to the conduction band and the material becomes a rather poor insulator or a rather poor conductor. It is called an intrinsic semiconductor. The word intrinsic here indicates that the material would conduct appreciably at this higher temperature even if it were absolutely pure and if its crystal structure were perfect. The term semiconductor indicates that, at the temperature considered, its resistivity lies in the large range between that of a metal ($\sim 10^{-5}$ ohm cm) and that of an insulator ($\sim 10^9$ ohm cm).† The current in an intrinsic semiconductor, as in an insulator at high temperatures, is carried by both holes and electrons. In a pure material the number of positive holes is always equal to the number of electrons and the balance between them is dynamic, that is electron-hole pairs are continuously generated by thermal agitation and, in equilibrium, an equal number of recombination processes is taking place. The rates of generation and recombination increase rapidly with temperature according to a special exponential law, and it can be readily shown that the equilibrium number of electron-hole pairs must therefore also increase in a similar manner. These matters have an important bearing on the operation of transistors and they will be considered in some detail later.

Pure germanium which has a resistivity of about 50 ohm cm at room temperature and an energy gap of about 0·75 eV (electron volts), and pure silicon which has a resistivity of about 250,000 ohm cm at room temperature and an energy gap of about 1·1 eV, are intrinsic semiconductors.

1.2.3. *Extrinsic or impurity semiconductors*

Another type of semiconductor may be obtained by adding

† The system of units used in this book and the values of important constants are discussed in Appendix I.

impurities to an insulator or intrinsic semiconductor. The impurities are of two main types—those that release electrons and those that trap electrons. At low temperatures, impurities of the first type contain loosely bound electrons (usually one per impurity atom) which are released by thermal agitation as the temperature is raised. The released electrons are in the conduction band and increase the conductivity of the crystal. This increase of conductivity is due to one type of carrier only—electrons or negative carriers—and if this type of impurity

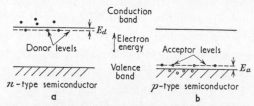

FIG. 1.3. Simple energy-level diagrams of: (a) An n-type semiconductor. (b) A p-type semiconductor.

semiconduction is predominant the material is said to be an n-type extrinsic semiconductor, or simply of n-type. The centres which supply the extra electrons are called donor impurities. Impurities of the second type contain empty states (again usually one per impurity atom) which are unoccupied at low temperatures. As the temperature is raised thermal agitation causes electrons from the valence band to occupy some of these empty states, leaving positive holes in the valence band. The material then has an additional conductivity because of the presence of positive holes and, if this type of conduction is predominant, the material is said to be a p-type semiconductor. The centres which receive electrons as the temperature is raised are called acceptor impurities.

The energy diagrams of n-type and p-type semiconductors are shown schematically in Fig. 1.3. The energy levels associated with the donor and acceptor impurities are seen to lie in the forbidden region and quite close to the conduction and valence band respectively.

For germanium and silicon the physical picture of these

impurity semiconductors is particularly simple. These materials have the same crystal structure as diamond and the effect of impurity may be described by reference to Fig. 1.4, which shows two-dimensional diagrams of the type described earlier. In Fig. 1.4 a an impurity (e.g. arsenic or antimony) having five valence electrons is inserted. Four of these five electrons are taken up in the valence-bond structure of the material but the fifth is very loosely bound. It is this electron whose energy state is just below the conduction band in Fig. 1.3 a, and it can

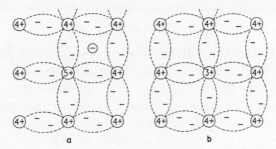

FIG. 1.4. Two-dimensional diagrams of the valence-bond structure in: (a) An n-type semiconductor. (b) A p-type semiconductor.

easily be released to wander through the crystal. In Fig. 1.4 b an impurity (e.g. gallium or indium) having three valence electrons has been inserted so that one electron of its bond structure is missing. An electron from an adjacent bond requires very little additional energy to make it jump into the vacant position and the positive hole which results can then wander through the crystal.

1.3. Calculation of the number of charge carriers

For an understanding of the electrical properties of a semi-conductor, it is necessary to know how the numbers of charge carriers depends upon the numbers of impurities, the width of the forbidden region between valence and conduction bands, and the temperature. This requires a few results from statistical mechanics which we shall quote without proof.

The number of electrons per c.c. having energies in a range dE

near the energy E in a solid in equilibrium is decided by the number of states $N(E)\,dE$ available to them in that range and by the chance (or probability) that an electron can be excited thermally to that energy region. The numbers and distributions of states in the conduction and valence bands can be calculated by well-known methods. The number and location of states in the forbidden region is decided by the numbers and types of impurities. The probability that an electron or hole occupies a single energy state within the range dE is given by the Fermi Distribution Function

$$f(E) = \frac{1}{1+\exp[(E-E_f)/kT]},$$ (1.1)

where T is the absolute temperature and k is Boltzmann's constant. The quantity E_f, which has the dimensions of energy, is known as the thermodynamic potential or Gibbs free energy per electron. It can be represented on the energy diagram as an imaginary energy level which is usually called the Fermi level. The position of the Fermi level on the energy diagram depends on the width of the forbidden region between valence and conduction bands, on the numbers and types of impurities, and on the temperature.

The total number of electrons per c.c. or density of electrons (N) in the valence band plus conduction band plus impurity centres must be equal to the sum of the number of states, each multiplied by the probability that it is occupied, i.e.

$$\int N(E)f(E)\,dE = N,$$ (1.2)

where the integration is carried out over valence band, energy gap, and conduction band. Evaluation of equation (1.2) leads to a relation between E_f, T, N_d, N_a, E_d, and E_a, where N_d and N_a are the densities of donors and acceptors per unit volume whose energy levels are displaced from the conduction and valence bands by E_d and E_a respectively (Fig. 1.3). Thus if the densities and types of impurities are known it is possible to calculate the position of the Fermi level at a given temperature. A typical position for a material containing more donors than acceptors is shown in Fig. 1.5. The Fermi level is displaced from the conduction band by an energy ϕ_e and from the valence band by an energy ϕ_h, so that $\phi_e + \phi_h = E_g$, the energy gap between valence and conduction bands. Note that if we are determining the number of electrons in the conduction band and $\phi_e \gg kT$ ($\simeq 0.025\,\text{eV}$ at room temperature), the unity in the denominator of (1.1) may be omitted and $f(E)$ becomes the more familiar Boltzmann distribution function. A similar remark applies for $\phi_h \gg kT$. In transistor technology these conditions apply almost invariably so that the Boltzmann distribution is generally used.

The densities (or concentrations) of electrons and positive

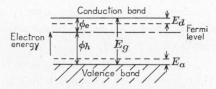

FIG. 1.5. Simple energy-level diagram of an n-type semiconductor showing the Fermi level.

holes can be expressed in terms of the Fermi level energy as follows:

$$n = C_e\, T^{\frac{3}{2}} \exp(-\phi_e/kT), \tag{1.3}$$

$$p = C_h\, T^{\frac{3}{2}} \exp(-\phi_h/kT), \tag{1.4}$$

$$C_e = 2(2\pi m_e k/h^2)^{\frac{3}{2}}, \tag{1.5}$$

$$C_h = 2(2\pi m_h k/h^2)^{\frac{3}{2}}, \tag{1.6}$$

where n is the density of electrons in the conduction band, p is the density of holes in the valence band, m_e and m_h the effective masses of electrons and holes respectively, and h is Planck's constant. C_e and C_h are therefore constant for a given material.

A general analysis of the variation of the position of the Fermi level and of the densities of carriers for all conceivable conditions is quite complicated. However, only a few special relations need be considered for transistor applications. These may be outlined as follows:

(a) The product

$$np = C_e C_h\, T^3 \exp[-(\phi_e + \phi_h)/kT] = C_e C_h\, T^3 \exp(-E_g/kT) \tag{1.7}$$

is, for a given material, dependent on temperature only and

independent of the number of impurities. Thus if n-type impurities are added to a germanium crystal, for example, the density of electrons in the conduction band at room temperature will increase but the density of positive holes must decrease to keep the product np constant.

(b) For an intrinsic semiconductor $n = n_i = p = p_i$, so that from equation (1.7)

$$n_i = p_i = (C_e C_h T^3)^{\frac{1}{2}} \exp(-E_g/2kT). \qquad (1.8)$$

Since E_g has the value 0·75 eV for germanium and 1·1 eV for silicon and since $kT \simeq 0.025$ eV at room temperature, the exponential factor is small but increases rapidly with temperature. n_i and p_i thus show the exponential dependence upon temperature mentioned in § 1.2.2.

Since m_e and m_h are of the same order it is seen from equations (1.3) and (1.4) that $\phi_e \simeq \phi_h$ for $n = p$, so that the Fermi level of an intrinsic semiconductor is near the centre of the energy gap.

(c) For an n-type impurity semiconductor in which N_d, the density of donors, is so large that intrinsic effects can be ignored and for which $E_d \gg kT$ we have

$$n = N_d^{\frac{1}{2}} C_e^{\frac{1}{2}} T^{\frac{3}{4}} \exp(-E_d/2kT). \qquad (1.9)$$

A similar expression applies for p-type material under the same conditions.

(d) In germanium, which has $E_d \simeq E_a \simeq 0.01$ eV, equation (1.9) applies only at very low temperatures. The impurity centres in this material are practically completely dissociated at ordinary temperatures so that $n \simeq N_d$ for an n-type material and $p \simeq N_a$ for a p-type material. The left-hand side of equation (1.3) or (1.4) thus becomes N_d or N_a. The value for $C_e T^{\frac{3}{2}}$ for germanium at room temperature is somewhat less than 10^{19} per c.c. and if the number of impurities is greater than this, equation (1.3) can only be satisfied if ϕ_e is negative, i.e. if the Fermi level lies in the conduction band. Similarly the Fermi level for p-type material containing a very large density of impurities lies in the valence band. Materials of this type are used in an important new device, the tunnel diode (Chapter VIII).

(e) For silicon, $E_d \simeq E_a \simeq 0.05$ eV and when the density of impurities is small (10^{15} to 10^{17} per c.c.), it satisfies equation (1.9) for temperatures up to about $0°$ C. For larger temperatures n approaches N_d asymptotically. If the density of impurity centres is very large there is interaction between the carriers trapped in them which lowers the magnitude of E_d or E_a and silicon behaves similarly to germanium under these conditions.

(f) If the number of donors or acceptors is small or the temperature is high, intrinsic effects are important (cf. § 1.4 below) and the Fermi level lies between the centre of the forbidden region and the position given by equation (1.9). This condition exists in the active (base) region of most transistors at room temperature and the activation energy ϕ_e in an n-type material or ϕ_h in a p-type material (equations (1.3) and (1.4)) may range from $0{\cdot}10$ to $0{\cdot}25$ eV. The carriers that exist in the larger concentration in a semiconductor are called majority carriers and we therefore say that the activation energy for majority carriers is in the above range. The activation energy for the carriers existing in the smaller concentration (minority carriers) in germanium is obtained by subtracting the above limits from E_g ($= 0{\cdot}75$ eV) and therefore lies between $0{\cdot}5$ and $0{\cdot}65$ eV. For silicon the majority-carrier activation energy is approximately the same and the minority-carrier activation energy lies between about $0{\cdot}90$ and $1{\cdot}05$ eV. For minority carriers the exponential terms in equations (1.3) and (1.4) therefore dominate the temperature dependence.

(g) For germanium or silicon containing both donors and acceptors the conductivity is characteristic of the impurity present in the greatest amount and the effective density of carriers is $|N_d - N_a|$. For example, in an n-type material containing acceptors, electrons from the donors fill up the acceptors and are removed from circulation so that the density of free carriers cannot exceed $(N_d - N_a)$. The same argument applies to a p-type material containing some donors. Such materials are said to be compensated.

Some idea of the usefulness of the Fermi level is obtained from these results. However, its value is greatest when contacts between semiconductors of different conductivities or between semiconductors and metals are considered. In equilibrium the Fermi levels of the adjoining materials must be at the same energy and this fact makes it possible to show quite easily how transistors operate.

1.4. Influence of impurities and temperature on the position of the Fermi level

The effect of impurity concentration (density) and temperature on the position of the Fermi level, which has been indicated to some extent in the preceding section, may be summarized as follows:

In an intrinsic material the Fermi level is near the centre of the energy gap. As n-type impurities are added (at constant temperature) it moves towards the conduction band, passing through the condition mentioned under (f) above and, for very large values of N_d, reaches a position about 0·1 eV above the bottom of the conduction band. Similarly if p-type impurities are added the Fermi level moves towards, and eventually into, the valence band.

The effect of temperature may be described by considering an n-type semiconductor with a fairly large density of impurities. At low temperatures the Fermi level is near the conduction band but as the temperature is raised intrinsic effects become more important and it shifts downwards. At sufficiently high temperatures intrinsic effects dominate and the Fermi level is approximately at the centre of the energy gap. A similar description applies to p-type material.

1.5. Mobility and conductivity

We have stated earlier that electrons in the conduction band and positive holes in the valence band contribute to a flow of current in the semiconductor when an electric field is applied. We now consider the magnitude of the current produced and the way in which it varies with the applied field.

If a crystal were to consist of a perfect array of completely immobile atoms the charge carriers would behave in much the same way as electrons in a vacuum. They would be accelerated

by an electric field and their transit times in the solid would be
of the same order as that of electrons in a vacuum tube of similar
dimensions. This ideal state of affairs is not approached in
practice for the following two reasons:

1. The array of atoms in the crystal is not perfect by any
means. There are many vacant lattice sites and regions of misfit
(dislocations) in the most carefully grown crystals and these
produce distortions in the electric field of the crystal which
impede and deflect the charge carriers. Impurity atoms, whether
added intentionally or not, produce a similar effect. Continuous
acceleration of the type described above is thus not possible.
The defects and impurity centres are said to act as scattering
centres for the charge carriers.

2. Even in a perfect crystal there would be a large amount of
scattering at ordinary temperatures because the thermal vibra-
tions of the atoms of the lattice about their mean position produce irregularities in the electric field in the crystal.

The effect of these two factors is to make a charge carrier in
a solid behave more like an ion in a gas than an electron in a
vacuum. If the crystal is in equilibrium the charge carrier
moves about in a completely random manner. When an electric
field is applied to the crystal a constant mean velocity or 'drift'
of the carriers is superimposed on the random thermal motion—
in contrast to the case of an electron in a vacuum where a
constant acceleration is produced. For ordinary field strengths
the drift velocity is proportional to the field strength and we
may put
$$v_e = -\mu_e F, \qquad v_h = \mu_h F, \qquad (1.10)$$

where v_e and v_h are the mean velocities of electrons and positive
holes respectively and F is the applied field. The constants μ_e
and μ_h are called the mobilities of the charge carriers. If F is
in volts/cm, μ_e and μ_h are in cm/sec per volt/cm or cm²/volt sec.
For germanium $\mu_e \simeq 3,900$, $\mu_h \simeq 1,900$ and for silicon $\mu_e \simeq 1,200$,
$\mu_h \simeq 500$. These figures apply to single crystals of good structure and high purity. For strained crystals, or crystals containing many impurities, the mobilities are lower. For poly-
crystalline materials there is a further reduction in mobility

because of scattering at crystal boundaries. This is not important in modern transistors and diodes, however, as single-crystal
material is invariably used.

There is a variation of mobility with temperature but this is
rather small. Thus in both germanium and silicon at ordinary
temperatures $\mu_e \propto T^{-1 \cdot 6}$ approximately and $\mu_h \propto T^{-2 \cdot 3}$ approximately.

The current densities j_e and j_h produced by the field F are
obtained by multiplying equations (1.10) by $-qn$ and $+qp$
respectively where q is the magnitude of the electronic charge
($= 1 \cdot 602 \times 10^{-19}$ coulomb). j_e and j_h thus have the same sign
and add together to produce the total current. The conductivity
σ, obtained from the relation $\sigma = j/F$, is

$$\sigma = q(n\mu_e + p\mu_h). \tag{1.11}$$

For an impurity semiconductor the density of majority carriers
is usually so much larger than the density of minority carriers
that only one term of (1.11) need be used. For an intrinsic
material $n = p$ and (assuming that both types of carrier can
enter the semiconductor easily) both terms must be considered.
More current will, however, be carried by electrons than holes
because $\mu_e > \mu_h$.

From a study of equations (1.8), (1.9), and (1.11) we can see
how the conductivities of germanium and silicon vary with
temperature. We first note that the temperature factor in the
mobility and that in front of the exponential in equations (1.8)
and (1.9) tend to cancel each other so that for a qualitative
picture we consider only the exponential term. The most useful
way of plotting the conductivity–temperature relation is there-
fore to plot $\log \sigma$ ($= -\log \rho$ where ρ is the resistivity) against
$1/T$. A schematic diagram of the type of curve obtained is
shown in Fig. 1.6. At low temperatures in the region AB the
exponential factor of equation (1.9) is dominant and the slope
of AB is approximately $E_d/2$ or $E_a/2$. At the point B a large
fraction of the donors or acceptors is dissociated and the slope
of the curve decreases. In the region CD the number of carriers
is practically constant and there is a slight drop in conductivity

because of the effect of temperature on the mobility. At D
intrinsic effects become important and the slope of DE is $E_g/2$
approximately, as obtained from equation (1.8). The positions
of the lettered points depend on the number and type of impurities. For n-type germanium having a resistivity of 4 ohm cm
at room temperature D occurs at about 90° C and C is well

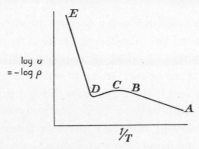

Fig. 1.6. Conductivity–temperature plot
for a semiconductor. Letters are referred
to in the text.

below —120° C. For 0·3 ohm cm n-type germanium, D occurs
at about 150° C, while C is still below —120° C. For 0·3 ohm cm
n-type silicon D occurs at about 600° C and C in the region of
room temperature. Since intrinsic effects must be avoided in
transistors it is seen that silicon is more suited to high-temperature operation than germanium.

This completes our rather hasty review of electrical conduction
in solids as it was known before the advent of transistors. The
latter event opened a whole new field of conduction phenomena
that depend on the properties of minority carriers. In the next
chapter we consider the more important of these from the point
of view of junction rectifier and transistor operation.

THE PROPERTIES OF MINORITY CARRIERS

2.1. Introduction

IN § 1.3 we mentioned minority carriers briefly and the discussion of § 1.5 implied that their contribution to the conductivity is qualitatively similar to that of majority carriers. This would be true if both types of carrier could enter and leave the semiconductor freely and if their densities did not differ appreciably from the equilibrium values. It is relatively easy, however, to change the density of minority carriers from its equilibrium value in certain semiconductors and thus to produce phenomena not ordinarily encountered in conduction processes. In this chapter we shall describe some of these phenomena and show how this ability to change the equilibrium number of carriers makes 'transistor action' possible. Later, when the concept of transistor action has been introduced, we shall consider some of the properties of minority carriers in more detail.

2.2. Current flow in semiconductors

In order to pass an electric current through a semiconductor or insulator we must attach electrodes to it. If these electrodes allow majority carriers to enter easily and if the effective resistance of the contact is independent of the direction of current flow we say that the connections to the sample are 'ohmic'. The application of a constant potential will then produce a steady majority-carrier current whose magnitude depends on the number of carriers and on their drift velocity through the specimen. In this steady state, majority carriers enter one end of the specimen and leave the other end at equal rates. If pure majority-carrier flow occurs the change in density of majority carriers within the specimen is negligible.

It is important to note that, in this case of pure majority-carrier flow, the rate at which a new condition is established in the specimen is not directly connected with the rate at which the carriers drift down the specimen. Thus, if the applied potential rises instantaneously to a constant value, the final steady current will be reached after a delay which depends upon the rate at which the electric disturbance created by the sudden change in potential is passed from carrier to carrier along the specimen. This is normally much more rapid than the velocity of the carriers themselves.

The delay in reaching the final state of steady majority-carrier current flow depends on the dielectric relaxation time [1] $t_D = \epsilon/4\pi\sigma$, where ϵ is the dielectric constant and σ is the conductivity. For metals t_D is less than 10^{-16} sec while for an insulator having a resistivity of 10^{12} ohm cm it is of the order of seconds. Germanium and silicon of 1 ohm cm resistivity —a fairly typical value for transistor materials—have relaxation times of about 10^{-12} sec. The steady-state condition in these materials is thus established very rapidly for majority carriers.

It will be apparent from the above that the density of majority carriers in a specimen cannot be readily changed by increasing the potential applied to it. Such a procedure merely increases the rate of flow of the carriers through the sample and the rates at which they enter and leave. The number of carriers in any chosen volume of the semiconductor changes by a negligible amount. In contrast to this, the density of minority carriers can be changed quite easily if special electrodes, to be described later, are used. Such electrodes can 'inject' minority carriers into the material, thus raising their density above the equilibrium value. These injected carriers tend to produce a space charge in the material which is quickly neutralized by an equal number of majority carriers entering through an ohmic contact—the time of the neutralization process being of the order of the above-mentioned dielectric relaxation time. Application of an electric field F to the material will produce motion of the injected carriers at a velocity μF and the majority carriers will readjust their positions in an attempt to neutralize the minority-carrier charge as it progresses along the specimen. This readjustment will, of course, be superimposed on any normal flow of majority carriers which results from application of the field.

An example of such minority-carrier flow may be discussed with the aid of Fig. 2.1. Here an n-type sample having ohmic electrodes at A and D has a potential V_1 applied across it in the direction shown. This produces a flow of electrons from D to A. When the switch S is closed a positive-hole injecting contact B is biased positively with respect to the underlying material so that holes are injected and flow or 'drift' towards D with velocity $\mu_h F$. The front of the positive hole cloud can be detected some time after the closing of the switch at a second injecting-type contact at C biased negatively with respect to the underlying material. It is thus possible, by measuring the elapsed time and the distance d, to determine the drift velocity and hence the 'drift mobility' μ_h of the positive holes.

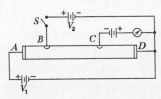

FIG. 2.1. Simple experimental arrangement for the determination of drift mobility.

This experiment which was first performed by Haynes and Shockley [2] is, in principle, very simple. There are some complications that arise with material of high resistivity [3] but these need not concern us here.

We may emphasize the difference between majority and minority carriers by noting that it would not be possible to measure the velocity of the electrons (majority carriers) in the material of Fig. 2.1. If we could measure the time required for the front of the majority-carrier current to travel through the specimen (e.g. times of the order of 10^{-12} sec in transistor materials) we would be measuring, not the velocity of the majority carriers, but the velocity with which an electric disturbance is propagated through the material.

The injection of minority carriers produces a non-equilibrium condition and processes within the crystal automatically attempt to restore equilibrium. Some, at least, of the injected carriers will therefore be removed in the body of the semiconductor before reaching the electrode by which they leave the crystal.

The ultimate process by which the excess carriers are removed, in the body of the semiconductor, is recombination of holes and electrons, but diffusion and electric-field effects which influence the spatial distribution of carriers are also important factors. All of these processes play important parts in the operation of transistors and so must be considered in some detail. In order that the discussion may not seem too academic and to relate it to practical problems involved in transistor design and operation we give below a brief description of transistor action. However, since the description of the transistor follows naturally from that of the p-n junction rectifier, we shall first consider this simpler device.

2.3. The p-n junction rectifier

The junction rectifier in its most common form consists of a single crystal of semiconductor of which one part contains a higher concentration of n-type than p-type impurities while in the remainder the p-type impurities predominate. The two parts are called the n and the p regions respectively. External ohmic connections are made to them by means of metal electrodes. The principles of operation can be outlined by considering a hypothetical case in which n- and p-type crystals of identical cross-section are brought together—it being assumed that the two parts eventually form a single crystal with no distortion of crystal structure or contamination at the area of contact.

The energy levels of the two crystals before they are brought together are shown in Fig. 2.2. Their initial positions relative to each other on the energy diagram are decided by the fact that electrons just outside and beyond the influence of each surface must have the same energy. This energy level, which may be arbitrarily called the zero energy level, is marked 00. It is spaced from the bottom of the conduction band by an energy ϕ_{0p} in the p-type material and by an energy ϕ_{0n} in the n-type material. The quantities ϕ_{0p} and ϕ_{0n} are probably roughly equal in magnitude. When the two parts of the crystal are separated as in Fig. 2.2 there are more electrons at an energy level AA in the conduction band in the n-type than in the p-type material, while at energy level BB in the valence band there are more holes in the p-type than in the n-type material.

If the two crystals are now brought together to form a single crystal, electrons and holes will diffuse from regions of high concentration just as a gas diffuses. Thus electrons diffuse from right to left and positive holes from left to right. Both processes tend to make the p-type material negative with respect to the n-type and the excess charge tends to prevent further diffusion

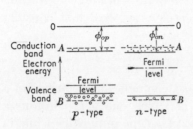

FIG. 2.2. Energy levels of p-type and n-type crystals that are not in contact.

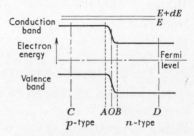

FIG. 2.3. Electron-energy diagram of a p-n junction.

of electrons and holes because of the electrostatic forces created. A balance is reached when the Fermi levels of the two parts of the crystal coincide and the energy diagram is then as shown in Fig. 2.3. The crystal is then in equilibrium and the densities of electrons at any chosen energy level (e.g. between E and $E+dE$) are the same in the two parts. There is no net flow of charge across the junction. This condition is also sometimes defined by considering conditions in the region between A and B. Balance is then assumed to result from equal currents of electrons flowing in opposite directions—one component being due to diffusion of electrons from the n-type to the p-type material and its counterpart being due to the flow of electrons (minority carriers) from the p-type to the n-type material under the influence of the field at the junction. As will be seen below, this point of view is better suited to the discussion of the non-equilibrium conditions that occur when a potential is applied to the crystal.

The flow of positive holes across the junction may be described in a manner completely analogous to the above description of electron flow—except that the flow of carriers is reversed. The condition of balance again arises when the Fermi levels of the two parts of the crystals coincide.

The region between A and B is often called the transition region because the change of potential or potential energy occurs there. Also, because electrons flowing from n- to p-type material or holes flowing from p- to n-type material require excess energy to mount the potential step, the latter is sometimes called the 'barrier'. The importance of this term will be evident from the discussion below.

The resistivity of the transition region is very high relative to the resistivities of the n- and p-type materials. At O, for example, the Fermi level lies half-way between the conduction and valence bands so that the material is intrinsic. Between O and A the resistivity is graded from the high intrinsic value to that of the p-type section of the crystal and between O and B it decreases towards the resistivity of the n-type section. The average resistivity in the region AB is thus considerably higher than that of the remainder of the crystal. In practical cases, even though the transition region is much shorter than the remainder of the crystal, its resistance is so high that it is a good approximation to assume that an externally applied potential will be taken up across it, thus changing the height of the barrier at AB.

A battery connected as shown in Fig. 2.4 will lower the height of the potential step so that electrons from lower states in the conduction band can cross the barrier from right to left. The number of such electrons increases very rapidly (exponentially) as the barrier height is decreased and this

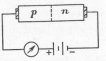

FIG. 2.4. Forward connection of the p-n junction.

component of the electronic current increases rapidly with voltage. On the other hand, the flow of electrons from left to right, which is decided by the number of electrons existing as minority carriers in the p-type material, does not change very much. Similar arguments apply to the flow of positive holes. The application of a battery voltage in the direction shown in Fig. 2.4 thus produces a large current flow through the device.

When the battery voltage is reversed the potential step becomes larger. The number of electrons with sufficient energy to mount the potential step and flow from right to left is now very small and the main component of the electron current is that flowing from left to right. This remains substantially unaltered at the low value decided by the density of minority carriers in the p-type material. A similar description again applies to positive holes. The net effect of applying a battery voltage in this direction is therefore to produce a very small current. The device thus acts as a rectifier whose forward direction is that of the battery shown in Fig. 2.4. It is called a p-n junction rectifier or, more simply, a junction rectifier. The theory and method of construction of these devices will be considered in more detail in later chapters.

It will be noted that the carriers supplying the large forward current of a p-n junction flow from a region where they are in the majority to one in which they are in the minority so that the p-n junction is one of the means of injecting minority carriers referred to previously. In the present example we have implied that the components of current due to holes and electrons are of equal importance but this is not necessarily the case. In most applications the current consists largely of one type of carrier. In the transistor, which is described below, one of the design requirements is to achieve as large a difference as possible between the two components.

2.4. The junction transistor

It is possible to produce two junction rectifiers, with directions of rectification reversed, in the same crystal. If this is done under the special conditions outlined below, the device is a junction transistor. The electron-energy diagram of one such arrangement, with no external voltage applied, is shown in Fig. 2.5. It consists of two p-n junctions arranged so that the p-type material is common to the two junctions. Another version of the device exists in which a section of n-type material is sandwiched between two p-type sections.

A schematic diagram of the n-p-n transistor is shown in Fig. 2.6. Here external potentials are applied through ohmic contacts F, G, and H in such a way that the junction on the left is biased

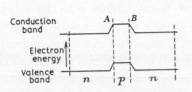

FIG. 2.5. Electron-energy diagram of an n-p-n transistor with no applied voltage.

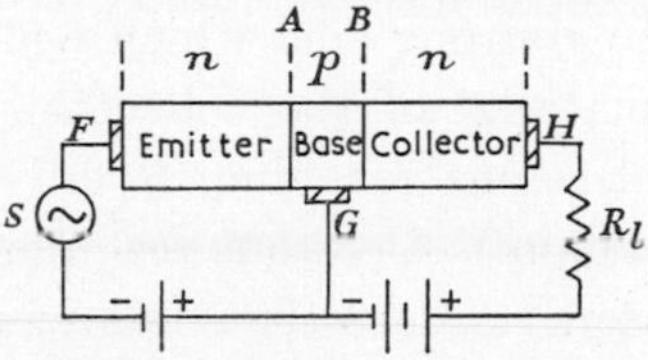

FIG. 2.6. Schematic diagram of a correctly biased n-p-n transistor.

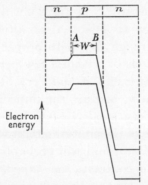

FIG. 2.7. Electron-energy diagram of a correctly biased n-p-n transistor.

in the forward direction and the right-hand junction in the reverse direction. The energy diagram for this arrangement is shown in Fig. 2.7. The potential step at the left has been reduced and a large current of electrons diffuses from the left into the p-type region which is common to the two junctions. This region, which thus has many minority carriers injected into it, is called the base. The material from which these injected carriers come (in this case the n-type material on the left) is called the emitter and the junction between it and the base is called the emitter junction. The region to the right is called the collector and the junction between it and the base is called the collector junction.

If the base region is sufficiently thin and has other suitable properties, many of the electrons injected at A on the base side of the emitter junction will diffuse through the base to the base side of the collector junction at B. They will then be subjected to a strong field which will move them rapidly into the n-type material of the collector. (In terms of the energy diagram, electrons reaching B fall rapidly downhill into the collector region.) Electrons reaching the collector become majority carriers again so that, following the extremely short delay characteristic of majority-carrier flow, a flow of current occurs in the external resistance R_l of Fig. 2.6.

It will readily be seen that an alternating voltage such as that applied by generator S in Fig. 2.6 will modulate the height of the potential step at A so that an alternating current may be made to flow through R_l. With proper design this collector current will approach to within a few per cent of the current flowing in the emitter circuit and very little current will flow out of the base. Now, because the impedance of the forward-biased emitter is very small (a few hundred ohms at most), the total impedance of the emitter circuit will be decided chiefly by that of the generator and will probably rarely exceed a few thousand ohms. In contrast, the impedance of the collector circuit is decided by that of the collector junction, which may be several megohms, since in this case the bias is in the reverse direction. A load resistance R_l of several hundred thousand ohms will therefore have little influence on the current flowing in the collector circuit. The device thus passes most of the emitter current from a low-impedance generator to a high-impedance load and, when connected in the manner described, acts as a voltage and power amplifier.

This process, whereby the same current can be made to flow through junctions connected in opposite directions by the flow of minority carriers in the region common to the two junctions, is called transistor action. In order for it to give an appreciable amount of amplification, a large fraction of the emitter current must flow through the collector. This requires a high efficiency of injection of minority carriers into the base from the emitter and also that most of these injected carriers reach the collector. To achieve these objects it is necessary to consider the mechanisms whereby minority carriers enter and pass through the base and to take account of any process which prevents them from reaching the collector. The chief force which drives minority carriers through the base is diffusion, and the most important process that tends to remove them before they reach the collector is recombination with majority carriers in the body, or at the surface, of the base region. These properties and some of the important constants that depend on them are considered in the section that follows.

2.5. Properties of minority carriers

2.5.1. *Diffusion*

The diffusion of current carriers, which is strictly analogous to the diffusion of gases, appears whenever the concentration of carriers (majority or minority) varies in different parts of the material. The concentration gradient (i.e. the variation of carrier density with distance) produces a flow of carriers which tends to make their distribution more uniform. The diffusion current thus produced is $qD_n \nabla n$ for electrons or $-qD_p \nabla p$ for positive holes where D_n and D_p are constants, called diffusion coefficients, and ∇ is the symbol for a gradient. For a one-dimensional system these expressions become $qD_n(dn/dx)$ and $-qD_p(dp/dx)$, where x is the single distance coordinate. From this definition it can be shown quite readily that the rates of increase of density of electrons and holes due to diffusion are $D_n(d^2n/dx^2)$ electrons and $D_p(d^2p/dx^2)$ holes respectively per unit volume per second.

In the example of Fig. 2.1 we note that the front of the positive-hole cloud which is produced by the sudden closing of the switch S will, because of diffusion, become progressively less sharp as it moves through the material.

It is important to note that this tendency for the carriers to diffuse away from regions of high concentration does not depend upon the fact that they are charged. The neighbours of each minority carrier will tend on the average to be majority carriers and electrostatic repulsion between minority carriers of the same sign will not be an important factor. Similarly, the neighbours of majority carriers will tend to be either minority carriers (if large numbers of these have been injected) or charged impurity centres. Diffusion therefore occurs, as in a gas, because of the random motion of the carriers and collisions between them.

An analysis of any system (such as a p-n junction) in which charged particles are in equilibrium under the influence of diffusion and electrical forces [4] makes possible a determination of the following relation between diffusion coefficient and mobility:
$$D = kT\mu/q. \tag{2.1}$$
This is usually called Einstein's relation.

2.5.2. Recombination and minority-carrier lifetime

We have pointed out earlier that, although the number of carriers in equilibrium in an intrinsic semiconductor is constant, generation and recombination of hole-electron pairs takes place continually. A similar description applies to impurity-type semiconductors. In n-type materials, for instance, the release of electrons from some donors and the recapture of electrons by others are taking place continually. The generation and recombination of hole-electron pairs also occurs in these materials but the number of such 'intrinsic' processes is much smaller at ordinary temperatures than the number of processes involving impurity centres. A similar description applies to p-type materials. The expressions for the numbers of carriers given in equations such as (1.3), (1.4), (1.7), (1.8) result from the balance between these competing processes.

These same processes attempt to restore equilibrium when the number of carriers is altered as a result, for example, of the injection of minority carriers. Since such injection increases both the number of holes in the valence band and the number of electrons in the conduction band, the main process tending to restore equilibrium will be the recombination of hole-electron pairs. The rate at which such recombinations take place decides how long the injected carriers exist, i.e. it determines their 'lifetime'.

This lifetime is an important factor in the expression for current gain of the transistor and in the formulae for the variation of parameters with frequency. To define it, we must consider in more detail the generation and recombination processes described above. The rate of generation is usually expressed in carriers per c.c. per sec and is denoted by g. For a given material at a given temperature it is constant. The rate of recombination depends on the number of times per second that positive holes and electrons come into contact with each other. The chance that a positive hole comes into contact with an electron is obviously proportional to n, the number of electrons per c.c. and since there are p holes per c.c. the total number of collisions, and hence the number of recombinations, must be proportional to pn. In equilibrium the rates of generation and recombination must be equal so that

$$g = rp_0 n_0, \qquad (2.2)$$

where r is a constant for a given material at a given temperature and p_0, n_0 are the equilibrium densities of holes and electrons.

When a number of minority carriers is injected, both n and p are increased as outlined above, and the rate of change of density of either type of carrier becomes

$$\frac{dp}{dt} = \frac{dn}{dt} = g - rpn = -r(pn - p_0 n_0). \qquad (2.3)$$

Let us now assume that positive holes are being injected into n-type material and consider the case in which the density of injected holes is much smaller than the density of electrons present in the material in equilibrium. Then, since the density of holes initially present in the n-type material is also much smaller than the electron density, we must have $p \ll n_0$. The recombination rate is then approximately rpn_0 and equation (2.3) becomes

$$\frac{dp}{dt} \simeq -rn_0(p - p_0) = -\frac{1}{\tau_p}(p - p_0), \qquad (2.4)$$

where the constant $1/rn_0$, which has the dimension of time, has been replaced by τ_p. Integration of equation (2.4) gives

$$p-p_0 = C\exp(-t/\tau_p), \tag{2.5}$$

where C is a constant. If we now consider a small volume of the semiconductor in which the density of positive holes has been increased, by injection or otherwise, to p_1 holes/c.c. at time $t = 0$ we obtain, using (2.5), $C = p_1-p_0$. Hence

$$p-p_0 = (p_1-p_0)\exp(-t/\tau_p). \tag{2.6}$$

Equation (2.6) shows that the excess of minority carriers will decrease to $1/e$ ($= 37\%$) of its initial amount in time τ_p. This quantity τ_p is therefore called the lifetime of positive holes in n-type material. A similar quantity τ_n is defined for electrons in p-type material.

The recombination defined by equations (2.4) and (2.6) is called constant lifetime recombination. Strictly speaking, it only applies when the density of injected carriers is small compared with the density of majority carriers. If this is not the case, equation (2.3) must be used and a constant lifetime of the type we have discussed cannot be defined or, to put it in another way, the lifetime varies with minority-carrier density. The process described by equation (2.3) is often called mass-action recombination since it is analogous to the chemical law of mass action in that variations in the amounts of both reacting materials (in this case holes and electrons) must be taken into account.

The mathematical treatment of mass-action recombination is complicated and analyses of transistor action are usually based upon the constant-lifetime approach. When the injection level is high (i.e. when the number of minority carriers approaches the number of majority carriers) the error thus introduced may be large but in many cases the results of calculations still apply approximately.

The above description is idealized in that it assumes that direct recombination of holes and electrons is the most probable process. This would be the case in materials of exceptional purity and structure but even in the best present-day transistor materials other recombination processes, depending on the presence of hole or electron traps whose energy levels lie in the forbidden energy region, are more important. When such traps are present recombination takes place in two stages. In an *n*-type material, for example, an electron may drop from the conduction band into the energy level of the trap, thus losing some of its energy to the surrounding lattice. Later, a hole collides with this trapped electron, and if conditions are suitable, recombines with it. The probability of satisfying the momentum and energy requirements of the recombination process is greater for a mechanism of this type than for the direct process described above. Recombination therefore takes place more readily and the minority carrier lifetime is smaller than it would be if the traps were not present.

One process involving traps has been treated by Hall [5] and by Shockley and Read [6]. It seems to describe satisfactorily the recombination process in germanium. On this model the general features of the idealized case described above are still present. At low minority-carrier levels, for instance, a simple lifetime similar to, but much smaller than, that described above can be used. Equations (2.4) and (2.6) are therefore still applicable. At higher levels the lifetime again varies with minority-carrier density.

The recombination processes so far discussed take place in the body of the semiconductor. There is, however, another aspect of the lifetime problem that is very important in practical applications. This concerns the effect of the semiconductor surface on the recombination of positive holes and electrons. One of the objects of transistor technology is to minimize the rate of recombination of holes and electrons at the surface which may be quite different from that in the body of the semiconductor. Some minority carriers are bound to reach the surface by diffusion and, if the rate of recombination there is very large, many of these will be removed from circulation with consequent deleterious effects on the properties of the device. As would be expected by analogy with conditions in the body of the semiconductor, the rate of recombination is increased and the surface lifetime lowered by the presence of surface contaminations and by mechanical imperfections such as those produced by sand blasting. By careful treatment, however, it is possible to make the effect of the surface negligible, at least as far as the main features of transistor operation are concerned, and we shall not consider it explicitly in the sections that follow.

Since the lifetime of minority carriers in present-day materials depends not only on the number of impurities but also on the number of structure faults in the lattice (lattice vacancies and regions of misfit), we should expect it to depend markedly on the thermal history of the specimen (e.g. the extent to which it has been heat-treated or annealed) and this is found to be the case. Also, because impurities or defects that trap electrons may have characteristics quite different from those of their hole-trapping counterparts, the lifetime of minority carriers may be quite different in p-type and n-type materials of similar quality. In transistor-grade germanium the lifetime of electrons and holes may range up to several hundred microseconds (μsec). The figures for silicon are similar. In general the lifetime will be lower for crystals of lower resistivity. An exception occurs when the sample is highly compensated, i.e. contains relatively large but nearly equal numbers of p-type and n-type impurities. A material of this type may have high resistivity and short lifetime.

2.5.3. Diffusion length

We have so far considered separately the effects of diffusion and recombination in dispersing a non-equilibrium distribution of minority carriers. However, these two mechanisms will, in general, be working simultaneously and another parameter, called the diffusion length, is then useful for the description of the process. For our purpose this can be defined easily by considering the steady-state process that occurs in a junction rectifier when a constant current flows through it. Assuming one-dimensional geometry we consider an element of length dx and unit cross-section in the n-type region of the rectifier and assume that a current of minority carriers (positive holes) is flowing into it. (We choose holes as our minority carriers, with a view to our later discussions, to avoid complications that arise when the velocity of a carrier and the electric current have opposite signs.)

The number of holes entering this region per second due to diffusion is $D_p (d^2p/dx^2) dx$, and the number removed by re-combination is $(p-p_n) dx/\tau_p$, where p_n is the equilibrium density of holes in the (n-type) region concerned. In the steady state of constant current flow, the number of holes in a chosen volume element must be independent of time so that

$$D_p \frac{d^2p}{dx^2} = \frac{p-p_n}{\tau_p}. \qquad (2.7)$$

Note that this equation will also apply for $p < p_n$. The left-hand side then indicates the number of holes lost per c.c. per sec by diffusion, and the right-hand side is the number gained by generation.

We have introduced equation (2.7) in a rather specialized way suited to the condition we are considering. It can of course be obtained from the more fundamental equation (A3.7) in Appendix III by putting $\partial p/\partial t = 0$, and omitting the field term.

The solution of equation (2.7) with the condition that all injected holes recombine in the n-type material, given by equation (A2.4) in Appendix II, is

$$p-p_n = (p_1-p_n)\exp(-x/L_p), \qquad (2.8)$$

where p_1 is the number of holes/c.c. capable of entering the n-type material. The flow of current arises from diffusion due to the fact that p_1 exceeds p_n. The constant $L_p = (D_p \tau_p)^{\frac{1}{2}}$ is called the diffusion length for holes in n-type material. From equation (2.8) we see that the excess of holes per c.c. decreases from (p_1-p_n) at the junction ($x = 0$) to $(p_1-p_n)/e$ at $x = L_p$. Similar conclusions apply when electrons are injected into p-type material. The diffusion length in this case is $L_n = (D_n \tau_n)^{\frac{1}{2}}$.

A typical value for L_p or L_n in germanium is about 0·10 cm. For silicon, smaller diffusion coefficients and somewhat smaller lifetimes combine to reduce this by a factor of about three. Heat treatment in the construction of semiconductor devices

D

may cause a further reduction so that reasonable 'practical' values of L_n or L_p may be 0·03 cm in germanium and 0·01 cm in silicon.

The importance of the diffusion length in transistor design can be seen from our description of the junction transistor in § 2.4. It was pointed out there that, for efficient operation, most of the carriers injected into the base must reach the collector. It is apparent from equation (2.8) (or its electron equivalent) that this condition can only be met if the base width (W in Fig. 2.7) is much smaller than the diffusion length.

THE CONSTRUCTION OF *p-n* JUNCTIONS AND TRANSISTORS

3.1. Introduction

EARLY in Chapter II we introduced simple descriptions of the *p-n* junction rectifier and the junction transistor. In later chapters we shall present analyses of these devices from the physical and circuit viewpoint and it will be seen that some of their properties depend on the methods by which they are made. A certain background knowledge of these methods is therefore desirable. In this chapter we will describe them briefly, concentrating on those aspects that affect the electrical properties of commonly used devices. We will not discuss detailed technology except in so far as it affects characteristics considered in the chapters that follow. Later, in Chapter VIII, when the factors affecting the operation of junction rectifiers and transistors at high frequencies and under high-speed transient conditions have been described in more detail, we will describe the methods of construction of devices for operation in this region.

3.2. Preparation of semiconductor materials for junction devices

While it is possible to produce junction rectifiers and transistors from many different semiconductors, the devices in successful commercial production are, without exception, made from either germanium or silicon. This is due chiefly to the fact that these two materials are elements while all other materials having suitable energy gaps between valence and conduction bands are compounds. In the latter materials any unbalance (non-stoichiometry) between constituents degrades physical properties such as mobility and lifetime to a marked extent. The attempt to keep the proper proportion between the basic components, while eliminating unwanted impurities and adding donors or acceptors, introduces an added order of difficulty in the manufacturing process. Consequently compound materials, though often possessing desirable properties such as high mobility combined with large energy gaps (e.g. InP and GaAs among the intermetallic compounds), have not yet been applied commercially in junction diodes and transistors. We shall therefore confine our remarks to the semiconducting elements germanium and silicon.

The most important operations in the preparation of materials for junction devices are the following:

1. Chemical purification of the semiconductor.
2. Purification by physical means (zone refining).
3. The growth of single crystals.

These have been discussed in considerable detail in semiconductor literature. A recent summary has been given by Shepherd [1].

We shall not discuss item (1) in detail but shall merely note that silicon, because of its high melting temperature (1,420° C compared with 936° C for germanium) and high reactivity at the melting-point, is more difficult to purify than germanium. For this and other reasons discussed below, progress in its application to transistors has been slower.

3.2.1. *Zone refining*

The physical method of purification mentioned above depends on the following property: When a solid is formed from a liquid containing an impurity, the concentration of impurity in the solid is usually smaller than in the liquid. A molten semiconductor frozen slowly in a certain direction will therefore have smaller concentrations of most impurities in the part frozen early in the process than in that frozen later. Such impurities are said to be segregated. Most of the common impurities in germanium and silicon are readily segregated in this manner.

In practice, impurity segregation is obtained by sweeping a molten zone slowly along an ingot of the semiconductor. This zone tends to carry impurities of the above type with it. The process, which may be repeated many times until a large fraction of the ingot has attained a high degree of purity, is called zone refining.

The factor that decides the effectiveness of the zone refining process is the ratio of the impurity concentrations in solid and liquid phases in contact at the same temperature. This is called the distribution coefficient and is usually identified by the symbol k. For efficient removal of impurities of the above type k should be considerably smaller than unity. This is the case for all of the impurities that affect the electrical properties of

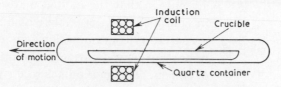

FIG. 3.1. Horizontal-zone refining apparatus.

germanium and silicon with the exception of boron, an acceptor impurity whose equilibrium distribution coefficient is 17 in germanium and 0·8 in silicon. In germanium boron is moved readily to the *beginning* of the ingot but removal of it from silicon is difficult. The effect of its distribution coefficient on the technology of silicon will be discussed below.

Two forms of zone refining are used in the purification of semiconductors. A schematic diagram of the simpler and more commonly used process is shown in Fig. 3.1. An ingot of semiconductor is placed in a horizontal crucible of high-purity quartz, which is drawn slowly through an induction coil. The crucible and semiconductor are isolated from the coil by means of a quartz tube which is evacuated or contains a pure inert gas. The coil produces a molten zone, of approximately its own length, in the semiconductor by radio-frequency induction. Motion of the crucible from right to left causes this zone to move along the semiconductor ingot and to sweep impurities with it as described earlier.

In more elaborate versions of this horizontal-zone refining process several coils are placed along the specimen and a corresponding number of molten zones is produced. One pass of the specimen is then equivalent to several passes in a single-coil apparatus and the removal of impurities is accelerated.

In the second process an ingot of small cross-section is held vertically by means of chucks at its ends as shown in Fig. 3.2. The whole apparatus, including an enclosing quartz tube, is moved vertically relative to a fixed induction coil. The molten zone produced by the coil is supported only by surface tension and for this reason the procedure is called the Floating-Zone Technique. It has the advantage that the molten material is not in contact with a crucible which might be a source of contamination—an especially important consideration in the purification of silicon. The method has so far been confined to samples of relatively small cross-section, the maximum diameter for silicon being about 1 inch.

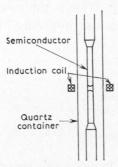

FIG. 3.2. Floating-zone apparatus.

Semiconductor

Induction coil

Quartz container

Many articles on zone refining have been published. A good introduction to the horizontal method has been given by Pfann [2] who is a pioneer in the field. The floating-zone technique is described in the original note on this subject by Keck and Golay [3]. Both methods are discussed in a recent book by Pfann [4] which summarizes most of the important work on the subject.

At this point it is worth while to compare the procedures used in the purification of germanium and silicon to see how transistor technology has been affected by them. Because its melting-point is relatively low and the distribution coefficients of its important impurities are small, germanium may be purified rapidly by the horizontal-zone melting method. Silicon, on the other hand, has a high melting-point and an impurity, boron, whose distribution coefficient is close to unity. The removal of boron from silicon therefore requires many passes of the molten zone with the resulting danger of contamination if a crucible is used. The most promising procedure is, therefore, to remove as much boron as possible by chemical means and to use the floating-zone process in the final stage of purification. Until relatively recently (1954) neither of these methods was as effective for the commercial purification of silicon as the horizontal-zone refining method was for germanium. The large distribution coefficient of boron in silicon and the high reactivity of silicon at the melting-point have therefore delayed the development of silicon as a transistor material.

3.2.2. *Methods of growing single crystals*

The high mobilities and long lifetimes required in the manufacture of junction rectifiers and transistors cannot be obtained in multicrystalline substances because of the presence of violent discontinuities and large numbers of trapping centres at grain boundaries. Single-crystal material is therefore used exclusively. This is obtained commercially by one of the following methods:

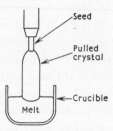

FIG. 3.3. Czochralski or crystal-pulling apparatus.

(*a*) *Crystal-pulling.* This technique, which was introduced by Czochralski [5], was apparently first applied to germanium and silicon by Teal and Little [6]. A schematic diagram of the apparatus used is shown in Fig. 3.3. A crucible contains a charge of germanium or silicon whose temperature is just above the melting-point. A small single crystal, known as the seed crystal, is inserted in the melt and withdrawn slowly in the vertical direction. During this process material from the melt freezes on the seed, building up new rows of atoms whose crystal axes are the same as those of the seed. A large single crystal having the same orientation as the seed is thus formed. To minimize the formation of improperly oriented crystallites on the surface of the main crystal and to compensate for lack of uniformity in heat loss from its surface, the seed is rotated slowly as it is withdrawn. By variation of the rate of withdrawal or the temperature of the melt, the cross-section of the pulled crystal can be controlled. In this way single crystals with cross-sections up to 4 sq. in. and lengths up to 8 in. have been grown. The pulling process is accompanied by segregation of impurities of the type occurring in zone refining so that the part of the crystal adjacent to the seed tends to have a lower density of impurities than that grown later. This effect can, however, be reduced to some extent—while retaining a constant-crystal cross-section— by varying the temperature of the melt and the rate of growth as the crystal lengthens.

(b) *Crystal growth by zone melting*. This process, which has been described by Pfann [4] and Cressell and Powell [7], is an adaptation of the horizontal-zone refining process to the growth of single crystals. In it, a seed crystal is placed in contact with the ingot at one end of the crucible. Part of the seed is melted and combines with the first part of the ingot to form the molten zone at the beginning of the process. As the semiconductor freezes, in the wake of the molten zone, it assumes the orientation of the seed and the whole ingot eventually becomes a single crystal. Crystals that have a uniform distribution of impurities are produced more easily by this method than by the pulling technique but the best materials obtained by the two methods are apparently approximately equivalent in quality [4]. When applied to silicon, however, the method has the usual disadvantages of the horizontal-zone melting technique. It is therefore rarely used in the production of silicon single crystals.

(c) *Floating-zone crystal growth*. The floating-zone refining process may also be used for the production of single crystals by placing a seed crystal in one chuck and a long ingot, held by the other chuck, in contact with it. As in the horizontal-zone melting process, the molten zone is produced initially at the junction between seed and ingot and subsequently moved along the ingot to create a single crystal. The method is applied chiefly in the production of high-quality silicon crystals for research and development.

3.3. The construction of ohmic contacts

One of the most important techniques required in the construction of junction rectifiers and transistors is the making of ohmic connections to the n-type and p-type semiconductors. In this section we shall discuss briefly the theory of the contact between a metal and a semiconductor and deduce therefrom the methods by which ohmic connections may be made.

3.3.1. *Ohmic connections to n-type semiconductors*

The development of the energy diagram for the simplest type of contact between a metal and an *n*-type semiconductor is

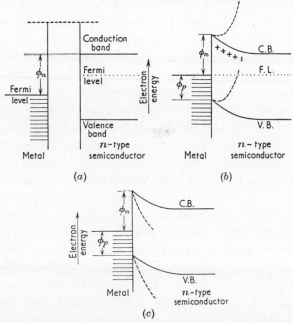

FIG. 3.4. The contact between a metal and an *n*-type semiconductor. (*a*) Energy levels when metal and semiconductor are well separated. (*b*) Energy diagram when metal and semiconductor are in contact. Full line: no voltage applied. Dashed line: forward voltage applied. (*c*) Same as (*b*) except that the dashed line results from the application of reverse voltage.

shown in Fig. 3.4. In part (*a*) of the figure, the metal and semiconductor are some distance apart and the positions of their energy levels are decided by their work functions as in the case of the *p-n* junction discussed in Chapter II. The Fermi level of the semiconductor is above that of the metal. When the two materials are brought together, electrons from the conduction band of the semiconductor drop into positions near the Fermi level of the metal, thus making the metal negative and the semiconductor positive. This process continues until the Fermi level of the semiconductor has been depressed to the same level as that of the metal, giving the energy diagram of Fig. 3.4 b. The positive charge in the semiconductor is supplied by donors that have lost their electrons and is therefore distributed through the semiconductor. It gives rise to the curved barrier shown by the full line in Fig. 3.4 b. The height, ϕ_n, of this barrier above the Fermi level is approximately equal to the original difference in energy between the Fermi level of the metal and the bottom of the conduction band of the semiconductor.

It may be seen from the following description that the contact thus created has a rectifying action. When no potential is applied across the contact, the currents of electrons from metal to semiconductor, and in the opposite direction, are equal so that the net current flow is zero. When the semiconductor is made negative with respect to the metal its energy levels are raised as shown by the dashed lines of Fig. 3.4 b and the barrier to the flow of electrons from semiconductor to metal is decreased in height, allowing a large increase in the flow of electrons in this direction. The flow of electrons from metal to semiconductor remains unchanged at its original low value since the barrier height ϕ_n is substantially unaffected by the applied field. There is thus a large net flow of electrons across the barrier as a result of the applied potential. This is the forward direction of the rectifying contact.

When the semiconductor is positive its energy levels take the position shown by the dashed lines of Fig. 3.4 c. The field now opposes the flow of electrons from semiconductor to metal and the current flowing in this direction becomes negligible even for quite small applied potentials. The flow of electrons from metal to semiconductor remains at its former small value and the net flow of current is in this direction. This is the reverse direction of the rectifying contact.

The contact formed between n-type germanium or silicon and a metal differs somewhat from that described above in that, owing to the existence of electron-trapping levels at the surface of the semiconductor, there is a barrier even when no metal is present [8]. This makes the contact relatively insensitive to the work function of the metal but does not change the essentials of the above picture.

Two measures may be taken to minimize the effect of the barrier thus described and make the contact essentially ohmic in practical cases. The first is to increase the area of contact so that the resistance, even in the reverse direction, is quite low. Because of limitations in the size and shape of the semiconductor this is not always possible. The second measure is to grade the density of donors from the normal small value in the body of the semiconductor to a large value near the metal. It can be seen from Fig. 3.4 *b* that the barrier ϕ_n is smaller if the conduction band is close to the Fermi level as in a heavily doped (n^+-type) semiconductor. The distance that the barrier extends into the semiconductor is also smaller in the case of a heavily doped semiconductor (cf. reference [9] p. 88). However, there now exists an additional rise in potential, similar to that of a *p-n* junction, between the n^+-type and *n*-type semiconductors so that the energy diagram of the contact is as shown in Fig. 3.5. If the change from n^+-type to *n*-type is sufficiently gradual, electrons diffusing from the n^+-type material will recombine with holes before reaching the *n*-type material and the n^+-*n* junction will be non-rectifying. Alternatively, insertion of a region having a high recombination rate will prevent the occurrence of rectification if the current is not too large. These same considerations apply to the *p-n* junction and they have been analysed in detail by Shockley [10]. The original barrier has thus been reduced to the very small one at the metal to n^+ contact. The area of the contact can usually be made large enough that the asymmetry of current flow produced by this small barrier is negligible.

This type of contact has the additional important property of preventing the injection of positive holes into the *n*-type material. The barrier to the entry of positive holes is the energy ϕ_p that the holes have to overcome when the contact is biased in the forward direction. In Fig. 3.5 this is considerably larger than in Fig. 3.4 *b* so that the probability of injection is small.

In practice, ohmic contacts to n-type material are usually made by soldering or evaporating on an alloy whose main constituents are inert from the point of view of semiconductor doping but to which an n-type impurity (e.g. antimony) has been added. Heating during soldering or subsequent to evaporation causes some of the n-type impurity to diffuse into the semiconductor to form an n^+-type layer. Careful control of temperature is required to ensure that the n^+-n junction is properly

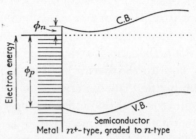

Fig. 3.5. Electron-energy diagram of an ohmic contact to an n-type semiconductor.

graded. A common electrode material for this purpose is antimony-tin-lead solder.

3.3.2. *Ohmic connections to p-type semiconductors*

The behaviour of the contact between a metal and p-type germanium is quite different from that exhibited when the germanium is n-type. At first glance this is rather surprising since, on the simple model described above, one would expect an energy diagram of the type shown in Fig. 3.6. This is the analogue of Fig. 3.4 b and predicts rectification of positive-hole current. In practice this does not occur because of the existence of trapping levels, mentioned in the preceding section, at the surface of the semiconductor. These cause the energy levels at the surface of the p-type material to behave in a manner similar to those of an n-type semiconductor. The energy diagram for this case is shown in Fig. 3.7. The rise in the energy levels of the semiconductor does not present a barrier to the flow of holes so that the contact is ohmic. Also, because the barrier to electrons is relatively high there is negligible injection of these carriers into the p-type material.

Data on metal-germanium contacts have been presented by Bocciarelli [11], who obtains remarkable agreement between theory and experiment. His theoretical analysis is based on the assumption of zero electron flow across the contact. This condition can only be satisfied if a barrier of the type shown in Figs. 3.4 b and 3.7 exists at the surface of the semiconductor.

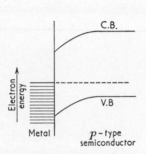

FIG. 3.6. Electron-energy diagram of a rectifying contact between a metal and a p-type semiconductor.

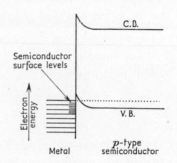

FIG. 3.7. Electron-energy diagram of the contact between a metal and p-type germanium.

The above picture, which is the result of the experience of many workers with metal-semiconductor contacts, is thus confirmed by detailed investigation.

It thus appears that there is little difficulty in making an ohmic contact to p-type germanium. Added insurance that the contact is ohmic can, however, be obtained by using a p-type impurity in the electrode material and thus creating a p^+-type layer in the surface of the semiconductor. This functions in a manner similar to the n^+-type layer in n-type material. This state of affairs comes about automatically in the alloy method of making junctions described below.

For silicon the effect of surface traps is apparently not as great as in germanium and the use of a contact metal containing p-type impurities seems to be obligatory. For example, aluminium, which alloys with silicon fairly readily, is used for the base connections in high-frequency n-p-n transistors [12].

3.4. Methods of making junction rectifiers and transistors

All processes for the manufacture of junction rectifiers and transistors make use of one or more of three basic techniques. In this section we shall describe these techniques briefly and indicate how some of the simpler devices are made. In later chapters we will see how device properties are influenced by these manufacturing processes.

The three basic techniques referred to may be defined in terms of the following types of junction produced by them:

1. Grown junctions.
2. Alloy junctions.
3. Diffused junctions.

We now consider these in turn.

3.4.1. *Grown junctions*

Grown junctions are produced by a modification of the pulling method for the production of single crystals, in which the density of impurities is altered during the growing process. In the production of a germanium p-n junction, for example, the melt may have initially a small concentration of n-type (donor) impurity (e.g. arsenic). At a later stage in the single-crystal growing process a sufficiently large quantity of p-type impurity is added to make the remainder of the crystal p-type. In order to obtain better control of the amount of impurity, heavily doped p-type material, having a known concentration of acceptors determined by electrical measurement, is used in preference to pure p-type impurity. Upon removal from the furnace the central section containing the junction is cut out—the lengths of the p-type and n-type materials adjoining the junction being usually several times greater than the diffusion length. By further slicing, parallel to the direction of crystal growth, a large number of bars of rectangular cross-section, each containing a p-n junction, is made. Following the attachment of ohmic contacts and leads to its ends the device is encapsulated to form a commercial p-n junction.

In the manufacture of n-p-n grown-junction transistors, the *p*-type section is grown for a very short time to give a thin base layer. A charge of heavily doped *n*-type material is then added to make the melt *n*-type and growth is continued. Upon completion the crystal is cut into a large number of *n-p-n* transistors to which ohmic electrodes are attached. The technique of finding the base layer and attaching an ohmic electrode to it is rather complicated, because of the small base thickness and the possibility of short-circuiting the junctions, but it is now done regularly on a commercial scale. For reasons to be discussed later, the final *n*-type section of the crystal, which contains the largest concentration of impurity and thus the lowest resistivity material, is made the emitter of the finished transistor.

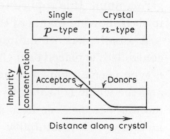

This straightforward method of growing *p-n* junctions produces rather gradual changes in the densities of impurities. A schematic diagram of the impurity distributions produced is shown in Fig. 3.8.

FIG. 3.8. Schematic diagram of impurity concentrations in a grown *p-n* junction.

Several modifications of the above procedure are now being used to produce transistors. The following are typical examples:

(*a*) Rate-grown transistors [13] are produced by varying the rate of growth of a single crystal from a melt containing both *p*- and *n*-type impurities. Because the distribution coefficients of the two impurities vary differently with the growth-rate, the type of conductivity of any section of the crystal depends on the rate at which it is grown. Thus, by controlled variation of the rate of growth and the temperature of the melt, transistors can be produced.

(*b*) Three developments that make use of the same principle as the rate-growing process are the remelt process [4], the 'melt-quench process' [14], and the 'melt-back process' [15]. In each of these a single crystal containing different amounts of *p*-type and *n*-type impurities is grown and segregation of impurities is obtained by subsequent melting and refreezing. Germanium n-p-n transistors can be grown by all three methods.

(c) A different modification of the growing process is used in the manufacture of 'grown-diffused' transistors. We will defer the discussion of this until high-frequency transistors are considered in Chapter VIII.

3.4.2. *Alloy junctions*

The process of junction formation that is used most widely in the manufacture of transistors is the alloying of indium and germanium. It is applied to the construction of p-n-p transistors in the following manner [16]:

A small piece of indium, the weight of which is carefully controlled, is placed on a thin wafer of relatively high-resistivity n-type germanium (4 ohm cm for general-purpose transistors) and the whole is heated to a temperature of about 500° C. The indium becomes molten at about 150° C and dissolves germanium. The solubility of germanium in molten indium increases with temperature, and at a temperature of 500° C enough germanium dissolves in the indium to produce a depression in the germanium disk. Equilibrium is reached quite rapidly and the solution is then at the saturation point corresponding to that temperature. The depression therefore reaches a depth that depends on the amount of indium used and the temperature. The temperature is now lowered, reducing the solubility of germanium in indium, and part of the germanium containing indium as a p-type impurity crystallizes out. This recrystallized germanium forms a single crystal of the same orientation as the germanium disk and, except for the p-type impurity, is indistinguishable from it. Its resistivity is very low and the p-n junction that it forms with the original n-type material is very sharp.

A similar junction is also formed on the opposite side of the wafer thus completing a transistor whose construction is shown schematically in Fig. 3.9. For general-purpose (low-frequency) transistors the ohmic connection to the base usually consists of an oblong tab soldered to it as shown in the figure. For higher frequencies a ring base-contact may be used. The important dimensions of the device, as given by Giacoletto [17] are also shown in Fig. 3.9.

The following points of difference between alloy-junction and grown-junction transistors are noted here for future use:

1. Because the emitter junction in an alloy-junction transistor lies well below the surface of the base material, the emitter current tends to spread out radially from the emitter junction. Thus, in order to ensure that a large fraction of the emitter current reaches the collector, the latter is made larger in area than the emitter. This has the disadvantage, which must be accepted, of making the collector capacitance larger than that of an otherwise equivalent grown-junction transistor.

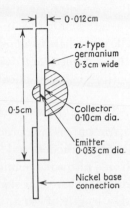

FIG. 3.9. Construction of an alloy-junction transistor.

2. The resistivities of the emitter and collector regions in alloy transistors are low and approximately equal. The base resistivity is relatively high. In grown-junction transistors the resistivity of the collector exceeds that of the base—which in turn has a larger resistivity than the emitter.

3. The abrupt character of the alloy junction, which is a result of the fact that the diffusion coefficient of indium in germanium is very small at 500° C, is in marked contrast to the 'graded' character of the grown junctions described earlier.

4. The properties of the impurities concerned are such that it is relatively easy to make *p-n-p* alloy-junction transistors from germanium while grown germanium transistors are usually of the *n-p-n* type. For the same dimensions the latter have the better high-frequency response because, in addition to the lower collector capacitance mentioned above, the higher mobility of electrons leads to a more rapid diffusion of minority carriers across the base region.

5. Silicon transistors are largely of the *n-p-n* grown variety. It is more difficult to make good alloy-junction transistors of silicon than germanium, although silicon-alloy transistors are now made by at least two American manufacturers. Silicon-alloy junction rectifiers are produced in larger quantities. Because of their high reverse resistance and their ability to operate at high temperatures they have displaced germanium-alloy rectifiers to a large extent. It now seems, however, that the diffused rectifiers described in the next section will displace both in many applications.

3.4.3. *Diffused junctions*

An important process in the present-day manufacture of junction diodes and transistors is the diffusion of impurity atoms into solid semiconductors. Diffusion of this type (i.e. of atoms rather than electrons or holes) can take place in a reasonable length of time only if the temperature is high, although still well below the melting-point of the semiconductor. In this high-temperature region the diffusion coefficients of these atomic impurities, which vary exponentially with temperature, can be controlled between wide limits. The thickness of the diffused layer can thus be defined very precisely by control of the temperature and the time of diffusion.

The diffusion process may be applied to the manufacture of transistors in many ways [18]. Two of these, which were outlined in the earliest papers on the subject, will suffice to indicate the power of the method. The first [12], which is applied to silicon, makes use of the fact that donor and acceptor impurities of slightly different atomic weights (e.g. antimony and aluminium) diffuse in this material at widely different rates—the rate for acceptors being 10 to 100 times that for donors at the same temperature. Thus, if a certain concentration of donor impurities and a smaller concentration of acceptor impurities are established at the surface of a wafer of single-crystal *n*-type silicon, the concentrations within the material, following a period at high temperature, may be represented by the schematic diagram of Fig. 3.10. The layer *OA* immediately below the surface will be *n*-type, the layer *AB* will be *p*-type, and the remainder will have the *n*-type conductivity of the original wafer. An *n-p-n* diffused-junction transistor is thus created in a single operation.

In the second application [19] a slice of single-crystal *p*-type germanium is used as the starting material. A donor impurity (arsenic) is diffused into it to produce a thin surface layer of *n*-type material. A dot of the acceptor indium is then melted into this *n*-type layer to form an alloyed emitter junction. The diffused layer forms the base, and the original material the collector, of a high-frequency *p-n-p* transistor.

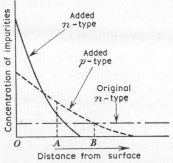

Fig. 3.10. Concentrations of *n*-type and *p*-type impurities obtained in *n*-type silicon by diffusion.

We have not discussed methods of making ohmic contacts to either of the devices described. It is sufficient to say that they are made by alloying p^+ or n^+ electrodes as required. Details may be obtained from the original papers.

It is apparent that the solid-state diffusion technique can also be applied to the manufacture of junction rectifiers. Indeed, its first published application was in the construction of silicon *p-n* junctions [20] and it will doubtless become the dominant technique in the manufacture of large area devices of this type.

This completes our brief survey of the techniques whereby ohmic contacts and *p-n* junction devices are produced. In a later chapter, when the properties of these devices have been considered in some detail, we will consider further the effect of these techniques on specific properties of junction rectifiers and transistors, particularly properties required in the handling of high-speed transients and high-frequency alternating currents.

THE p-n JUNCTION

4.1. Introduction

In the preceding chapters brief descriptions of the operation and manufacture of p-n junctions have been given with the intention of familiarizing the reader with them and with some of the parameters which enter into the operation of junction devices in general. In the present chapter a more complete outline of the physics of the p-n junction will be given. Before proceeding with this it is perhaps worth while to mention some of the reasons for the relatively large concentration of effort on this device. These are:

(a) The p-n junction is an important device in its own right, which may function as a rectifier, voltage regulator, or photovoltaic cell.

(b) Junction theory plays an important part in transistor design, particularly in the process of making an efficient emitter and in the effort to minimize temperature effects.

(c) The equations that govern the flow of current in p-n junctions also apply to transistors although the boundary conditions used are different.

A rigorous analysis of the p-n junction, applicable under all operating conditions, would be very complicated. In view of the apparent simplicity of the physical picture of the device this is, perhaps, rather surprising. Such complications are, however, characteristic of systems in which current flow is governed by both electrical and diffusion forces and, in the present instance, are intensified by the existence of two types of carrier with the possibility of carrier generation and recombination. A preliminary manipulation of the equations involved (Appendix III) shows that some quite drastic approximations and assumptions are necessary if theoretical results in readily usable form are to be obtained.

The first and most complete analysis of the p-n junction was made in Shockley's classic paper [1] dealing with a junction in which the transition from n- to p-type material within the crystal is gradual. It seems to apply quite accurately, within limits decided by the approximations used, to grown junctions. Another analysis dealing with junctions in which the transition is more sudden has been given by Hall [2].

Excellent outlines of the Shockley and Hall theories have been given by Goudet and Meuleau [3] and a comparison of various modifications of simple p-n junction theory has been given by Saby [4]. A detailed discussion of these analyses cannot be given in this book but we shall outline a simplified theory of the d.c. characteristic which applies to p-n junctions of both the graded and abrupt types in which the p- and n-type regions each have lengths greater than a few diffusion lengths. It is emphasized that this simple analysis is mainly descriptive and does not apply to power rectifiers of the alloy type in which a near-intrinsic region is usually assumed to exist between the p- and n-type material. The range in which it applies can only be ascertained by the study of more complete theories. It does, however, reveal most of the features that are important in deciding the static characteristics of p-n junctions and transistors. In the case of a.c. characteristics of p-n junctions we shall be content to outline the results of Shockley's theory for small alternating voltages and to give the order of magnitude of transient effects.

4.2. The d.c. characteristic

We consider again the electron-energy diagram of a p-n junction as shown in Fig. 4.1 and observe that the potential step between A and B exists because the density of electrons in the region OB is less than $(N_d - N_a)$ and the density of positive holes in the region AO is less than $(N_a - N_d)$, where N_d, the number of (positively charged) donors, and N_a, the number of (negatively charged) acceptors, both vary with distance through the region AB. The two parts of region AB thus have space charges of opposite sign because of the 'depletion' of mobile

carriers. For this reason the region AB is often referred to as
the space-charge or depletion region. A third term, common in
transistor literature, is 'transition region'. Because of the loss
of carriers this region has high effective resistance and, even for
quite large forward currents, the voltage drop across remaining
parts of the device is small compared with that across AB.
This condition applies to an even greater extent for reverse-
applied voltages when the current flowing through the device

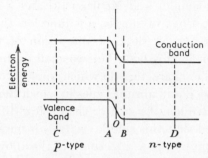

Fig. 4.1. Electron-energy diagram of a *p-n* junction.

is very small. Consequently, as in most other analyses of *p-n*
junctions, the basic assumption is made that the applied potential merely changes the size of the energy step at AB so that
the number of carriers capable of crossing the barrier is altered.
This number is decided by conditions in the regions CA and BD
on either side of the energy step. The region AB is so thin that
processes, such as generation and recombination, taking place
within it can usually be ignored.

In deriving the current-voltage characteristic it is advantageous to consider the flow of positive holes rather than electrons
since the direction of current flow is then the same as the direction
of flow of the carriers and there is less confusion concerning signs.
The hole-energy diagram for a *p-n* junction with no applied
voltage is given by the full lines in Fig. 4.2 *a*. The effect of a
potential V, applied in the forward direction, is to lower the
Fermi level of the *n*-type material by an amount qV with respect
to the *p*-type material and to decrease the height of the barrier
by the same amount, as shown by the dashed line. In the

diagram this decrease is shown, for convenience, as a change in the energy of the n-type material but the important quantity is the difference in energy between the n- and p-type materials. We now consider the effect of this difference in energy on the flow of positive holes across the barrier under d.c. conditions.

The number of holes per c.c. in the p-type material having

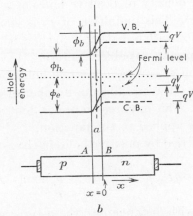

FIG. 4.2. (a) Positive-hole energy diagram of a p-n junction. (b) Schematic diagram of the single crystal containing the junction.

energies greater than the height of the barrier may be calculated from equation (1.4) by replacing ϕ_h by $[\phi_h+(\phi_b-qV)]$. It is

$$p_1 = C_1 \exp[-(\phi_b-qV)/kT],$$

where C_1 is constant at constant temperature. When $V = 0$, p_1 must be equal to p_n the equilibrium number of holes in the n-type material, as a flow of current would otherwise be produced by diffusion of holes across the junction. Hence

$$p_n = C_1 \exp(-\phi_b/kT)$$

and $$p_1 = p_n \exp(qV/kT). \tag{4.1}$$

Note that, because holes are majority carriers in the region to the left of the barrier, p_1 does not vary significantly with distance in this region.

Positive holes crossing the barrier from left to right become minority carriers and, in the steady-state condition with the assumption of constant lifetime, must obey equation (2.7). As in that case, the solution is

$$p - p_n = (p_1 - p_n) \exp(-x/L_p), \tag{4.2}$$

where x is positive in the direction of positive-hole flow and $x = 0$ on the n-side of the transition region as shown in Fig. 4.2. p_1, the density of positive holes at $x = 0$, is defined by equation (4.1). This definition of p_1 is equivalent to that given in connection with equation (2.8) since both represent the number of holes per c.c. capable of entering the n-type material.

The assumption of constant lifetime holds only if p is very much less than n_0 (the equilibrium number of electrons in the n-type material). This imposes an upper limit on p_1 and hence on V, the voltage applied to the junction.

The current carried by positive holes in the n-type material is

$$I_{px} = -qD_p \frac{dp}{dx} = \frac{qD_p}{L_p} (p_1 - p_n) \exp(-x/L_p). \tag{4.3}$$

This diminishes with distance into the n-type material because of recombination, and the function of carrying the current is taken over by electrons which enter the n-type material through the ohmic connection shown at the right of Fig. 4.2 b. This current, which arises from the injection of holes into the n-type material, thus satisfies the law of continuity, but in the region immediately to the right of the barrier the current is carried largely by holes while at greater distances it is carried almost entirely by electrons.

Electrons are injected into the p-type material in a manner completely analogous to that outlined for holes. The corresponding component of current is carried largely by electrons in the p-type region immediately to the left of the barrier but is transferred to positive holes as the left-hand terminal of the device is approached. This component is superimposed on that due to the injection of holes and they may be treated independently.

The component I_{px} is carried entirely by holes at $x = 0$ so that substitution of this condition in (4.3) gives the current I_p

produced by the injection of holes into the n-type material, i.e.

$$I_p = \frac{qD_p}{L_p}(p_1 - p_n), \tag{4.4}$$

or $$I_p = \frac{qD_p p_n}{L_p}[\exp(qV/kT) - 1], \tag{4.5}$$

where p_1 has been substituted from equation (4.1). When V is positive I_p is positive and increases very rapidly with voltage. When V is negative I_p is negative, indicating a reverse current, and for $|V|$ large, becomes constant at the value

$$I_p = -I_{ps} = -\frac{qD_p p_n}{L_p}. \tag{4.6}$$

In this case the barrier is very large and I_{ps}, which is called the hole saturation current, arises from the generation of minority carriers in the n-type material. These diffuse to the barrier and, under the influence of the large barrier field, move rapidly into the p-type material. From paragraph (f) § 1.3 we see that p_n and I_{ps} are rapidly varying functions of temperature.

The current resulting from the injection of electrons into the n-type material may be derived by an identical procedure which gives an expression for I_n of the same form as (4.5). The total current is therefore

$$I = I_p + I_n = I_s[\exp(qV/kT) - 1], \tag{4.7}$$

where $$I_s = \left(\frac{qD_p p_n}{L_p} + \frac{qD_n n_p}{L_n}\right) \tag{4.8}$$

is the magnitude of the total saturation current. The expression (4.7) is the equation of the d.c. characteristic of our simple p-n junction.

The d.c. characteristic of an ideal p-n junction is sketched schematically in Fig. 4.3. Note that it is continuous through the origin as expected from equation (4.7) and that rectification is a

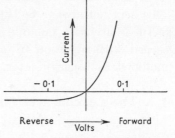

FIG. 4.3. Schematic diagram of the d.c. characteristic of an ideal p-n junction.

direct result of the properties of the exponential function.

As mentioned in Chapter I, n_p and p_n both vary exponentially with temperature although their activation energies ϕ_e and ϕ_h are, in general, different. The carrier having the smaller activation energy contributes the dominant component of the saturation current. Thus, taking account of the variation of D_p and D_n with temperature,

$$I_s \propto T^2 \exp(-E'_g/kT), \qquad (4.9)$$

where E'_g differs from the energy gap by 0·10 to 0·25 eV. This equation will be considered later in this chapter when the effect of temperature on *p-n* junction characteristics is discussed.

4.2.1. *Injection properties*

The method whereby a *p-n* junction can be made into a good hole or electron injector can be deduced from equation (4.8). Using equations (2.1) and (2.4) for diffusion coefficient and lifetime it can be shown [1] that the ratio of the two components of (4.8) is given by

$$\frac{I_{ps}}{I_{ns}} = \sqrt{\left(\frac{\sigma_p}{\sigma_n}\right)}, \qquad (4.10)$$

where σ_p and σ_n are the conductivities of the *p*- and *n*-type materials. The current crossing a junction of high-conductivity *p*-type material and low-conductivity *n*-type material thus consists largely of holes and such a junction can be used as a positive-hole injector.

We should note that equation (4.10) will only apply exactly if the definition of lifetime has the general form of equation (2.4). This may not always be the case but for our purpose equation (4.10) is accurate enough. In transistors, where we are concerned with injection from emitter to base, this equation is modified, as discussed later, because of the small base thickness.

4.3. The a.c. characteristic

The d.c. characteristic of the *p-n* junction describes a highly non-linear resistive device. At high frequencies, however, it exhibits pronounced capacitive properties which affect its performance under steady state a.c. or pulse conditions. These properties are defined by two distinctly different parameters normally called the 'transition-region capacitance' and the 'diffusion capacitance' respectively. We now consider these briefly.

4.3.1. *Transition-region capacitance*

We have indicated earlier that the potential step at the p-n junction of Fig. 4.1 exists because depletion of mobile charge carriers in the region AB produces adjacent layers of positive and negative space charge. It can be shown from simple electrostatics [5] that the potential step at such a double layer is proportional to the electric moment ($\sum qd$, where q is a charge at distance d from O) of the space-charge region. Thus when the potential step becomes larger because of increased applied potential in the reverse direction the amounts of negative space charge in the region AO and of positive space charge in the region OB must increase. These increases are obtained by the removal of holes from the left-hand side and electrons from the right-hand side of the transition region. The junction thus contains an insulating region, depleted of mobile charge, whose thickness increases with reverse voltage. On the boundaries of this region the semiconducting regions contain mobile charge and thus act as the plates of a condenser having the transition region as a dielectric. An incremental capacitance $C_T = \delta Q/\delta V$, usually called the transition-region capacitance, may thus be defined. Here δQ is the change of charge produced in the region AO or OB by a change δV in applied voltage. This capacitance, which may be measured by superimposing a small a.c. voltage upon a d.c. reverse voltage, would be constant if the transition thickness did not vary with applied voltage. In practice, however, the transition-region thickness and capacity both vary with d.c. reverse voltage. Formulae expressing these quantities in terms of applied voltage and densities of impurity centres are derived in Appendix IV. For a graded junction in which the densities of impurity centres vary linearly with distance

$$C_T \propto (V_0 - V_a)^{-\frac{1}{3}}, \tag{4.11}$$

where V_a is the applied voltage, which is negative when in the reverse direction, and $V_0 = \phi_b/q$ is the built-in voltage of the junction. For an abrupt junction, in which $|N_d-N_a|$ changes suddenly from one constant value to another,

$$C_T \propto (V_0-V_a)^{-\frac{1}{2}}. \qquad (4.12)$$

Relation (4.11) usually seems to apply to grown junctions while (4.12) is more characteristic of alloy junctions. V_0, which is about 0·4 volts for germanium and 0·7 volts for silicon, may be ignored when the applied reverse voltage is large.

For abrupt junctions an interesting aspect of the expansion of the space-charge region with reverse voltage arises if the conductivities of the p and n regions of the crystal differ considerably. To fulfil the requirement that the amounts of charge on the two sides of the double layer be equal, the edge of the space-charge region will advance more rapidly into the high-resistivity material than into the low-resistivity material as the reverse voltage is increased. This effect, which is considered quantitatively in Appendix IV, has an important bearing on the design of transistors and high-voltage junction rectifiers.

Equations (4.11) and (4.12) show that the transition-region capacitance is diminished when the applied d.c. voltage is in the forward direction. C_T is then masked by the diffusion capacitance discussed below.

4.3.2. *Diffusion capacitance and stored charge*

Another variation of charge in the vicinity of the junction arises from the injection or extraction of minority carriers under conditions of forward or very small reverse bias respectively. For very small changes of applied voltage

$$(\delta V_a \ll kT/q \simeq 25 \text{ mV})$$

the corresponding change in injected charge δQ is a linear function of voltage and a parameter $C = \delta Q/\delta V$, called the 'diffusion capacitance' may be defined. For small low-frequency alternating voltages, with no superimposed d.c. potential, Shockley [1] has shown that the diffusion capacitance is

$$C_d = q^2(p_n L_p+n_p L_n)/2kT. \qquad (4.13)$$

For higher frequencies C_d increases with frequency and is accompanied by a conductance term which also increases with frequency. The behaviour under these higher frequency low-voltage conditions has also been analysed in detail by Shockley.

For larger alternating applied voltages, when the forward current is large, a capacitance defined in the ordinary way would be a function of time and forward current, and a determination of the effect of frequency on the rectifier properties could not be made by ordinary circuit methods. The problem is then usually treated by considering the transient response of the stored minority-carrier charge when an applied d.c. voltage is altered suddenly. This has been done by many workers, the most complete paper being that of Henderson and Tillman [6] who give references to most earlier work. We shall not consider this approach further for *p-n* junctions but shall have occasion to refer to it later in connection with transistors.

Some indication of the effect of this high-level carrier storage on the frequency response of a *p-n* junction rectifier can be obtained by considering our earlier equations for the densities of injected carriers. By the elimination of (p_1-p_n) from equations (4.2) and (4.4) it is seen that

$$p-p_n = \frac{L_p I_p}{q D_p} \exp(-x/L_p), \tag{4.14}$$

and the total charge stored per sq. cm. in the *n*-type material when a steady forward current I_p flows through it is

$$Q = q \int_0^\infty (p-p_n)\, dx = \frac{L_p I_p}{D_p} \int_0^\infty \exp(-x/L_p)\, dx = \frac{L_p^2 I_p}{D_p} = \tau_p I_p. \tag{4.15}$$

(We assume that the length of the *n*-type region is much greater than L_p so that the upper limit of the integral may be made infinite without appreciable error.) We see from this that the total charge stored is proportional to the total forward current. We note that the amount of this stored charge is independent of the area of the rectifier and depends only on the total current. If the area is increased, with the total current constant, the current density I_p and the charge per sq. cm. Q decrease so that the total charge remains constant. This is in contrast to the stored charge in the transition region which increases with area.

We now consider a practical rectifier whose forward current is carried largely by positive holes so that I_p in (4.15) is the total current. This device is connected in series with a load of resistance R as shown in Fig. 4.4. An applied alternating voltage V then produces a half-cycle of (forward) current whose average value is I_A. The amount of charge stored in the rectifier as a result of this current flow is approximately $Q_A = \tau_p I_A$.

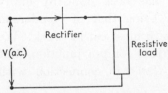

FIG. 4.4. Half-wave rectifier in series with a resistive load.

We now assume that the stored charge is released during the following reverse half-cycle, i.e. during a time $1/2f$ where f is the frequency. The average reverse current is thus $2fQ_A$. For efficient rectification this should be much smaller than I_A—say 1 per cent or less. Thus $2fQ_A \leqslant I_A/100$ or $f \leqslant 1/200\tau_p$, and for $\tau_p = 1$ μsec —a reasonable value for a good junction—the upper limit of frequency is about 5 kc/sec.

It must be emphasized that this result represents an order of magnitude only and that it applies to a junction for which the length of the n-type region is much greater than L_p. The effect of shortening the length of the n-type region is considered in the next section.

4.4. Minimization of carrier storage

The above frequency limitation and the accompanying deterioration of transient response restrict the application of the type of device so far discussed. It is, however, possible to improve performance by reducing the amount of carrier storage. The two most obvious ways of doing this are the following:

1. *To decrease the minority-carrier lifetime.* For the above case this decreases L_p, which is proportional to $\tau_p^{\frac{1}{2}}$, and increases the reverse saturation current as may be seen from equation (4.8). This and the degradation of other properties limit the extent to which this method can be applied, but for special

devices it may be quite effective. A silicon computer diode [7] has a minority carrier storage time of less than 5×10^{-9} seconds.

2. *To shorten the region into which the minority carriers are injected* (the n-type region in the present case). Most injected carriers will then pass through this region to recombine rapidly at the ohmic connection to it. Junction rectifiers of this type are often called narrow-base diodes. The magnitude of the improvement attainable by this method may be estimated by the calculation that follows.

For an n-type region of length $W \ll L_p$ the density of the injected holes is given by equation (A2.5) of Appendix II. Thus

$$p - p_n = (p_1 - p_n)\left(\frac{W - x}{W}\right) \qquad (4.16)$$

and
$$I_{px} = I_p = -qD_p\frac{dp}{dx} = \frac{qD_p}{W}(p_1 - p_n). \qquad (4.17)$$

Elimination of $(p_1 - p_n)$ from equations (4.16) and (4.17) gives

$$p - p_n = \frac{I_p}{qD_p}(W - x) \qquad (4.18)$$

and the stored charge becomes

$$Q = q \int_0^W (p - p_n)\, dx = \frac{I_p W^2}{2D_p} = \frac{\tau_p I_p W^2}{2L_p^2}. \qquad (4.19)$$

Comparing this with equation (4.15) we see that a considerable reduction in stored charge (or in diffusion capacitance if the signal is small enough that this quantity can be defined) is possible if $W \ll L_p$. Equation (4.17) when compared with equation (4.4) indicates that the level of current flow in both directions through the device will be increased by a factor L_p/W, but in the case of power rectifiers this change can be readily tolerated and may even be desirable since the forward voltage drop will be decreased. The accompanying increase of current in the reverse direction is often not important. For small devices to be used in pulse circuits the lowering of effective resistance may be more serious. Carrier storage is the most serious limitation in the design of diodes for such applications.

Finally it should be observed that the above analysis applies only to very simple junctions in which such factors as surface leakage, surface recombination, and poor connections have not been considered. In practice one or more of the following cases may occur:

(a) The junction may be more complicated [2, 4].

(b) The reverse characteristic may be influenced by surface effects or by the generation of carriers in the transition region [8, 9].

(c) The resistance of the semiconductor or the 'ohmic' contact that it makes with an electrode may affect the forward characteristic.

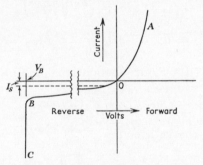

FIG. 4.5. Schematic diagram of a practical
p-n junction characteristic.

These considerations may modify the above results somewhat although the general conclusions will still apply. A practical p-n junction characteristic is shown in Fig. 4.5. The reverse current in this case is seen to rise above the theoretical saturation value I_s because of surface effects or the generation of carriers in the transition region. The reverse breakdown section BC of the characteristic will be discussed below.

4.5. Effect of temperature on the p-n junction characteristic

It can be seen from equations (4.7) and (4.9) that the forward and reverse currents of an ideal p-n junction are both functions of temperature. The reverse saturation current varies rapidly with temperature, but the variation in forward current is less rapid because of the cancellation produced by the $\exp(qV/kT)$ factor. We note also that the percentage change of reverse current with temperature is greater for silicon than germanium. The magnitude of the reverse saturation current in silicon is so small, however, that the effect of temperature on the reverse current of the rectifier can be ignored below operating temperatures of about 150° C. For germanium, in which the reverse current is much larger at ordinary temperatures, the upper limit of rectifier operation is usually taken as 100° C.

The reverse saturation current plays an important part in the operation of the collector of a transistor, where it forms one component of the current that flows between collector and base when the emitter current is zero. This current is called the collector-leakage or cutoff current. It contains two other important components, both arising at the surface. One is due to the presence of states that would be present even if the surface were perfect. It varies with temperature in much the same way as the body-saturation component and is substantially independent of the voltage applied across the junction. For practical purposes it may be assumed to form part of I_s. The second surface component, which is due to the presence of impurities, increases slowly with reverse voltage and is similar to the slowly rising p-n junction current shown in Fig. 4.5. It does not vary rapidly with temperature so that, at junction temperatures above about 35° C, the collector leakage current of germanium transistors is dominated by the body and surface saturation components. For silicon transistors the slowly rising component seems to be dominant until at least 100° C. The variation of reverse saturation current may be expressed, over a limited range of temperature, by a straight line on a $\log I$ vs. T plot. The collector leakage current is usually presented in this way by transistor manufacturers.

The effect of temperature on the forward characteristics of junction rectifiers can usually be ignored. In transistors, however, the variation of the emitter resistance with temperature is sometimes important. In such applications the standing or bias current rather than the voltage is kept constant. Differentiation of equation (4.7) when $\exp(qV/kT) \gg 1$ and $dI/dT = 0$, using equation (4.9) for I_s, then shows that, for germanium transistors, having emitter currents of the order of one milliampere,

$$\frac{dV}{dT} = -\frac{1}{T}\left[\frac{2kT}{q} + \frac{E'_g}{q} - \frac{T}{q}\frac{dE'_g}{dt} - V\right]. \qquad (4.20)$$

Now $E'_g \simeq E_g$ at $T = 0$ and decreases roughly linearly as T increases. Hence $E'_g - T(dE'_g/dT) \simeq E_g$ and since $V \simeq 0.15$ volts we obtain

$$\frac{dV}{dT} \simeq -2.3 \ \text{mV/°C}. \qquad (4.21)$$

This figure also applies approximately to silicon since the increase in E'_g is compensated for by a corresponding increase in V under normal operating conditions. Equation (4.21) will be used in our study of methods of biasing transistors.

4.6. Electrical breakdown of p-n junctions

Our description of the reverse characteristic has not indicated that there is any upper limit to the voltage that can be applied across a p-n junction in the reverse direction. That such a limit must exist is apparent from equations (A4.6) and (A4.21), which show that the transition layer, across which the reverse voltage is applied, increases in thickness as $V^{\frac{1}{3}}$ for a graded junction and as $V^{\frac{1}{2}}$ for an abrupt junction. The electric field strength thus increases with applied voltage until breakdown occurs.

4.6.1. *Avalanche breakdown*

The mechanism usually responsible for breakdown at higher voltages is avalanche formation due to the cumulative increase of the number of carriers by collision processes. The essentials of the mechanism may be seen by reference to Fig. 4.6 which shows the electron-energy diagram of a p-n junction subjected to a large reverse voltage. The field strength in the transition region between G and H is indicated by the slope of the bottom of the conduction band and the top of the valence band. An electron entering the transition region at A from the p-type region is accelerated by the field, and its velocity (v) and kinetic energy ($\frac{1}{2}m_e v^2$) increase rapidly. The kinetic energy of the electron at any point is given by its distance above the bottom of the conduction band. For example, an electron at B has a kinetic energy BC. If the electron suffered no loss of energy when moving at high velocity the point representing its energy would move along the line AJ. It does, however, lose small amounts of energy in collision with the atoms of the lattice so that its position on the energy diagram actually follows the line AB.

Upon arrival at position B the electron has a kinetic energy BC equal to E_g, the gap energy. Once this condition has been reached it can, in a collision with a lattice atom, impart energy to a valence electron and put it into the conduction band at C. The first electron loses the energy $BC = C'D \simeq E_g$ and there are then two electrons in the conduction band at C and C' and a positive hole in the valence band at D. All three carriers can continue the process—the subsequent positions of the electrons falling along the lines CE, $C'E'$

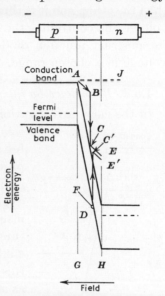

Fig. 4.6. Electron-energy diagram illustrating avalanching in a p-n junction.

and those of the hole along DF. The numbers of carriers in both conduction and valence bands are thus rapidly multiplied and the effective resistance of the device drops to a very low value as shown by the section BC of the p-n junction characteristic in Fig. 4.5. The voltage V_B at which this sudden decrease in resistance occurs is called the breakdown voltage.

It can readily be seen that the magnitude of V_B depends on the resistivity of the junction material. Equations (A4.6) and (A4.21) show that, for a given applied voltage, the width of the transition or space-charge region will vary inversely with the density of impurity centres in the semiconductor. The electric field in the transition region will therefore decrease, and the breakdown voltage increase correspondingly, as the resistivity of the semiconductor is increased.

In most p-n junctions, especially those of the alloy type, one section of the crystal will have a considerably higher resistivity than the other, and it is this section that decides the breakdown voltage. By controlling the resistivity of this section it is possible to construct junction diodes having their reverse breakdown voltage in a chosen range.

4.6.2. *Breakdown by internal-field emission (Zener breakdown)*

In the early investigations of p-n junctions, another process

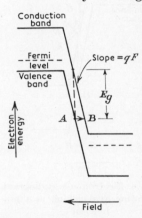

FIG. 4.7. Electron-energy diagram illustrating breakdown of a p-n junction by internal-field emission.

was believed responsible for electrical breakdown in the reverse direction. This process, called 'internal-field emission' [10], was originally proposed by Zener to explain the high-voltage breakdown of insulating solids. It depends on a quantum mechanical theorem that has no analogue in classical mechanics. Briefly, this theorem states that a particle such as an electron can pass through a high-potential barrier if the barrier is sufficiently thin. According to classical mechanics such a process is impossible and the only way an electron can cross a barrier is to gain sufficient energy to go over it.

The application of this quantum mechanical process, which is often called Tunnel Effect, to the p-n junction is shown schematically in Fig. 4.7. An electron in the valence band at A is separated from a vacant state of the same energy in the conduction band at B by a distance that depends on the applied field. Since the vertical distance between valence and conduction bands is constant and equal to E_g, we have $qF = E_g/AB$, where F is the field strength in the transition region. Thus AB decreases as F is increased. When the distance AB becomes sufficiently small, large numbers of electrons can tunnel through the potential barrier from valence to conduction band and contribute to a current which rises very rapidly with field strength. The applied voltage at which this rapid rise in current occurs is called the breakdown voltage.

4.6.3. *Breakdown in commercial p-n junctions*

From a practical point of view, the chief difference between the avalanche and Zener mechanism appears in the temperature coefficient of the breakdown process. For avalanche breakdown this quantity is positive because the loss of energy to atoms of the lattice (that is, in the region AB of Fig. 4.6) increases with temperature. In field emission the chief effect of temperature arises from the decrease of the gap energy E_g as the temperature is increased—which leads to a negative temperature coefficient of breakdown voltage.

Avalanche breakdown is expected to be dominant when the transition-region thickness is large and hence when the breakdown voltage is high. In practice it is found that most junctions which break down at applied potentials of 5 volts or higher have positive temperature coefficients so that avalanche breakdown is probably the dominant mechanism in this region. Lower voltage units usually have negative temperature coefficients indicating the existence of Zener effect. In such devices the transition region is apparently too thin to allow appreciable carrier multiplication to take place and Zener breakdown occurs before the critical avalanche condition has been reached. In the region around 5 volts both mechanisms probably contribute to the breakdown current.

4.6.4. *Punch-through*

A third process that can lead to a drastic lowering of the reverse resistance of a transistor collector or a narrow-base junction rectifier, is called punch-through. It is not a breakdown in the ordinary sense. For transistors it can be described with the help of the energy diagram of the *p-n-p* transistor shown in Fig. 4.8. As the collector voltage is increased the transition region of the collector-base junction lengthens and, if the base region is very thin, the collector transition region may eventually occupy the whole of the base region. Upon further increase of collector voltage the emitter barrier will be lowered and a very large current will flow through the transistor producing a collector to emitter breakdown. This phenomenon often occurs at a field strength below that required to produce avalanche breakdown and is responsible for the low voltage ratings of many high-frequency transistors.

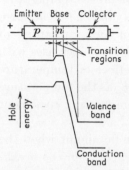

Fig. 4.8. Positive-hole energy diagram illustrating the approach to punch-through in a *p-n-p* transistor.

The method of manufacture of the collector junction is important in determining the susceptibility to punch-through as may be seen by comparing the behaviour of grown and alloy junctions. At high field strengths, the collector transition regions of both types of transistor extend into regions in which the numbers of donors and acceptors are constant so that both may be represented by the abrupt model of Appendix IV. As seen from equation (A 4.24) the extension of the transition region into the collector or base region is proportional to the resistivity of the region concerned. Thus for alloy junctions in which the base resistivity is considerably higher than that of the collector, most of the extension of the collector transition region takes place at the expense of the base layer. For grown junctions, on the other hand, the collector resistivity exceeds that of the base so that most of the extension is into the collector. We should therefore expect high-frequency alloy-junction transistors to be more susceptible to punch-through than the grown-junction variety. Other high-frequency transistors, such as those made by solid-state diffusion, are usually designed to have a base resistivity lower than that of the collector so that their behaviour, as far as punch-through is concerned, is similar to that of grown-junction transistors.

A somewhat different form of punch-through can occur in a narrow-base junction diode. At the time of writing it does not

seem to have been considered in detail in the literature but the
mechanism is probably the following, which we describe with
the aid of Fig. 4.9. Part *a* of the figure shows the electron-energy
diagram of a *p-n* junction in which most of the current is carried
by holes and the *n*-type 'base' region is very thin. The restriction
on the length of the base prevents the formation of a graded
ohmic contact of the type described in § 3.3 so that there is a
barrier adjacent to the metal. In some rectifiers this barrier is

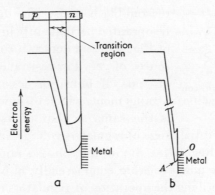

FIG. 4.9. Electron-energy diagram of
a narrow-base junction diode. (*a*) In
the normal reverse-voltage condition.
(*b*) When punch-through is imminent.

incorporated by design to increase the reverse resistance of the
device [11].

For the applied reverse potential shown in Fig. 4.9 *b* the
potential in the transition region adds to that of the barrier to
prevent the entry of electrons from the metal, but the sole
deterrent to the entry of holes (treated as bubbles on the diagram) is the energy step *OA*. As the field strength in the *n*-type
semiconductor is increased, the height of this step is decreased
by the encroachment of the transition (depletion) region of the
p-n junction and by the electrostatic image force or Schottky
effect [12]. Owing to this decrease in height, and possibly to
tunnel effect in the region near *A*, an increased number of holes
can enter the semiconductor. The current of holes thus produced

rises very rapidly with applied potential and leads to a 'punch-through' type of breakdown.

4.7. Practical applications of the breakdown process—regulating diodes

The breakdown process in junction diodes is not destructive provided the breakdown current is limited, by a series resistance

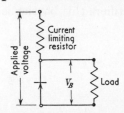

for example, so that mechanical and thermal effects produced by it are kept within reasonable bounds. The device can then be operated permanently in the region BC of Fig. 4.5, and acts as a constant voltage source of very low resistance (of the order of tens of ohms or less). The circuit arrangement, which is shown in Fig. 4.10, is the same as that of its vacuum-tube counterpart but the range of regulated voltage available is very much larger. Regulating diodes for voltages ranging from 2 to 1,500 volts are now available commercially in North America. Formulae describing the operation of regulators of this type are derived in Appendix XIII.

FIG. 4.10. Circuit connection of a regulating diode.

4.8. Irradiation effects in *p-n* junctions

We have indicated three methods whereby electrons may be excited from the valence band to the conduction band in a semiconductor, viz. by thermal agitation, by collision processes, and by internal-field emission. The same result may be produced when the semiconductor is irradiated by light, X-rays, or by high-energy particles. A photoconductive current can thus be produced in the body of a semiconductor if an electric field is applied to it during the irradiation process.

If the semiconductor contains a *p-n* junction its built-in electric field may be used instead of an externally applied field to produce a photocurrent when the junction is irradiated. The method by which this is accomplished may be demonstrated by means of the electron energy diagram of Fig. 4.11. The junction is subjected to irradiation in the region shown by the arrows

and hole-electron pairs are produced on both sides of the central
plane OO. Electrons generated in the region between the planes
AA and OO can reach OO by diffusion since the distance AO
is equal to the diffusion length L_n. Upon reaching the potential
step they are swept into the n-type section of the crystal by the
built-in field. Positive holes undergo a similar process and move
into the p-type region. If the crystal is connected to an external
circuit a current is produced therein. If no connections are made

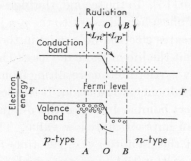

Fig. 4.11. Electron-energy diagram
illustrating the operation of a p-n
junction as a solar battery.

to it a potential will exist between its terminals, as long as the
radiation persists, because of the separation of charge produced
by the junction. The device can thus be used to transform energy
contained in the incoming radiation directly into electricity
provided the energy of the radiation is greater than that of the
semiconductor energy gap. Most of the radiation from the sun
is in the region of 1·0 eV and above so that 'solar batteries' can
be made from germanium or silicon. The efficiency of the process
is greater when silicon is used and commercial solar batteries
(sometimes called 'solar cells') are at present made from this
material. Somewhat greater efficiencies may be obtained eventually by the use of a semiconducting compound having a larger
energy gap than that of silicon (the optimum is about 1·5 eV)
but the technology of these materials has not yet reached a
suitable stage for commercial application. The construction
[13, 14] of solar batteries is different from that implied in Fig. 4.11
in that the junction usually has a large area and light parallel to

FF reaches it through the p-type material whose thickness is of the order of L_n.

'Nuclear batteries' in which the radiation consists of fast electrons from a β-emitter have also been built. These are of two types. In the first, the high-energy β-ray electrons lose their energy (which may be several hundred thousand electron volts) directly in a series of excitation processes in the p-n junction so that about 10^5 hole-electron pairs may be produced by each impinging electron [15]. In the second, the high-energy electrons are absorbed in a phosphor adjacent to the p-n junction and the light produced creates electron-hole pairs in the junction [16].

Two factors limit the life of these devices. The first is the decrease in minority-carrier lifetime resulting from lattice damage produced by the high-energy radiation. It is especially important in the case of direct bombardment of the p-n junction and may limit the life to an impracticably low value. The second factor is the half-life of the β-emitter (i.e. the time for its output to decay to one-half of its initial intensity) which may be relatively short. Promethium 147, which has a large output of β-electrons whose energy is below the threshold of damage of many substances (silicon is an exception) has a half-life of 2·6 years. It is used in nuclear batteries of the second type described above. One such device, $\frac{1}{2}$ inch diameter and $\frac{1}{4}$ inch thick has an output of 1 volt and 20 μA for a period of about two years. The cost of the isotope prevents commercial application at present but increases in isotope production will probably overcome this difficulty.

In another interesting application the p-n junction is used as a detector of radiation [14]. In this case a reverse voltage is applied and minority carriers produced in the neighbourhood of the junction by the incident radiation are swept rapidly away to produce a current in the external circuit that is very much larger than the (reverse) current flowing in the absence of radiation. The junction is thus an efficient radiation detector. The operation is similar to that of a solar cell but, because the junction is operated in the reverse direction its resistance is very large. When used in this manner the p-n junction is the solid-state counterpart of the vacuum-tube photocell.

LOW-FREQUENCY EQUIVALENT CIRCUITS

5.1. Introduction

IN our description of the junction rectifier we have shown that approximate values of circuit parameters of that device may be obtained from a study of the physical processes taking place within it. Further, the way in which these parameters depend on applied variables such as voltage and temperature may be determined. A similar procedure may be followed for the transistor. Both the physical processes and the circuit characteristics are, however, more complicated than those taking place in the junction rectifier so that more formal ways of expressing results are necessary. These usually take the form of equivalent circuits which can be used to represent the transistor under different circuit conditions. The development of equivalent circuits, especially those applying for small changes of voltage and current, has now reached a fairly advanced stage and we shall consider them in some detail later. As an introduction to the subject and to show which parameters are important it seems advisable to consider one of the simpler forms which can be developed intuitively from the physical ideas of the transistor that we already have. Historically this was the first transistor equivalent circuit to be used generally and many manufacturers still present transistor data in terms of it.

5.2. Intuitively developed equivalent circuit

The schematic diagram of a p-n-p transistor is shown in Fig. 5.1. This device operates in the same way as the n-p-n transistor of Fig. 2.6, except that the important carriers are positive holes so that the flow of carriers coincides with the flow of electric current. The emitter current flows through the low resistance of the forward-biased emitter junction in the region of A and most of it passes through the high resistance of the reverse-biased collector junction at D. The difference between these is the base current which flows transversely through the base region and leaves it at B. Since the width AD of the base region is small there is appreciable resistance to this transverse current.

The equivalent circuit that arises from these considerations is called the low-frequency T equivalent circuit or simply the T-circuit. It is shown in Fig. 5.2, in which r_e represents the low resistance of the forward-biased emitter, r_c the very high resistance of the reverse-biased collector, and r_b the resistance through the transverse base current flows. Since the emitter and collector-junction characteristics are non-linear these resistances can be considered as constants only for small excursions of current and voltage about fixed d.c. values, that is, the circuit is a small-signal equivalent circuit. As mentioned earlier r_e is usually less than 100 ohms while r_c may be several megohms. r_b, whose magnitude has not been so far considered, is usually a few hundred ohms.

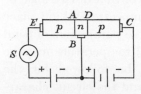

FIG. 5.1. Schematic diagram of a p-n-p transistor.

In our description of the transistor in Chapter II we mentioned that appreciable transistor action is obtained only if i_c the collector current is a large fraction of i_e the emitter current, or $i_b \ll i_e$. Since $r_c \gg r_b$ the current condition cannot be met unless an auxiliary voltage or current generator is inserted in the collector or base arm. If it is in the collector arm the generator must increase i_c and if in the base arm it must decrease i_b. The former position seems to fit the physical conditions better since the flow of minority carriers by diffusion increases the collector current over that which would flow in a simple passive resistance circuit. Similarly, a current generator seems more appropriate than a voltage generator since an additional current diffusing into the collector is more in accord with the physics of the device than an additional 'diffusion voltage'. However, a voltage generator is sometimes more convenient to use in circuit calculations and equivalent circuits of both types will be considered.

The above discussion shows that it is the current generator arising from the diffusion force that makes the transistor an 'active' circuit device that can be used as an amplifier or oscillator. In contrast, the active part of the other common amplifying device, the vacuum tube, is better described by a voltage generator.

Two common methods of drawing the current generator are

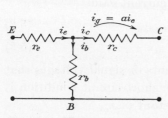

FIG. 5.2. *CB* low-frequency T equivalent circuit (current generator represented by arrow).

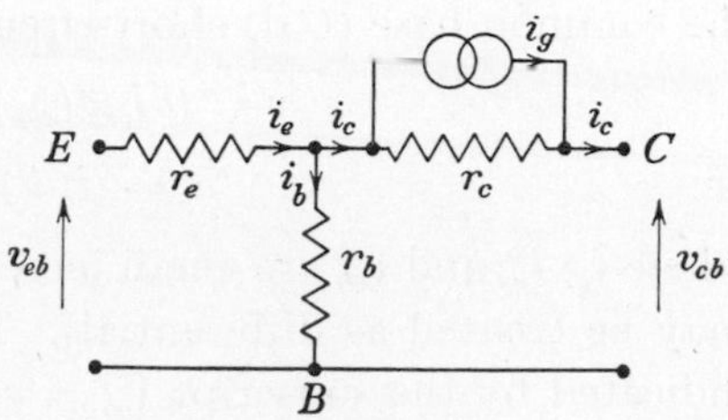

FIG. 5.3. *CB* low-frequency T equivalent circuit (current generator represented by double circle).

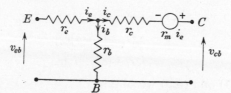

FIG. 5.4. *CB* low-frequency T equivalent circuit with voltage generator.

shown in Figs. 5.2 and 5.3. These are equivalent and each represents a source of infinite impedance, in parallel with r_c, whose current output i_g is independent of the voltage across its terminals. The double-circle symbol of Fig. 5.3, whose connection in parallel with r_c is clearly shown, will be used in this book.

For small signals the ratio i_g/i_e is approximately constant and is usually denoted by the symbol a so that $i_g = ai_e$. When a voltage generator is used, as in Fig. 5.4, its output is written as $r_m i_e$ where r_m has the dimensions of resistance. Since Figs. 5.3 and 5.4 are equivalent we can equate the voltage drops in the collector arm, obtaining

$$i_c r_c - r_m i_e = (i_c - i_g) r_c = (i_c - a i_e) r_c$$

or
$$r_m = a r_c. \tag{5.1}$$

The voltage generator has zero internal impedance and acts in series with other voltages in the output circuit.

It is almost universal practice to define the current ratio of a transistor by a parameter which differs slightly from a. This is the common base (CB) short-circuit current gain

$$\alpha = (\partial I_c / \partial I_e)_{V_{cb}=\text{constant}} \tag{5.2}$$

or
$$\alpha = (i_c / i_e)_{v_{cb}=0}, \tag{5.3}$$

where i_e, i_c, and v_{cb} are small increments or signal voltages that may be treated as differentials. The short-circuit condition is indicated by the subscript $V_{cb} = \text{constant}$ or $v_{cb} = 0$.

We may determine i_g or a in terms of α by an analysis of the circuit of Fig. 5.3 when a short circuit is applied between B and C. Then, since $i_c = \alpha i_e$

and
$$v_{eb} = i_e r_e + i_b r_b = i_e r_e + (i_e - i_c) r_b,$$
$$v_{eb} = i_e [r_e + (1 - \alpha) r_b]. \tag{5.4}$$

Also
$$v_{eb} = i_e r_e + (\alpha i_e - i_g) r_c. \tag{5.5}$$

Equating (5.4) and (5.5) we obtain

$$a = \frac{i_g}{i_e} = \alpha - (1 - \alpha) \frac{r_b}{r_c}. \tag{5.6}$$

Since, usually, $(1-\alpha) \ll 1$ and $r_b \ll r_c$ we may ignore the last term of (5.6) and put
$$i_g = \alpha i_e. \tag{5.7}$$

We have thus derived a simple equivalent circuit for the junction transistor, from our physical picture of it, by intuitive reasoning. We have not considered several factors such as transition-region capacitances, diffusion capacitances, and the transit time of minority carriers in the base region, which affect the response of the device at high frequencies. These will be considered in a later chapter. In the remainder of this chapter we shall first consider the effect, on the equivalent circuit, of different methods of connecting the transistor. Later we shall describe other equivalent circuits that are becoming increasingly popular and shall show how circuit properties (e.g. input resistance, power gain, etc.) can be calculated.

5.3. Transistor connections

The connection of Fig. 5.1 may be represented schematically by the circuit diagram of Fig. 5.5. The symbol used here is the standard symbol of the (American) Institute of Radio Engineers [1] for a p-n-p transistor. The emitter is represented by the sloping line with the arrow. For an n-p-n transistor the arrow, which indicates the conventional direction of emitter-current

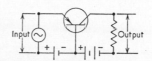

FIG. 5.5. Circuit diagram of *CB* connection.

flow, would be reversed. The other sloping line represents the collector and the vertical line is the base connection. The horizontal line may be considered to represent the transistor crystal. As shown in the figures that follow, the diagram may be oriented in any suitable way.

It is apparent from Figs. 5.2 to 5.5 that operation of the transistor is described by four variables, viz. input voltage V_1, input current I_1, output voltage V_2, and output current I_2. It is sometimes called a two terminal-pair or a two-port device. One of the terminals is common to both 'pairs' or 'ports' and is used to specify the way in which the transistor is connected. The connection of Fig. 5.5 is thus called the common base (CB) connection. There are, strictly speaking, two CB connections but amplification is obtained in only one of them, i.e. when the emitter is the input terminal. The term CB therefore applies invariably to the circuit of Fig. 5.5. It will be recalled from our earlier description that voltage and power amplification are possible in this connection but that current gain does not occur in normal operation. Two other amplifying connections are possible and are known as the common emitter (CE) and common collector (CC) connections respectively. The CE connection usually gives current, voltage, and power gain while the CC connection gives current and power gain only. Schematic diagrams of them are shown in Figs. 5.6 and 5.7. The common electrode in each connection is readily ascertained when it is assumed that the battery impedance is zero. The diagram of Fig. 5.7 *a* follows literally from the above description of the *CC* connection. That of Fig. 5.7 *b* is equivalent but is drawn to show the resemblance to the cathode follower vacuum-tube circuit. For this reason the *CC* connection is often called the 'emitter follower'.

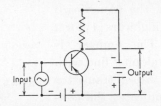

FIG. 5.6. Circuit diagram of *CE* connection.

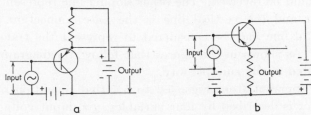

FIG. 5.7. Circuit diagram of *CC* connection (emitter follower). (*a*) With collector as common d.c. terminal. (*b*) With one side of load as common d.c. terminal.

The simple *T* equivalent circuits for the *CE* and *CC* connections can be derived from the *CB* connection as outlined in Appendix V. The resulting *T* equivalent circuits are shown in Figs. 5.8 and 5.9. The directions of current flow in these figures are chosen for convenience in analysis and, unlike those of Fig. 5.3, are not necessarily related to the direction of flow in the device itself. The ratio of two variables calculated using Fig. 5.8 or Fig. 5.9 may therefore have a negative sign in some cases, indicating that one of the variables should be reversed.

5.4. Other low-frequency equivalent circuits

The low-frequency *T* equivalent circuit is one representation of a transistor that has found considerable use in circuit calculations. There are other representations that may be more useful in certain applications. These may be derived by considering quite general relations between the four variables shown in the schematic diagram of Fig. 5.10. If any two of these are chosen as independent variables the remaining two may be expressed in terms of them. As an example we choose the currents I_1 and

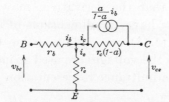

FIG. 5.8. *CE* low-frequency *T* equivalent circuit.

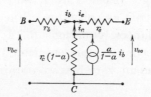

FIG. 5.9. *CC* low-frequency *T* equivalent circuit.

FIG. 5.10. Schematic representation of variables in a two-port four-terminal network.

I_2 as independent variables. The voltages V_1 and V_2 may then be expressed as functions of I_1 and I_2 as follows:

$$V_1 = f_1(I_1, I_2), \tag{5.8}$$

$$V_2 = f_2(I_1, I_2). \tag{5.9}$$

The capital letters are here used to indicate 'total' variables consisting of a small a.c. signal superimposed on a fixed direct current or voltage. Differentiating (5.8) and (5.9), we obtain

$$dV_1 = \frac{\partial f_1}{\partial I_1} dI_1 + \frac{\partial f_1}{\partial I_2} dI_2, \tag{5.10}$$

$$dV_2 = \frac{\partial f_2}{\partial I_1} dI_1 + \frac{\partial f_2}{\partial I_2} dI_2. \tag{5.11}$$

If the a.c. signal is small enough that it may be treated as a

G

differential we may put

$$v_1 = \frac{\partial f_1}{\partial I_1} i_1 + \frac{\partial f_1}{\partial I_2} i_2 = z_{11} i_1 + z_{12} i_2, \tag{5.12}$$

$$v_2 = \frac{\partial f_2}{\partial I_1} i_1 + \frac{\partial f_2}{\partial I_2} i_2 = z_{21} i_1 + z_{22} i_2, \tag{5.13}$$

where we have assumed that f_1 and f_2 are linear over the small ranges decided by i_1 and i_2 so that the derivatives may be written as constants. Since these have the dimensions of impedances, equations (5.12) and (5.13) are said to define the impedance representation. When the voltages are used as independent variables we obtain the admittance representation

$$i_1 = y_{11} v_1 + y_{12} v_2, \tag{5.14}$$

$$i_2 = y_{21} v_1 + y_{22} v_2. \tag{5.15}$$

There are six representations altogether, corresponding to the six possible choices of two independent variables from i_1, i_2, v_1, v_2. These are described in articles and books on network theory [2]. We shall be concerned only with three, the impedance and admittance representations given above and a representation in which i_1 and v_2 are chosen as the independent variables. This last, which is usually called the hybrid representation, is described by the equations:

$$v_1 = h_{11} i_1 + h_{12} v_2 = h_i i_1 + h_r v_2, \tag{5.16}$$

$$i_2 = h_{21} i_1 + h_{22} v_2 = h_f i_1 + h_o v_2. \tag{5.17}$$

Since the subscripts 1 and 2 on the variables apply to input and output respectively we see that the h's define the following circuit parameters:

$h_{11} = h_i$ = input impedance with output short-circuited ($v_2 = 0$),

$h_{12} = h_r$ = reverse voltage ratio with input open-circuited

($i_1 = 0$),

$h_{21} = h_f$ = forward current ratio with output short-circuited,

$h_{22} = h_o$ = output admittance with input open-circuited.

The second set of symbols shown here are alternative h-parameter symbols contained in the (American) Institute of Radio Engineers Standards on Letter Symbols for Semiconductor Devices

[3]. They have the advantage that the subscript gives an indication of the property referred to. Also a second subscript b, e, or c may be used to indicate the transistor connection. When the above numerical subscripts are used a total of three subscripts is normally required. The alphabetical subscripts will therefore be used in the derivations that follow. A single-letter subscript will be used for relations that apply to all three transistor connections.

The foregoing three sets of equations may be presented in matrix form. Thus, for the hybrid representation equations (5.16) and (5.17) become

$$\begin{bmatrix} v_1 \\ i_2 \end{bmatrix} = \begin{bmatrix} h_i & h_r \\ h_f & h_o \end{bmatrix} \begin{bmatrix} i_1 \\ v_2 \end{bmatrix}. \tag{5.18}$$

Using the rules of matrix algebra, relations between the z, y, and h matrices may be obtained. A table of these relations is given in Appendix VI. Note that they apply to any method of connecting the transistor (CB, CE, or CC) but that the z's, y's, and h's are different for the three connections. The most useful relations between the h's for the three connections, and an example of the way in which they are derived, are given in Appendix VIII. Values of h-parameters for commercially available transistors usually refer to one connection (CB or CE) only, so that these relations are needed if one of the other connections is used. The relative magnitudes of h-parameters for the different connections are discussed, for a typical general purpose transistor, in § 5.8.

The matrix methods used in the derivation of Appendix VI are helpful in the application of transistors in complicated circuits and, though we cannot consider them further here because of lack of space, a study of them is well worth while. Outlines of matrix theory are contained in references [2] and [4].

5.5. The relation between the low-frequency T-circuit and other low-frequency equivalent circuits

The development of the low-frequency T equivalent circuit in paragraph 5.2 was completely intuitive. We now show that it can be derived formally from the low-frequency impedance representation of equations (5.12) and (5.13).

To form a T-circuit from these relations we must have an impedance common to the input and output circuits, through which i_1 and i_2 both flow. We may obtain such an element for the input circuit by expressing equation (5.12) in the form (using resistances instead of impedances for the low-frequency case):

$$v_1 = r_{11}i_1 + r_{12}i_2 = (r_{11}-r_{12})i_1 + r_{12}(i_1+i_2). \qquad (5.19)$$

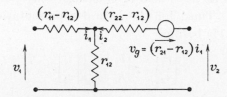

Fig. 5.11. Low-frequency T equivalent circuit derived from the impedance matrix representation.

The resistance r_{12} must therefore be the element that is common to both circuits and the output circuit must contain the term $r_{12}(i_1+i_2)$. We therefore have

$$v_2 = r_{21}i_1 + r_{22}i_2 = r_{12}(i_1+i_2) + (r_{21}-r_{12})i_1 + (r_{22}-r_{12})i_2. \qquad (5.20)$$

The equivalent circuit representing equations (5.19) and (5.20) is shown in Fig. 5.11. The quantity $(r_{21}-r_{12})i_1$ is the output of a voltage generator which is the active part of the device. If r_{21} and r_{12} were equal the device would be passive and could be represented simply by a combination of resistances.

Comparing Fig. 5.11 with the CB circuit of Fig. 5.4 we see that

$$\left. \begin{array}{ll} r_e = r_{11}-r_{12}, & r_c = r_{22}-r_{12} \\[2mm] r_b = r_{12}, & r_m = r_{21}-r_{12} \\[2mm] a = \dfrac{r_m}{r_c} = \dfrac{r_{21}-r_{12}}{r_{22}-r_{12}} \end{array} \right\} \qquad (5.21)$$

and from equation (5.6) $\alpha = \dfrac{r_{21}}{r_{22}},$ \qquad (5.22)

whence

$$r_{11} = r_e+r_b, \quad r_{22} = r_c+r_b,$$

$$r_{12} = r_b, \quad r_{21} = r_m+r_b = ar_c+r_b. \qquad (5.23)$$

Using equations (5.21) and Appendix VI the constants of the low-frequency T equivalent circuit may also be expressed in terms of the admittance and hybrid parameters. The relations between T equivalent circuit parameters and h-parameters are given in Appendix IX.

5.6. Low-frequency circuit properties

The purpose of an equivalent circuit is to make possible the calculation of the circuit properties. For transistor applications in the low-frequency region the most important of these are the following:

(1) Current gain A_i (2) Voltage gain A_v
(3) Input impedance Z_i (4) Operating power gain G
        (5) Output admittance Y_o (or impedance Z_o)

In this section we illustrate the method of obtaining these properties in terms of the h-parameters. The use of the h-equivalent circuit for this purpose has the following advantages:

(a) The same calculation applies to all three transistor connections. This advantage also applied to the other equivalent circuits that can be represented by matrices such as the impedance and admittance types but not to the T equivalent circuit.

(b) The low-frequency h-parameters are more generally available in manufacturers' data than parameters of the other representations.

(c) Although the results that follow are derived specifically for the low-frequency case in which the h-parameters are considered to be independent of frequency they may also be used at higher frequencies if the h-parameters are given in complex form as functions of frequency. Such applications will be discussed in more detail when high-frequency equivalent circuits are considered.

The general h-parameter equations, here repeated for convenience, are:

$$v_1 = h_i i_1 + h_r v_2, \tag{5.24}$$

$$i_2 = h_f i_1 + h_o v_2. \tag{5.25}$$

It may be seen by inspection that these equations are satisfied by the simple equivalent circuit of Fig. 5.12 in which, following our earlier practice, a voltage generator is represented by a single circle and a current generator by a double circle. The input generator of voltage v_g and internal impedance Z_g and the load of impedance Z_l may be connected or not depending on which of the above properties we are considering. For the

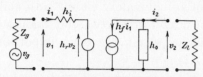

FIG. 5.12. Equivalent circuit of the hybrid matrix representation.

calculation of the 'forward' properties (1) to (4) we connect Z_l so that $v_2 = -i_2 Z_l$. Equations (5.24) and (5.25) then become

$$v_1 = h_i i_1 - h_r Z_l i_2, \qquad (5.26)$$

$$0 = h_f i_1 - (1 + h_o Z_l) i_2. \qquad (5.27)$$

Following the procedure of Appendix VII we have from (5.26) and (5.27)

$$\Delta = \begin{vmatrix} h_i & -h_r Z_l \\ h_f & -(1 + h_o Z_l) \end{vmatrix} = -h_i - \Delta_h Z_l, \qquad (5.28)$$

where Δ_h is defined in Appendix VIII.

$$i_1 = \frac{1}{\Delta} \begin{vmatrix} v_1 & -h_r Z_l \\ 0 & -(1 + h_o Z_l) \end{vmatrix}, \qquad (5.29)$$

$$i_2 = \frac{1}{\Delta} \begin{vmatrix} h_i & v_1 \\ h_f & 0 \end{vmatrix}. \qquad (5.30)$$

Dividing (5.30) by (5.29) we obtain the current gain

$$A_i = \frac{i_2}{i_1} = \frac{h_f}{(1 + h_o Z_l)}. \qquad (5.31)$$

We note that, when the output is short-circuited ($Z_l = 0$), the current gain becomes h_f. For the CB case, using equation (5.3), we therefore have

$$h_{fb} = -\alpha. \qquad (5.32)$$

The minus sign in equation (5.32) arises because the currents i_2 in Fig. 5.12 and i_c in Fig. 5.2 flow in opposite directions.

The voltage gain A_v may be obtained from equation (5.30)

$$A_v = \frac{-i_2 Z_l}{v_1} = \frac{h_f Z_l}{\Delta} = \frac{-h_f Z_l}{h_i + \Delta_h Z_l}. \tag{5.33}$$

The input impedance may be determined from equation (5.29)

$$Z_i = \frac{v_1}{i_1} = \frac{-\Delta}{1 + h_o Z_l} = \frac{h_i + \Delta_h Z_l}{1 + h_o Z_l}. \tag{5.34}$$

The power gain may be defined in several ways (see § 5.7) but for the moment we consider the operating power gain G which is the ratio of the power consumed in the load to the power entering the transistor. Its value is

$$G = |i_2|^2 R_l / |i_1|^2 R_i = |A_i|^2 R_l / R_i, \tag{5.35}$$

where R_l and R_i are the real components of Z_l and Z_i respectively. In the low-frequency case, when $Z_l = R_l$ and $Z_i = R_i$,

$$G = A_i A_v. \tag{5.36}$$

The output impedance is the ratio v_2/i_2 determined with the load Z_l removed and the generator inserted but no generator voltage applied. The equations for this case are

$$-i_1 Z_g = h_i i_1 + h_r v_2, \tag{5.37}$$

$$0 = (h_i + Z_g) i_1 + h_r v_2, \tag{5.38}$$

$$i_2 = h_f i_1 + h_o v_2, \tag{5.39}$$

whence
$$\Delta_0 = \begin{vmatrix} h_i + Z_g & h_r \\ h_f & h_o \end{vmatrix} = \Delta_h + h_o Z_g, \tag{5.40}$$

$$v_2 = \frac{1}{\Delta_0} \begin{vmatrix} h_i + Z_g & 0 \\ h_f & i_2 \end{vmatrix}, \tag{5.41}$$

$$Z_o = \frac{v_2}{i_2} = \frac{h_i + Z_g}{\Delta_o} = \frac{h_i + Z_g}{\Delta_h + h_o Z_g}. \tag{5.42}$$

The relations of Table A9.2 make it possible to determine the circuit properties $A_i A_v$, etc. in terms of the T-circuit parameters r_e, r_b, etc. The resulting expressions are also available in several places in the literature [4, 5, 6]. The corresponding expressions for the z and y representations are contained in Appendix X.

5.7. Definitions of power gain

The operating power gain G, defined in the preceding sections, may be described by reference to Fig. 5.13 which shows the impedances of the transistor and the device that feeds or drives it. Thus G is the ratio of the power entering the load at CD to that entering the transistor stage at AB. It gives no indication

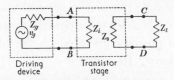

Fig. 5.13. Schematic impedance diagram of a transistor stage and its driving device.

of the extent to which the power available in the driving device is used.

In many audio and low radio-frequency amplifiers, having resistance-capacity coupling between stages, the power gain of the transistor stage may be the main criterion in deciding which of several types of transistors should be used and the number of stages required. One of the most important factors affecting these decisions is the efficiency with which the power available in the driving device is used. To take account of this factor, power gain may be defined in terms of the transducer gain G_T, which is the ratio of the power consumed in the load to the maximum power available from the generator. This maximum power would of course be obtained if the internal impedance Z_g of the driving device were the complex conjugate of the input impedance of the transistor, i.e. if $Z_i = Z_g^* = R_g - jX_g$. This is the condition of conjugate match. (As seen from equation (5.34) Z_i will be complex if Z_l is complex even though the h-parameters are real. At higher frequencies Z_i will be complex even though Z_l is real.) The current flowing in the input circuit in the condition of conjugate match is

$$i_1 = v_g/(Z_g + Z_g^*) = v_g/2R_g \tag{5.43}$$

and the maximum power available from the source is

$$P_a = i_1^2 R_g = v_g^2/4R_g. \tag{5.44}$$

The transducer gain is therefore

$$G_T = \frac{|i_2|^2 R_l}{v_g^2/4R_g} = \frac{4|A_i|^2 R_l R_g}{|Z_g+Z_i|^2}, \tag{5.45}$$

where we have inserted the magnitude of the input current $i_1 = v_g/|Z_g+Z_i|$ and the current gain $A_i = i_2/i_1$. With the help of equations (5.31) and (5.34) G_T can be expressed in terms of the h-parameters.

Knowledge of transducer gain is useful when different circuits for amplifying the output of a given source are to be compared. Such amplifiers usually contain several stages but the concept of transducer gain is applicable only to the first. The power consumed in the load of the first stage is actually the power entering the second stage (if we ignore the relatively small losses in the collector and base bias resistors) and the pertinent parameter for the second and the following stages is the operating power gain G. Thus the transducer gain of the complete amplifier is

$$G_T = G_{T1} G_2 G_3..., \text{ etc.} \tag{5.46}$$

If the gain is expressed in decibels† (db) we have

$$G_T(\text{db}) = G_{T1}+G_2+G_3+, \text{ etc.} \tag{5.47}$$

When the input impedance of the first stage is conjugate matched to the source its transducer gain becomes equal to its operating power gain G_1, and the transducer gain of the amplifier becomes $G_1 G_2 G_3....$. If the output impedance of each stage is now conjugate matched to its load, the input impedance of each stage (with the exception of the first which has already been considered) is thereby automatically matched and the amplifier then has the 'maximum power gain'

$$G_m = G_{m1} G_{m2} G_{m3}. \tag{5.48}$$

The condition of conjugate match can be obtained quite readily when tuned transformer coupling is used as in many

† The transducer gain in decibels is 10 log G_T, where G_T is the power ratio just defined. Other power gains may be expressed similarly. We use the same symbol to indicate both the ratio and the decibel value of the gain but the latter is followed by the symbol db.

radio-frequency applications. This case will be discussed in a later section.

Transformer coupling may also be used in untuned amplifiers operating at lower frequencies and it is theoretically possible to use conjugate matching in this case also. However, matching of the reactive components would require the addition of inductance or the design of special transformers. Since reactive effects are usually small at these frequencies this is hardly worth while and the general practice is to ignore reactances and to design for maximum power gain by the adjustment of resistances only. The required generator and load resistances may be obtained by expressing equation (5.45) in terms of R_l, R_g and the transistor parameters, and determining the values of R_l and R_g, treated as independent variables, that make G_T a maximum. These values are found to be $R_l = R_o$ and $R_g = R_i$ as would be expected from the simplification of the condition for conjugate match that occurs at low frequency. The given load and generator resistances are, of course, transformed to these matching values by the insertion of transformers between them and the transistor terminals.

In some cases (e.g. when the required impedance ratio is very high as in the CB connection) it is difficult to design transformers with the required ratio while in others it may be desirable to use an available transformer whose ratio differs from the calculated value. These factors are of such importance that the perfectly matched transformer-coupled low-frequency amplifier is the exception rather than the rule. Transformers are nevertheless often used to increase the power gain, particularly in battery-operated equipment where the total power consumption must be kept to a minimum.

Other definitions of power gain are considered in the literature but the ones discussed here are suitable for all but the most specialized applications.

5.8. Characteristic curves and numerical values

Our description of low-frequency equivalent circuits based on the general theory of the two-port network has, of necessity, been rather abstract and has given the reader very little 'feeling' for the magnitudes involved. In this section we shall consider a typical example of a commercially available transistor and give magnitudes of device parameters and circuit properties resulting therefrom.

An example of a good, reasonably priced, general-purpose transistor available in North America is the Texas Instruments 2N369. The manufacturer's specification for this device contains more information than is available for most other general-purpose transistors and we have therefore chosen it for our demonstration of transistor characteristics and properties. We emphasize that many transistors made by other manufacturers could be used for this purpose. A European device that could have been used equally well is the OC71.

The 2N369 is a p-n-p alloy-junction transistor having the ratings and parameters listed in Appendix XI. Its CB and CE output characteristics are available from the manufacturer's data. However, we prefer to use the results of measurements taken in the laboratory on a typical unit and these are shown in Figs. A11.1 and A11.3. An expanded view of Fig. A11.1 for small values of v_c is shown in Fig. A11.2. From a consideration of these curves we note the following:

(*a*) The CB curve for $I_e = 0$, which is barely distinguishable from the v_c axis, has as its main component the reverse saturation current of the collector junction. The curves for other values of I_e are similar in form but displaced along the I_c axis by an amount αI_e, where $\alpha = -h_{fb}$ has a design centre or mean value of 0·982.

(*b*) For any CB curve, I_e is constant or $i_e = 0$ so that these output curves are drawn for the open-circuited input condition and their slope is h_{ob}. Thus, from the simple picture of the transistor so far developed, we expect h_{ob}^{-1} to be of the same order as the resistance of a junction rectifier in the reverse direction. From Appendix XI we see that h_{ob}^{-1} ranges between 0·7 and 7 megohms. This is lower than the reverse resistance of a good junction rectifier of the same area. The difference is, however, readily accounted for when the theory of the transistor is considered in detail. This is done in the next chapter. For the CE connection the slope of the output curves (h_{oe}) is much greater. This is confirmed by the relation $h_{oe} \simeq h_{ob}/(1+h_{fb})$ in Table A8.1. Since $h_{fb} \simeq -0.982$, $h_{oe} \simeq 55h_{ob}$, i.e. the output resistance of the CE connection is 52 kilohms compared with 2·9 megohms for the CB connection. The change of h_{oe} with emitter or collector current is much greater than the change of h_{ob}. This is due chiefly to changes in h_{fb}, the effects of which are amplified in the CE connection. This amplification increases as α ($= -h_{fb}$) approaches unity, so that the CE output characteristics of high-gain transistors will, in general, have larger slopes than those of low-gain transistors of the same power rating.

(c) The CE collector characteristics in Fig. A11.3 show a pronounced increase of slope at high voltages that is absent from the CB characteristics. This difference is not due to thermal effects which should be approximately the same in the two connections. It is probably explained by the mechanism discussed in § 6.6.1, viz. the increase in α that occurs as the collector transition region encroaches on the base. (This phenomenon leads to punch-through at higher voltages.) Avalanche effects of the type discussed in Chapter VIII may also play a part but are not expected to predominate at these low voltages. We will not discuss this phenomenon further here but merely note the following:

(c.1) The 2N369, which has a maximum collector-to-base rating of 30 volts, should not be operated above about 15 volts (collector-to-emitter) in the CE connection.

(c.2) When two alloy-junction transistors have the same maximum V_{cb}, the maximum V_{ce} will usually be lower for the one having the higher frequency response or the higher α, since thin base regions are required for both of these properties. The 2N369, whose cutoff frequency is about 50 per cent higher than that of most general-purpose transistors, therefore has a relatively low maximum value of V_{ce}.

(d) The expanded portion of the CB output characteristic in Fig. A11.2 shows that, in the CB connection, the transistor retains its pentode-like characteristic for collector voltages well under 0·5 volt so that the transistor, unlike the vacuum tube, can be used as an efficient amplifier of small signals even when the supply voltage is very low. This property which also applies to a lesser extent to the CE connection, is often very useful, especially in portable equipment. A point of interest in connection with Fig. A11.2 is that collector current continues to flow in the normal (reverse) direction even when low forward voltages are applied to the collector junction. This is due to the diffusion force which drives carriers from emitter to collector. The collector current is not reduced to zero until this force has been overcome.

(e) The input resistance h_{ib} is the slope of the CB input characteristic of Fig. A11.4 which is similar to that of a forward-biased junction rectifier. This parameter obviously varies considerably with emitter current especially when the latter is small. (The analytical form of this variation is given in Chapter VI.) Similar variations occur in CE input resistance h_{ie} which is the slope of the input characteristic of Fig. A11.5. As seen from this characteristic and Table A8.1, $h_{ie} \simeq 55h_{ib}$ for this transistor.

The CE and CC h-parameters, determined with the help of Table A8.1, are listed in Table A11.3. Substitution in the formulae of Appendix X then gives the curves of Figs. A11.12 to A11.16 inclusive. A careful study of these curves will give the student a very good understanding of the way in which the transistor operates. We cannot discuss them in great detail because of lack of space but shall be content to make the following observations:

1. The curves are calculated from the low-frequency parameters and for each curve there is an upper limit of frequency, which depends on the transistor connection, beyond which the curve is inaccurate. The determination of the effect of frequency is complicated and a discussion of it is reserved for Chapter VII. We shall then give approximate upper frequency limits for Figs. A11.12 to A11.16.

2. The best general criterion of the gain of a transistor stage is probably the operating power gain. From Fig. A11.15 we see that the CE connection has a big advantage over the other

two in this respect and it is used invariably in audio and low radio-frequency applications unless the special impedance matching properties of the CC or the CB connection are required. The change of properties with frequency acts in favour of the CB connection at high frequencies as discussed in Chapter VII.

3. From the voltage-gain expression of Appendix X it is readily seen that phase inversion occurs in the CE but not in the CB and CC connections. In this respect and in the relative magnitudes of its current and voltage gains the CE connection is analogous to the grounded cathode connection of the vacuum tube while the CB and CC connections correspond to the grounded-grid and cathode-follower connections respectively.

4. The input and output resistances of the CE connection lie between those of the other connections and vary in the opposite way with load and generator resistance. This difference is also a consequence of the difference in sign of h_f.

5. The input resistance is much lower and the output resistance usually higher than the corresponding quantities for vacuum tubes. This is not as great a disadvantage as would at first appear. The curves of Appendix XI show that the low-power transistor is essentially a current device, i.e. its response is linear in terms of input current rather than voltage. The resistance of the source or generator supplying it should therefore be considerably larger than the input resistance of the transistor if reasonably linear operation is to be attained. (This is particularly true if the signal to be amplified is large; for small signals the output current-input voltage characteristic will also be reasonably linear.) When the source is a transistor stage this condition is automatically attained.

6. A complication from the point of view of multistage amplifier design arises from the fact that the load resistance of transistor stage is decided primarily by the input resistance of the stage that follows it. This and the fact that the transistor is a current-amplifying device demands an approach to amplifier design that is rather different from that used with vacuum tubes. It will be discussed in a later chapter.

PHYSICAL FACTORS AFFECTING THE D.C. AND LOW-FREQUENCY OPERATION OF TRANSISTORS

6.1. Introduction

IN this chapter we shall try to show how the d.c. and low-frequency properties of transistors can be interpreted in terms of the physical processes taking place within them. We have given a rather crude general description of such processes in Chapter II and in the second section of Chapter V. From this description and from an analysis of the device as a two-port network we have determined the transistor parameters r_b, α, h_{ib}, etc. These procedures cannot, however, give certain information that is needed if the transistor is to be used intelligently. Examples of such information are the effects produced by the following:

1. Changes of operating variables such as d.c. voltages, d.c. currents and temperature.
2. Differences in semiconductor properties and methods of manufacture.

Effects produced by the operating variables may be determined by measurement or, in some cases, from the manufacturers' specifications. However, such information is often incomplete and a knowledge of the theory of the device is then useful as it makes possible a qualitative prediction of its behaviour. Information of the second type, especially that dealing with the effect of methods of manufacture, is often useful when a transistor must be chosen for a special application since some characteristics of transistors depend on the way in which they are made (e.g. whether of alloy- or grown-junction type).

This chapter borrows heavily from two important papers [1, 2]. Another useful reference which treats many of the factors involved in considerably greater detail is the book [3] by Middle-brook.

6.2. Direct-current equations for the intrinsic transistor

As a first step we consider a simple transistor in which the processes associated with the diffusion of minority carriers are

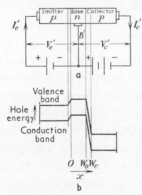

separated from those that depend on other properties of the device. This simplified version is usually called the intrinsic transistor. In this connection the word 'intrinsic' does not describe the semiconductor used in the device but indicates that only those properties related to transistor action *per se* are being considered. Other properties that have an important bearing on the circuit characteristics but are not associated with the diffusion process will be considered later in this chapter and in the next chapter.

FIG. 6.1. The p-n-p transistor. (*a*) Schematic diagram. (*b*) Positive-hole energy diagram.

We consider first the solution of the diffusion equation for an intrinsic p-n-p transistor in the CB connection. (We note in passing that all studies based on the physics of the transistor are most easily made for the CB connection. Results for the other connections can then be derived with the help of the transformations described earlier.) The schematic diagram and the positive-hole energy diagram for this case are shown in Fig. 6.1. Potentials V'_e and V'_c, applied as described earlier, produce a one-dimensional flow of current from left to right in the x-direction. To conform with the notation of Chapter V we should use V'_{eb} and V'_{cb} but since no confusion is likely to arise we shall drop the second suffix in this chapter. Also, for the moment, all variables have primes associated with them to indicate that they may differ from those of a real transistor. The origin of the x-coordinates, on the base side of the emitter junction, forms one boundary of the base as shown in Fig. 6.1 b. The other boundary is on the base side of the collector junction at $x = W_0$. As mentioned in Chapter II, $W_0 \ll L_p$, the diffusion length for holes in the n-type base region, so that most of the holes injected by the emitter diffuse through the base to the collector. In order to simplify the analysis that follows we make the very important assumption that the density of positive holes in the base region is at all times small compared with the density of electrons (majority carriers) there. When holes are injected, an equal number of electrons must enter the base electrode to cancel the space charge of the holes. However, electrons cannot enter the collector and they distribute themselves in such a way that an electron field-current, which cancels the electron diffusion-current, is produced. The net electron current in the base is thus small (see below) while the positive-hole (diffusion) current may be quite large.

The diffusion equation to be solved for the d.c. condition is (A2.1) and the boundary conditions applying to the transistor are the following:

(a) The number of holes per c.c. capable of entering the base from the emitter at $x = 0$, determined from equation (4.1), is

$$p_1 = p_n \exp(qV_e'/kT). \tag{6.1}$$

(b) The number of holes per c.c. at $x = W_0$ is assumed equal to zero since, as described in Appendix II, any holes that reach the collector are rapidly removed by the field in the collector transition region.

The solution obtained when these boundary conditions are used and $W_0 \ll L_p$ is given by equation (A2.6), which is here rewritten

$$p(x) - p_n$$
$$= \frac{1}{\sinh(W_0/L_p)} \{(p_1 - p_n)\sinh[(W_0 - x)/L_p] - p_n \sinh(x/L_p)\}. \tag{6.2}$$

The current due to the diffusion of holes through the base is

$$I_p' = -qD_p(dp/dx)$$
$$= \frac{qD_p}{L_p \sinh(W_0/L_p)} \{(p_1 - p_n)\cosh[(W_0 - x)/L_p] + p_n \cosh(x/L_p)\}. \tag{6.3}$$

The hole components of the emitter current (I'_{pe}) and the collector current (I'_{pc}) are the values of I_p at $x = 0$ and $x = W_0$ respectively. Thus, using the abbreviation $m = W_0/L_p$,

$$I'_{pe} = \frac{qD_p}{L_p \sinh m} \{(p_1 - p_n)\cosh m + p_n\} \qquad (6.4)$$

or $\qquad I'_{pe} = \frac{qD_p p_n}{L_p} \{[\exp(qV'_e/kT) - 1]\coth m + \mathrm{cosech}\, m\}, \qquad (6.5)$

and $\qquad I'_{pc} = \frac{qD_p}{L_p \sinh m} \{(p_1 - p_n) + p_n \cosh m\} \qquad (6.6)$

or $\qquad I'_{pc} = \frac{qD_p p_n}{L_p} \{[\exp(qV'_e/kT) - 1]\mathrm{cosech}\, m + \coth m\}. \qquad (6.7)$

In addition to these hole currents there are small electron currents at the two junctions. The electron component I'_{ne} crossing the emitter junction is a forward current which may be obtained from equations (4.7) and (4.8) by putting $V = V'_e$ and omitting the hole component. Thus

$$I'_{ne} = \frac{qD_n n_{pe}}{L_{ne}} [\exp(qV'_e/kT) - 1], \qquad (6.8)$$

where n_{pe} is the number of electrons in equilibrium in the p-type emitter and L_{ne} is their diffusion length.

The electron current crossing the collector junction consists of the following components:

1. The reverse saturation current. This is the electron component of equation (4.8) and is given by

$$I'_{nc} = qD_n n_{pc}/L_{nc}. \qquad (6.9)$$

It is a d.c. current which, in the ordinary range of transistor operation, is not directly influenced by a.c. voltages or currents in the transistor.

2. An electron component flowing from collector to base under the influence of the electric field created by the positive holes that enter the collector body from the base. The expression for the total current (d.c.+signal) arising from this effect is complicated and will not be given here. The collector signal current will be considered in the next section.

3. An electron-avalanche current produced in the transition region of the collector junction. In ordinary transistors this component will arise only at high collector-voltages. There will, of course, be a corresponding increase in positive-hole current. The effect of this phenomenon will also be discussed in the next section.

6.3. Physical interpretation of the short-circuit current gain

The low-frequency parameters of the intrinsic transistor may be determined from the equations of the preceding section. Probably the most important of these is α'_0, the low-frequency value of the short-circuit current gain α'. In this section we shall outline briefly the interpretation of this parameter in terms of the physical constants of the transistor.

The current gain α' is usually expressed in the form

$$\alpha' = \gamma\eta\alpha^*, \tag{6.10}$$

where the three factors on the right are defined as follows:

1. The emitter efficiency γ is the fraction of the emitter current that consists of minority carriers (in the present case, holes) injected into the base.

2. The transport factor η is the ratio of the minority-carrier current reaching the collector junction to the minority-carrier current injected at the emitter junction. In most transistor literature the letter β is used for this quantity. The use of η avoids confusion with the CE current gain for which the symbol β is often used in transistor specifications.

3. The collector multiplication factor α^* is the ratio of the total collector current to the positive-hole current entering the collector from the base.

These quantities are all functions of frequency except at the lower end of the frequency range where they become constants normally designated γ_0, η_0, and α_0^*. In this chapter we shall be concerned with these low-frequency values. The general form of the variation of α' with frequency will be considered in the next chapter.

6.3.1. *The calculation of emitter efficiency*

The factor γ_0 may be calculated from equations (6.5) and (6.8) by using differentials as approximations for small changes of current and voltage. Since W_0 is a constant when the collector is short-circuited (cf. § 6.4 below), we have

$$i'_{pe} = (q^2 D_p p_n v'_e / kT L_p) \exp(qV'_e/kT) \coth m, \qquad (6.11)$$

$$i'_{ne} = (q^2 D_n n_{pe} v'_e / kT L_{ne}) \exp(qV'_e/kT), \qquad (6.12)$$

where i'_{pe}, i'_{ne}, and v'_e are small changes of current and voltage superimposed upon the d.c. values. Also from the above definitions

$$\gamma_0 = i'_{pe}/(i'_{pe}+i'_{ne}) = 1/[1+(i'_{ne}/i'_{pe})].$$

Since $m \ll 1$ we may put $\coth m \simeq \operatorname{cosech} m \simeq L_p/W_0$, whence

$$\gamma_0 = \frac{1}{1+(D_n n_{pe} W_0/D_p p_n L_{ne})}. \qquad (6.13)$$

Since $\exp(qV'_e/kT) \gg 1$, i'_{pe} in equation (6.11) may be expressed in terms of I'_{pe} in equation (6.5) giving

$$i'_{pe} \simeq (qv'_e/kT)I'_{pe}. \qquad (6.14)$$

From this we see that, in order for i'_{pe} to be small compared with the d.c. current I'_{pe}, we must have $v'_e \ll kT/q$ ($\simeq$ 25 mV at room temperature). No such limit applies to the collector-voltage variation v'_c because the collector is biased so far into the reverse saturation region that fluctuations in collector voltage have little direct effect on the collector current. There is a second-order effect which arises from the effect of collector voltage on base width. This will be discussed later in this chapter. From equation (2.1) $D_n/D_p = \mu_n/\mu_p$ and from equation (1.7)

$$n_{pe} p_e = \text{constant} = p_n n_b, \qquad (6.15)$$

where n_b is the density of electrons in the n-type base. Thus $n_{pe}/p_n = n_b/p_e$ and using equation (1.11) with the assumption that the conductivities in emitter and base are decided practically entirely by their majority-carrier densities, we obtain

$$\gamma_0 = \frac{1}{1+(\sigma_b W_0/\sigma_e L_{ne})}. \qquad (6.16)$$

The emitter efficiency therefore increases with the ratio of emitter to base conductivity and with the ratio of electron-diffusion length in the emitter region to the base width. We note that γ_0 is related to the injection efficiency of a p-n junction (equation 4.10), but because $W_0 \ll L_{pb}$, the diffusion length for holes in the base region, the injection efficiency in the present case can be made much greater than that of a p-n junction of the type considered in Chapter IV. Typical values given by Early [2] are $\gamma_0 \simeq 0.992$ for an n-p-n grown-junction transistor and $\gamma_0 \geqslant 0.995$ for a p-n-p alloy-junction transistor. The former is the smaller because of the lower conductivity of the emitter region for the grown-junction transistor.

As the frequency is increased γ decreases by a small amount. This effect, which is discussed by Middlebrook [3], will not be considered further here.

6.3.2. *The calculation of transport factor*

The value of η_0 is given by the ratio i'_{pc}/i'_{pe}, in which the numerator is obtained by differentiation of equation (6.7) and the denominator from equation (6.11). Thus

$$i'_{pc} = \frac{q^2 D_p\, p_n\, v'_e}{kT L_p} \exp(qV'_e/kT)\, \text{cosech}\, m \qquad (6.17)$$

and
$$\eta_0 = i'_{pc}/i'_{pe} = \text{sech}\, m \simeq 1 - m^2/2, \qquad (6.18)$$

where the final expression again results from the assumption that $W_0 \ll L_p$. The values of η_0 for the two transistors described by Early are each 0.993.

As the frequency is increased, η decreases to a much greater extent than either γ or α^*. The decrease is due to the finite time that it takes minority carriers to diffuse across the base region. It will be discussed in some detail in the next chapter.

6.3.3. *The form of the collector multiplication factor*

The low-frequency collector multiplication factor may be expressed in the form

$$\alpha^* = (i'_{pc} + i'_{nc})/i'_{pc}, \qquad (6.19)$$

where i'_{nc}, the collector electron current mentioned in the preceding section, may consist of a component due to the electric field of the positive-hole signal current entering the collector and a component due to avalanche multiplication in the collector depletion region. The latter is not usually important when the collector voltage is small and will not be further considered here. Calculation of the first-mentioned component is rather complicated and we shall merely summarize Early's results. These state that α^* ranges from $1+(\sigma_{nc}/2\sigma_{pc})$ to $1+(\sigma_{nc}/\sigma_{pc})$ as the positive-hole component of the collector current density ranges from low to high values. Here σ_{nc} and σ_{pc} are the conductivities due to electrons and holes respectively in the p-type collector. For a p-n-p alloy-junction transistor the collector conductivity is high and the number of electrons in the collector body is small. Thus $\sigma_{nc} \ll \sigma_{pc}$ and $\alpha^* \simeq 1$. For a p-n-p grown-junction transistor the collector conductivity may be small and the number of electrons in the collector body correspondingly larger. In this case α^* may exceed unity by a small amount at room temperature. At higher temperatures α^* will be larger because of the increase of n_{pc} with temperature (cf. § 1.3). For a germanium n-p-n grown-junction transistor considered by Early (which shows an analogous effect) $\alpha_0^* = 1\cdot03$ at $70°$ C.

6.3.4. *Calculated values of current gain*

Early has combined the three factors mentioned to obtain the following values of α_0' for typical p-n-p alloy-junction and n-p-n grown-junction transistors:

(a) For the p-n-p transistor $\alpha_0' = 0\cdot988$ over the useful temperature range.

(b) For the n-p-n transistor $\alpha_0' = 0\cdot985$ at $25°$ C and $1\cdot015$ at $70°$ C.

A value of α' in excess of unity can, under certain circumstances, cause instability in the operation of transistors. This fact is well known in point-contact transistor circuitry, where it is used to supply regeneration in pulse applications. In steady-state applications (e.g. small-signal applications) the effect is normally avoided. For some germanium grown-junction transistors it is therefore necessary to make sure that a combination of collector dissipation and a rise in ambient temperature will not drive the collector temperature to an excessive value.

6.4. Physical interpretation of other parameters of the intrinsic transistor

The low-frequency properties of the intrinsic transistor are decided by four parameters. The short-circuit current gain α_0' may be chosen as one of these and the remaining three expressed as h-parameters or as components of the low-frequency T-circuit. However, in the development of an equivalent circuit from the physical properties of the device a simpler method is to determine the admittance parameters and to calculate the parameters of other representations therefrom. The reason for this is that the currents I_{pe}' and I_{pc}' of equations (6.5) and (6.7) are functions of V_e' and V_c' and the small-signal equations obtained from them are therefore of admittance form.

The dependence of I_{pe}' and I_{pc}' on V_c' arises, through W_0, by the following mechanism: The thickness of the collector-junction transition region increases with V_c' according to the relations of Appendix IV. This increase takes place at the expense of the base and collector regions. In grown-junction transistors conditions approximate those in the graded-junction model of Appendix IV so that the base and collector regions are reduced equally. Alloy-junction transistors conform more closely to an abrupt-junction model in which the base resistance is much larger than that of the collector. In this case practically all of the increase of the collector transition region occurs at the expense of the base layer.

It is a relatively simple matter to determine the effect of a variation in V_c' on the base thickness W_0 with the help of equations (A4.6) and (A4.21), but for our present purpose this is not necessary. Instead we follow the usual procedure of expressing the variation of W_0 with V_c' in the form $\delta W_0 = (\partial W_0/\partial V_c')v_c'$. We then obtain equations for i_{pe}'' and i_{pc}'' in terms of v_e' and v_c' by differentiation of equations (6.5) and (6.7). The results may be expressed in the form

$$i_{pe}' = g_{11}' v_e' + g_{12}' v_c', \qquad (6.20)$$

$$-i_{pc}' = g_{21}' v_e' + g_{22}' v_c'. \qquad (6.21)$$

Here we have used the conductance symbol g instead of y to emphasize that we are considering the low-frequency case for which the parameters have no reactive components. Also, we have used the variable $-i'_{pc}$ in equation (6.21) because the direction of collector current flow chosen in this derivation is opposite to that used earlier in our discussion of the two-port network. The g' values of equation (6.21) therefore satisfy the relations involving y's in Appendix VI.

The values of the g-parameters obtained by the above procedure are

$$g'_{11} = (q^2 D_p p_1/kTL_p)\coth m, \tag{6.22}$$

$$g'_{12} = -(qD_p/L_p^2)(\partial W_0/\partial V'_c)[(p_1-p_n)\operatorname{cosech} m + \\ + p_n \coth m]\operatorname{cosech} m, \tag{6.23}$$

$$g'_{21} = -(q^2 D_p p_1/kTL_p)\operatorname{cosech} m, \tag{6.24}$$

$$g'_{22} = (qD_p/L_p^2)(\partial W_0/\partial V'_c)[(p_1-p_n)\operatorname{cosech} m + \\ + p_n \coth m]\coth m. \tag{6.25}$$

In equation (6.25) a term $p_n \coth^{-1} m$ has been omitted from the expression in the square brackets. It is very much smaller than $p_n \coth m \simeq p_n/m^2$ for $W_0 \ll L_p$.

Equations (6.22) to (6.25) arise from a consideration of positive-hole flow only. To obtain accurate values for the conductances we should, strictly speaking, add components arising from electron-current flow. However, this would complicate the analysis without a commensurate increase in accuracy. These electronic components will therefore be omitted. This will not affect the qualitative discussion of transistor parameters in the remainder of this chapter.

The intrinsic transistor equations (6.20) and (6.21) may be represented by the equivalent circuit of Fig. 6.2. From this we see that g'_{11} and g'_{22} may be defined as input and output conductance respectively while g'_{12} and g'_{21} are transfer conductances.

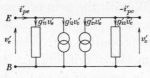

FIG. 6.2. The conductance (admittance) equivalent circuit of the intrinsic transistor.

Equations (6.22) to (6.25) may be simplified in form by making use of the d.c. current I'_{pe} of equation (6.4) and the factor η_0 of equation (6.18). We first note that $p_1 \gg p_n$ for practical emitter voltages so that

$$I'_{pe} \simeq (qD_p/L_p)p_1 \coth m. \tag{6.26}$$

Then, making further use of the fact that $p_1 \gg p_n$ and noting that because $W_0 \ll L_p$, $\coth m \simeq \operatorname{cosech} m \simeq 1/m \gg 1$, we obtain

$$g'_{11} \simeq qI'_{pe}/kT, \tag{6.27}$$

$$g'_{12} \simeq -(qD_p/L_p^2)(\partial W_0/\partial V'_c)p_1 \operatorname{cosech}^2 m$$
$$\simeq -(qD_p/L_p^2)(\partial W_0/\partial V'_c)p_1 \coth m \operatorname{sech} m \operatorname{cosech} m$$
$$\simeq -(I'_{pe}/L_p)(\partial W_0/\partial V'_c)\eta_0(L_p/W_0) \simeq -(\eta_0 I'_{pe}/W_0)(\partial W_0/\partial V'_c), \tag{6.28}$$

$$g'_{21} = -(q^2 D_p p_1/kTL_p)\coth m \operatorname{sech} m \simeq -\eta_0 qI'_{pe}/kT, \tag{6.29}$$

$$g'_{22} \simeq (qD_p/L_p^2)(\partial W_0/\partial V'_c)p_1 \coth m \operatorname{cosech} m$$
$$\simeq (I'_{pe}/W_0)(\partial W_0/\partial V'_c). \tag{6.30}$$

For the case of pure positive-hole flow represented by these equations, γ_0 and α_0^* are each unity and η_0 represents the current gain of the transistor. In line with the more usual terminology we now put $\eta_0 = \alpha'_0$. Then

$$g'_{12} = -\alpha'_0 g'_{22}, \tag{6.31}$$

$$g'_{21} = -\alpha'_0 g'_{11}. \tag{6.32}$$

Equations (6.27) to (6.30) apply to a transistor of unit area whose emitter current density is I'_{pe}. If we wish to obtain the conductance parameters of a practical transistor we multiply both sides of each equation by the area of the base (for an alloy-junction transistor the emitter area is probably the correct quantity). We shall assume that this has been done so that g''s are now the conductances of the practical transistor and I'_{pe} is the total current flowing rather than the current density.

6.5. Low-frequency parameters of the complete transistor

From equations (6.27) to (6.30) we can obtain a fairly accurate idea of the extent to which the parameters of the intrinsic transistor are influenced by temperature, emitter current, and collector voltage. (For the last we must also make use of Appendix IV.) The influence of these factors on the complete transistor is somewhat different from that indicated by these equations because of the effect of elements not considered in our analysis of the intrinsic transistor. Consequently, before we consider the effect of temperature and other variables in detail, we shall describe these additional elements (which are usually called 'extrinsic' components) and combine the more

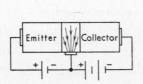

FIG. 6.3. Base-current flow in a grown-junction transistor.

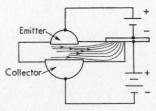

FIG. 6.4. Base-current flow in a low-frequency alloy transistor.

important ones with the above g-parameters to obtain the low-frequency parameters of the complete transistor.

The most important low-frequency extrinsic effects arise from resistance to the flow of majority carriers (in this case electrons) in the base. The current which flows out of the base electrode consists of a flow of electrons *into* the base to replace those electrons that recombine there with holes. (Note that we are not considering the flow of electrons from collector to base which is ignored in the derivation of equations (6.27) to (6.30).) The current is shown schematically for a grown-junction transistor in Fig. 6.3 and for an alloy-junction transistor in Fig. 6.4. Before reaching the base electrode it must pass transversely through the base region. Because the latter is very thin, its resistance is relatively high and must be taken into account when the equivalent circuit of the complete transistor is drawn. This extrinsic base resistance is shown as $r_{bb'}$ in Fig. 6.5. The subscripts indicate that it lies between the base connection of the intrinsic transistor and the external base connection.

The resistance $r_{bb'}$ is often called the base spreading-resistance because the base electrode, especially for grown-junction transistors, is usually small and the lines of current flow spread out from it to the various parts of the base. The geometry of the base-current flow in grown-junction transistors differs considerably from that in alloy-junction devices, as shown in Figs. 6.3 and 6.4, but it is found that the schematic representation of Fig. 6.5 is suitable for both cases.

There are two additional effects of the flow of base current

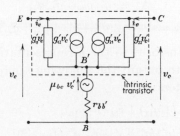

FIG. 6.5. Equivalent circuit of the
complete transistor.

that should be mentioned. The first is a vitiation of the assumption, made earlier, that current flow through the transistor is one-dimensional. The transverse potential, produced in the base by the base current, causes a variation in potential across the emitter junction and hence a variation in emitter current. To take this into account would complicate matters considerably. Since the effect is usually small, we shall follow the usual practice and ignore it.

The second effect that has been omitted arises from the modulation of the base width by the variation in collector voltage produced by the signal. This causes a change in base resistance in synchronism with the signal, and the flow of the base current through this changing resistance produces a voltage which may be represented by the voltage generator $\mu_{bc} v_c'$ shown, in series with the base lead, in Fig. 6.5. This effect is also small and will be ignored in the discussion that follows.

Another non-reactive extrinsic effect is sometimes added to the low-frequency equivalent circuit. This is a conductance from collector to base due to surface leakage. In good modern transistors this is negligible compared with g_{22}' and may be omitted,

Low-frequency g- or y-parameters for the complete transistor (in which electron flow has been neglected) may now be obtained from the equivalent circuit of Fig. 6.5 (omitting the generator $\mu_{bc} v'_c$). These are found to be

$$g_{11} = (g'_{11}+r_{bb'}\Delta_{g'})/\Delta, \qquad g_{12} = (g'_{12}-r_{bb'}\Delta_{g'})/\Delta, \qquad (6.33)$$

$$g_{21} = (g'_{21}-r_{bb'}\Delta_{g'})/\Delta, \qquad g_{22} = (g'_{22}+r_{bb'}\Delta_{g'})/\Delta, \qquad (6.34)$$

where

$$\Delta_{g'} = g'_{11} g'_{22} - g'_{12} g'_{21} \qquad (6.35)$$

and

$$\Delta = 1 + r_{bb'}(g'_{11}+g'_{12}+g'_{21}+g'_{22}). \qquad (6.36)$$

We may now transform to the h-representation with the help of Appendix VI to obtain the following approximate relations for the h-parameters:

$$h_{ib} \simeq (1/g'_{11})+r_{bb'}(1-\alpha'_0), \qquad (6.37)$$

$$h_{rb} \simeq (g'_{22}/g'_{11})[\alpha'_0+r_{bb'} g'_{11}(1-\alpha'^2_0)]$$
$$= -g'_{12}/g'_{11}+r_{bb'} g'_{22}(1-\alpha'^2_0), \quad (6.38)$$

$$h_{fb} \simeq -\eta_0 = -\alpha'_0, \qquad (6.39)$$

$$h_{ob} \simeq g'_{22}(1-\alpha'^2_0). \qquad (6.40)$$

These expressions have been simplified by making use of the following facts:

1. g'_{22} and g'_{12}, which are almost equal as equation (6.31) shows, are smaller than g'_{11} and g'_{21} by a factor between 10^3 and 10^4.

2. $r_{bb'}$ is usually a few hundred ohms and may be neglected when it is in series with $1/g'_{22}$ ($\simeq 100$ kilohms).

In Fig. 6.5 we have used the symbols v_e and v_c for the voltages of the real transistor, thus taking into account the effect of $r_{bb'}$. Also for ease in writing we have altered the current symbols to i_e and i_c although strictly speaking it is only necessary to change one set of variables.

We note from equations (6.38) and (6.40) that h_{rb} and h_{ob} are defined in terms of g'_{12} and g'_{22} which are functions of V'_c rather than V_c. However, the difference between V_c and V'_c is usually small and we may remove the inconsistency by replacing V'_c in equations (6.28) and (6.30) by V_c.

By making use of equations (6.27) to (6.32) and replacing

I'_{pe} by I_e we obtain the following approximate expressions for the h-parameters of the complete transistor:

$$h_{ib} \simeq (kT/qI_e) + r_{bb'}(1-\alpha_0) \simeq r_\epsilon + r_{bb'} \, m^2/2, \qquad (6.41)$$

$$h_{rb} \simeq (1/W_0)(\partial W_0/\partial V_c)[\alpha_0 kT/q + r_{bb'} I_e(1-\alpha_0^2)]$$

$$= \mu + r_{bb'} h_{ob}, \quad (6.42)$$

$$h_{fb} \simeq -\alpha_0 \simeq -(1-m^2/2), \qquad (6.43)$$

$$h_{ob} \simeq [I_e(1-\alpha_0^2)/W_0](\partial W_0/\partial V_c) \simeq (I_e W_0/L_p^2)(\partial W_0/\partial V_c). \quad (6.44)$$

In these equations α'_0 has been replaced by α_0 throughout since it can be shown that the resulting error is negligible. Also we have put

$$r_\epsilon = (kT/qI_e) \quad \text{and} \quad \mu = (\alpha_0 kT/qW_0)(\partial W_0/\partial V_c). \quad (6.45)$$

It should be noted that this μ differs from the μ_{bc} defined earlier. Although both arise from the effect of V'_c on base width, μ, which depends on the resulting changes at the emitter junction, is considerably larger than μ_{bc} which depends on the change in $r_{bb'}$.

6.6. Transistor parameters as functions of operating variables

In the derivation of the above theoretical expressions for the transistor parameters there is a tendency to lose sight of the physical processes in the detailed analysis. In order to compensate for this we shall now study briefly the terms of equations (6.41) to (6.44) and see how they are influenced by the more important operating variables, viz. collector voltage, emitter bias current, and temperature. We shall demonstrate the extent to which these equations apply to a practical transistor by comparing the behaviour predicted by them to that shown in published data on the 2N369.

6.6.1. The effect of collector voltage

The influence of collector voltage on the properties of the simple transistor arises from the change in base width produced by it. As the collector voltage is increased the collector transition region increases in width and produces a decrease in base width. For an alloy-junction transistor the equation for base thickness is (Appendix IV)

$$W_0 = W_b - C(V_0 - V_c)^{\frac{1}{2}}, \tag{6.46}$$

where W_b and C are constants and V_c, which is negative since the collector junction is reverse-biased, now replaces V_a in equation (A4.21). W_0, the base width under operating conditions, decreases as V_c is increased in magnitude.

In the present approximation, h_{rb} the reverse-voltage ratio and h_{ob} the output admittance can only exist if the base width depends on collector voltage. The mechanisms by which variation in base width give rise to these two h-parameters are the following:

1. A small increase $-\delta V_c$ in (negative) collector voltage causes a decrease in W_0 whose effect on emitter current and voltage is given by equation (6.5). Since h_{rb} and h_{ob} are measured with the emitter open-circuited to a.c., I_e and hence I'_{pe}, which differs very little from I_e, must remain constant. Hence, since

$$\coth(W_0/L_p) \simeq \operatorname{cosech}(W_0/L_p) \simeq L_p/W_0,$$

V'_e must decrease by an increment $-\delta V_e$. The ratio $(-\delta V_e)/(-\delta V_c)$ is the parameter μ of equations (6.42) and (6.45).

2. The decrease of base width reduces the volume of the base and thus the amount of recombination there. The electrons taking part in the recombination processes enter the base of the intrinsic transistor through $r_{bb'}$ and the voltage drop across this resistor changes by $-\delta V_{b'}$. The second term of equation (6.42) is equal to $(-\delta V_{b'})/(-\delta V'_c)$.

3. Because of the decreased recombination in the base the (negative) collector current is changed by an increment $-\delta I_c$. The ratio $(-\delta I_c)/(-\delta V_c)$ is the output admittance of equation (6.44).

This discussion shows that h_{rb} and h_{ob} arise in such an indirect manner that they might almost be regarded as second-order effects. Their magnitudes confirm this impression. Thus the reverse-voltage ratio h_{rb} is smaller by a factor of order 1,000 than the other dimensionless parameter h_{fb}. This is fortunate since h_{rb} is a feedback factor that gives an indication of the difficulty of isolating the input and output circuits of the transistor from each other at low frequencies. At higher frequencies h_{rb} is usually less important than a capacity feedback effect which will be described in the next chapter.

The magnitude of h_{ob} is also small compared with the conductance $1/h_{ib}$, as indicated earlier. Since the load resistance R_l is usually of the order of h_{ib}, we see that $h_{ob} R_l \ll 1$ so that the effect of h_{ob} in many of the formulae of Appendix X may be ignored.

In addition to the small changes of collector voltage which produce h_{rb} and h_{ob} the values of collector (d.c.) bias voltage may vary from one application to another and it is important to understand how these variations affect the circuit characteristics. From equations (6.41) to (6.44) we see that V_c the bias voltage, which enters through W_0, has some influence on all of the h-parameters. The magnitudes of the changes involved, as determined experimentally for the 2N369, are shown in Fig. A11.7. The general trends of the curves in this figure may be explained as follows:

(a) For h_{ib} the influence of V_c enters through the second term of equation (6.41). The magnitude of this term is small relative to the first term because $W_0 \ll L_p$. Consequently, as confirmed by the figure, the effect of V_c on h_{ib} is negligible.

(b) The variation of h_{fb} with V_c is obtained from equations (6.43) and (6.46). Thus

$$1+h_{fb} \simeq \frac{W_0^2}{2L_p^2} = \frac{[W_b - C(V_0 - V_c)^{\frac{1}{2}}]^2}{2L_p^2}. \qquad (6.47)$$

For V_c small $W_b \gg C(V_0 - V_c)^{\frac{1}{2}}$ and the variation of $(1+h_{fb})$ with collector voltage is slight, but for larger values of V_c the second term in the numerator of (6.47) becomes an appreciable fraction of W_b and the decrease of $(1+h_{fb})$ becomes more rapid. This condition can be detected for values of V_c approaching -20 volts in Fig. A11.7. It can be shown quite readily that the curve of $(1+h_{fb})$ in this figure satisfies equation (6.47) for values of V_c in the -5 to -20 volt range. This effect also appears in the rise at higher voltages of the CE output characteristics of Fig. A11.3 as mentioned in Chapter V.

(c) The variation of h_{rb} with V_c is decided chiefly by the first term of equation (6.42) and thus by the factor $(1/W_0)(\partial W_0/\partial V_0)$. Making use of equation (6.46) we find

$$h_{rb} \propto [(V_0-V_c)^{\frac{1}{2}}\{W_b-C(V_0-V_c)^{\frac{1}{2}}\}]^{-1}. \qquad (6.48)$$

For small negative values of V_c the variation of h_{rb} is decided chiefly by the first $(V_0-V_c)^{\frac{1}{2}}$ term, and in this voltage range h_{rb} decreases as the magnitude of V_c increases. However, for values of V_c in the -10 volt to -20 volt region the factor $W_b-C(V_0-V_c)^{\frac{1}{2}}$ varies quite rapidly and is responsible for the upturn which may be noted in Fig. A11.7.

(d) Expressing h_{ob} in terms of V_c, we obtain

$$h_{ob} \propto [W_b-C(V_0-V_c)^{\frac{1}{2}}]/(V_0-V_c)^{\frac{1}{2}}. \qquad (6.49)$$

As V_c is increased this equation predicts a decrease of h_{ob} which is confirmed by Fig. A11.7 until V_c reaches -5 volts. For larger voltages h_{ob} increases again. This effect is not predicted by our simple theory. It may arise from collector-to-base surface conduction, from avalanche effects, or from some other mechanism not taken into account in the simple one-dimensional model of the transistor used in this chapter.

6.6.2. *The effect of emitter current*

The effect of variation of emitter bias current on the CB h-parameters of the 2N369 is shown in Fig. A11.6. In terms of equations (6.41) to (6.44) we have the following explanations:

(a) As mentioned above, the magnitude of h_{ib} is decided chiefly by the first term so that we would expect a plot of $\log h_{ib}$ vs. $\log I_e$ to be approximately linear and of negative slope. Fig. A11.6 shows this to be the case. The approximate magnitude of h_{ib} can also be obtained from equation (6.41). Thus at room temperature $kT/q \simeq 0.025$ volt so that for $I_e = 1$ mA this term of h_{ib} is about 25 ohms. As seen from Appendix XI the value of h_{ib} for the 2N369 under these same conditions may range from 25 to 50 ohms with a design centre at 30 ohms. The curve of Fig. A11.6 is presumably drawn for the design centre case. For large currents h_{ib} tends to level off at a value determined by the second term of (6.41). The beginning of this levelling-off process can be seen in the figure.

(b) Equation (6.43) indicates an independence of emitter current for h_{fb} that is not confirmed by the curve for this parameter in Fig. A11.6. From this curve we see that

$$(1+h_{fb}) = (1-\alpha_0)$$

decreases with emitter bias current up to $I_e \simeq 3$ mA and then begins to increase, i.e. α increases and then decreases. The effect is amplified and thus shown more clearly by plotting $(1-\alpha_0)$ instead of α_0. Also, from the practical point of view the quantity $(1-\alpha_0)$ is the more important since it indicates approximately the way in which the reciprocals of h_{fe} and h_{fc} vary with emitter bias current. For general-purpose transistors this variation in current gain is not usually important but for power transistors the drop in current gain at the high current end must often be taken into account.

This behaviour of α_0 under medium- and high-current conditions results from the breakdown of our original assumption that the number of injected holes is very much smaller than the number of electrons in the base. It was first analysed by Webster [4]. The increase of α_0 at medium emitter currents arises because the diffusion force acting on electrons in the base prevents them from neutralizing the charge of the injected holes at all points in the base. The total charge in the base is very close to zero but it is distributed in such a way that an electric field exists in the direction of hole flow. This has the effect of increasing the hole current and hence α_0. The decrease in α_0 in the high emitter-current region arises because the injected holes increase the effective positive-hole conductivity of the base. As may be seen from equation (6.16) the emitter efficiency γ_0 is therefore reduced. Another factor contributing to the reduction in α_0 at high current levels is the increase in recombination that occurs because the concentrations of both holes and electrons are increased.

(c) The effect of I_e on h_{rb} arises chiefly through the second term of equation (6.42). Since this is normally considerably smaller than the first term the increase of h_{rb} with I_e is relatively small.

(d) As may be seen from equation (6.44) the variation of h_{ob} with I_e would be linear if α_0 were constant. A study of Fig. A11.6 shows that the departure from linearity of h_{ob} is approximately accounted for by the change in $(1+h_{fb}) \simeq (1-\alpha_0)$.

6.6.3. *The effect of temperature*

The effect of temperature—one of the most important variables in the application of transistors—is shown in Fig. A11.8. The curves of the h-parameters there shown may be interpreted as follows:

(a) The variation of h_{ib} follows equation (6.41) quite closely at temperatures up to 50° C approximately. Thus for a variation in temperature from $-50°$ C to $+20°$ C—approximately 25 per cent of the value of T ($\simeq 273$ at 0° C)—the variation in h_{ib} is about 25 per cent. At higher temperatures intrinsic conduction effects begin to appear and there is a quite rapid rise in h_{ib}. Operation of the transistor in this region is quite complicated and even a qualitative discussion would take us too far afield for this book.

(b) Equation (6.43) predicts no variation of α_0 with temperature and the measured variation for the 2N369 is, in fact, very small. If we assume $\alpha_0 = 0.982$ at 25° C the values at 75° C and $-50°$ C (determined from the $(1+h_{fb})$ curve of Fig. A11.8) are 0.990 and 0.976 respectively. This variation can probably be accounted for by the effect of temperature on the electronic component of collector current which has been ignored.

(c) For low temperatures the variation of h_{rb} follows quite closely that of h_{ib} as would be expected from a comparison of equations (6.41) and (6.42). The divergence between them at high temperatures is probably due to the fact that they are different functions of base width W_0 so that changes in W_0 as the intrinsic range is approached have different effects.

(d) The variation in h_{ob} apparently follows that of $(1-\alpha_0^2)$ at low temperatures as indicated by equation (6.44). At high temperatures intrinsic effects again become dominant. The activation energy determined from a plot of $\log h_{ob}$ vs. $(1/T)$ is about 0.32 eV at the high end of the temperature range shown in Fig. A11.8 and thus approaches quite closely to $E_g/2$, the activation energy for intrinsic conduction, which is about 0·37 eV for germanium.

For silicon transistors the intrinsic range is not approached even at the highest operating temperatures—as may be seen

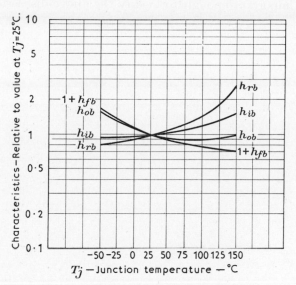

Fig. 6.6. CB h-parameters of the 2N336 grown-junction silicon transistor as functions of temperature.

from the curves for a high-gain silicon transistor, the 2N336, in Fig. 6.6—and the discussion of the low-temperature range applies in this case. (The increase in h_{rb} at the upper end of the temperature range may be due to an increase in surface conduction across the collector barrier.) For these devices the upper limit of operating temperature is apparently decided by lattice effects, such as the motion of impurities, or by surface effects, rather than the onset of intrinsic electronic conduction.

The results of this section show that the simple theory outlined in this chapter gives a surprisingly accurate picture of the operation of a general-purpose transistor at low frequencies. There are discrepancies, as we have indicated, but these can usually be explained, at least qualitatively. We should emphasize also that the quantitative differences between parameters of different types of low-power transistors (e.g. alloy-junction and grown-junction transistors) can usually be accounted for [2]. For high-power transistors, other factors such as the non-uniformity of current distribution across the base region may become important enough to modify the above discussion.

HIGH-FREQUENCY AND SWITCHING
PHENOMENA IN TRANSISTORS

7.1. Introduction

CHAPTER VI has shown that the phenomena taking place in transistors operating in the d.c. or frequency-independent a.c. region are quite complex. When operation at higher frequencies is considered these complexities increase many-fold due chiefly to transit-time effects in the flow of minority carriers. The development of equivalent circuits to describe transistor operation in this frequency-dependent region is therefore a very complicated procedure and many different approaches to it have been made. In this chapter we shall describe a general approach to this problem related to the physical properties and attempt to show how some practical high-frequency equivalent circuits are derived from our result. We will confine our discussions to circuits that we believe to be most useful to engineers or physicists who are not specialists in transistor applications but wish to make occasional use of the device in a reasonably intelligent way. Later we shall give our impressions of the present trends in the application of transistors at very high frequencies and end the chapter with a description of the processes involved in the amplification of large transients (pulses) and in switching phenomena.

It is perhaps worth while, at this point, to mention the broad reasons for the tremendous complexity of transistor high-frequency equivalent circuits compared with those normally used for vacuum tubes. As noted above, the chief cause of deterioration in response at high frequencies is the transit time of the charge carriers. For most general-purpose vacuum tubes in the common cathode connection this property becomes important at frequencies of the order of 100 Mc/sec. Designers of vacuum circuits for d.c., audio, and ordinary radio-frequency applications need not consider complications that arise when the frequency approaches this value. For junction transistors in the corresponding (CE) connection, effects associated with transit time arise, even in modern general-purpose transistors, at frequencies of the order of 10 kc/sec. This is often well within the range of interest and may be below the operating frequency in many applications. Thus most designers of transistor circuits have to take into account complications that concern only a small fraction of users of vacuum tubes.

7.2. Analysis of transistor operation above the frequency independent range

Application of the low-frequency T equivalent circuit of Chapter V very soon showed its inadequacy for estimating the performance of junction transistors in the CE and CC connections at frequencies exceeding a few kilocycles per second. It was recognized quite early that two factors that had not been taken into account were the collector transition region capacity and the decrease of short-circuit current gain α with frequency. The first attempts to extend the frequency range of the equivalent circuit consisted of *ad hoc* additions to take account of these two factors. These were soon shown to be inadequate in spite of various refinements that complicated the circuit considerably and it became evident that a more fundamental approach, based on an analysis of the physical processes taking place in the transistor, was necessary. The first reasonably complete study of this type was that of Early [1] referred to in the last chapter. The method of analysis was to solve the time-dependent diffusion equation (A3.7), omitting the field term, for the intrinsic transistor in the steady-state a.c. condition and, as in Chapter VI, to add the extrinsic elements later.

The density of holes in the base layer of a p-n-p transistor, in the high-frequency case, is again given by an equation of the form of equation (6.1),

$$p_1 = p_n \exp(qV_e/kT), \tag{7.1}$$

but in this case V_e contains a.c. and d.c. components. Thus

$$V_e = V_{e0} + V_{e1} \exp(j\omega t). \tag{7.2}$$

In order to make the diffusion equations tractable when the boundary condition (7.2) is introduced it is necessary to make $V_{e1} \ll kT/q$—a condition already used in the low-frequency case (equation (6.14)). The hole-density equations then become

$$p_1 = p_0 + p_2 \exp(j\omega t) \tag{7.3}$$

with $p_0 = p_n \exp(qV_{e0}/kT)$ and $p_2 = p_n\left(\dfrac{qV_{e1}}{kT}\right)\exp(j\omega t)$. (7.4)

The analysis proceeds along similar lines to that of Chapter VI and, for the case of pure positive-hole flow, leads to the following admittance parameters corresponding to the conductance parameters of equations (6.22) to (6.25). (We have here used the symbols $s = (1+j\omega\tau_p)^{\frac{1}{2}}$ and $m = W_0/L_p$.)

$$y'_{11} = sg'_{11} \tanh m/\tanh sm, \tag{7.5}$$

$$y'_{12} = sg'_{12} \sinh m/\sinh sm, \tag{7.6}$$

$$y'_{21} = sg'_{21} \sinh m/\sinh sm, \tag{7.7}$$

$$y'_{22} = sg'_{22} \tanh m/\tanh sm. \tag{7.8}$$

The most striking characteristic of these equations is their complexity. All of the y-parameters of the intrinsic transistor are complicated functions of frequency.

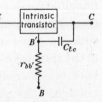

The y-parameter representation of the complete transistor can be obtained from equations (7.5) to (7.8) by the method of Chapter VI. However, we now have to consider another important extrinsic parameter. This is the collector transition region capacity C_{tc} which is usually shown as in Fig. 7.1. For

FIG. 7.1. Schematic diagram of a junction transistor showing the extrinsic elements.

some transistors, notably those of the alloy-junction type, the lower lead to C_{tc} should probably be connected to a tap part way along $r_{bb'}$ rather than to B'. However, the error introduced by connecting this lead to B' is small and the circuit of Fig. 7.1 is almost invariably used. An extrinsic leakage conductance between the collector and a tap on $r_{bb'}$ is also sometimes considered, as mentioned in Chapter VI, but it is usually small compared with the collector-to-base conductance of the intrinsic transistor and we shall neglect it.

In attempting to derive an equivalent circuit from equations (7.5) to (7.8) we choose the T-circuit of Fig. 7.2 as a convenient form. Following the ideas outlined in the development of the low-frequency T-circuit in Chapter V we assume that there are impedances z_e and z_c in the emitter and collector arms respectively. A current generator i_g is again inserted in the collector arm. The base resistance is now assumed to be $r_{bb'}$. We emphasize that this should not be assumed equal to the resistance r_b referred to previously. We shall show later that r_b is considerably larger than $r_{bb'}$.

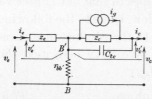

FIG. 7.2. First approach to a T-circuit representing the transistor at high frequencies.

We now attempt to obtain the constants of the 'intrinsic' part of Fig. 7.2 from equations (7.5) to (7.8). We note immediately that we have four complex equations representing four real and four imaginary parameters, while the intrinsic section of Fig. 7.2 contains only three real and three imaginary components (assuming that i_g as well as z_e and z_c are complex). To obtain a fourth set of components we can add a complex generator or another impedance. The physical picture of the transistor suggests an element that will represent the feedback effect arising from the change of base width with collector voltage. The simplest way to do this is to insert a voltage generator, whose voltage is proportional to v'_c, in the input circuit. The intrinsic transistor is then represented as in Fig. 7.3. The voltage generator is $\mu v'_c$ where μ is a complex number.

The y-matrix equations of the intrinsic transistor are

$$i_e = y'_{11} v'_e + y'_{12} v'_c, \tag{7.9}$$

$$-i_c = y'_{21} v'_e + y'_{22} v'_c. \tag{7.10}$$

We consider these equations, and Fig. 7.3 which represents them, under two conditions:

(1) $v'_c = 0$ (*output short-circuited*). Then, from equation (7.9),

$i_e = y'_{11} v'_e$, while from Fig. 7.3, $v'_e = i_e z_e$. Hence

$$z_e = 1/y'_{11}. \qquad (7.11)$$

From equation (7.10), $-i_c = y'_{21} v'_e = y'_{21} z_e i_e = (y'_{21}/y'_{11})i_e$. But from Fig. 7.3, $i_c = i_g$ since all current must go through the short-circuit rather than z_c. Hence

$$i_g = -(y'_{21}/y'_{11})i_e = \alpha'i_e \qquad (7.12)$$

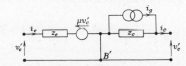

FIG. 7.3. Correct schematic representation of the intrinsic transistor.

and the frequency-dependent current gain is

$$\alpha = -y'_{21}/y'_{11}. \qquad (7.13)$$

Here, as in Chapter VI, we assume that the electron contribution to α' is negligible and that $\alpha = \alpha'$.

(2) $v'_e = 0$ (*input short-circuited*). Then, from equation (7.9), $i_e = y'_{12} v'_c$, and from Fig. 7.3, $\mu v'_c = -i_e z_e = -i_e/y'_{11}$. Hence

$$\mu = -y'_{12}/y'_{11}. \qquad (7.14)$$

Similarly, $-i_c = y'_{22} v'_c$ and $v'_c(1+\alpha\mu y'_{11} z_c) = -i_c z_c$.

Hence

$$z_c = y'_{11}/\Delta y' = 1/h'_{22}. \qquad (7.15)$$

The constants of Fig. 7.3 are now all expressed in terms of the y' parameters. Substituting for these from equations (7.5) to (7.8) we obtain

$$z_e = (1/g'_{11})\tanh sm/s \tanh m, \qquad (7.16)$$

$$\alpha = -(g'_{21}/g'_{11})\cosh m/\cosh sm, \qquad (7.17)$$

$$\mu = -(g'_{12}/g'_{11})\cosh m/\cosh sm, \qquad (7.18)$$

$$z_c = 1/g'_{22} s \tanh m \tanh sm. \qquad (7.19)$$

7.3. First-order approximations for the equivalent-circuit parameters

The non-linear expressions (7.16) to (7.19) are too complicated to use in circuit calculations and approximations to them are required. The usual procedure is to expand the hyperbolic functions on the assumption that $m^2\omega\tau \ll 1$ and to use as many terms as required of the series thus obtained. We shall use the 'first-order' approximation consisting of the first two terms in each series.

7.3.1. *The first-order approximation for* α

To obtain a first-order approximation for α we expand $\cosh sm$ as follows:

$$\cosh sm \simeq 1 + \frac{s^2 m^2}{2} = 1 + \frac{m^2(1 + j\omega\tau)}{2} \tag{7.20}$$

$$\simeq \left(1 + \frac{m^2}{2}\right)\left(1 + \frac{j\omega\tau m^2}{2}\right) \tag{7.21}$$

$$\simeq \left(1 + \frac{j\omega\tau m^2}{2}\right)\cosh m, \tag{7.22}$$

where the subscript on τ has been omitted, and terms containing powers of m higher than the second have been neglected.

Upon substituting (7.22) in (7.17) and using (6.32) (with the quite accurate assumption that the influence of γ, α^* and the extrinsic elements on the frequency dependence of α is negligible) we obtain

$$\alpha = \frac{\alpha_0}{1 + \frac{1}{2}j\omega\tau m^2}. \tag{7.23}$$

Equation (7.23) shows that the magnitude of α drops 3 db below its low-frequency value (i.e. α^2, which is proportional to the power, is reduced to 50 per cent or α is reduced to $1/\sqrt{2}$) at a frequency ω_c given by

$$\omega_c = 2\pi f_c = \frac{2}{m^2\tau}. \tag{7.24}$$

There is an accompanying phase shift so that α lags α_0 by 45° at $f = f_c$. Equations (7.23) and (7.24) therefore give, as the first-order approximation for α,

$$\alpha = \frac{\alpha_0}{1 + j(\omega/\omega_c)}. \tag{7.25}$$

The correct expression for α, derived from equation (7.17), is

$$\alpha = \frac{1}{\cosh m(1 + j\omega\tau)^{\frac{1}{2}}}. \tag{7.26}$$

As pointed out by Pritchard [2] this is decreased by 3 db at a frequency f_α given by

$$\omega_\alpha = 2\pi f_\alpha = \frac{2\cdot43}{m^2\tau}. \qquad (7.27)$$

Polar representations of equations (7.25) and (7.26) are given by the dashed and full curves respectively of Fig. 7.4. The magnitude of α at a chosen point on the curve is given by the

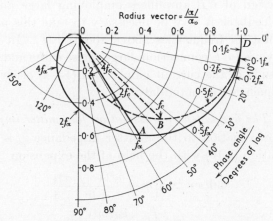

FIG. 7.4. Polar representations of CB short-circuit current gain α. Full line: The correct expression. Dashed line: The first-order approximation.

radius from O to that point and the phase angle is the angle between the radius and the horizontal axis. The points corresponding to some representative frequencies ($0\cdot1f_\alpha$, $0\cdot5f_\alpha$, etc.) are indicated by small arrows at right angles to the curves. The radii OA and OB are each equal to $1/\sqrt{2}$.

Experimentally determined curves for α fit the full curve of Fig. 7.4 quite well. The measured 3 db-down frequency, which is usually called the α-cutoff frequency, is therefore identical with f_α. However, in the most common approximation, α is assumed to satisfy equation (7.25) with ω_c replaced by the experimental value, i.e.

$$\alpha = \frac{\alpha_0}{1+j(\omega/\omega_\alpha)} = \frac{\alpha_0}{1+j(f/f_\alpha)}. \qquad (7.28)$$

This is equivalent to assuming that the f_c's on the dashed curve of Fig. 7.4 are f_α's. This approximation thus predicts a smaller phase shift than that obtained from equation (7.26). The error ranges from $3°$ at $0 \cdot 1 f_\alpha$ to $26°$ at $2 f_\alpha$. The magnitude of α is fitted to the experimental results at B and D and the error in it is negligible for frequencies less than $2 f_\alpha$.

It is worth noting that α has an appreciable phase shift at quite low frequencies. Thus at $f = 0 \cdot 2 f_\alpha$ the phase shift is $14°$. In the design of CB amplifiers employing large amounts of negative feedback it may be necessary to take this phase shift into account for frequencies above about $0 \cdot 1 f_\alpha$. In the more commonly used CE connection, large phase shifts and decreases in magnitude of the current gain $\beta = \alpha/(1-\alpha)$ occur at much lower frequencies, as noted later.

7.3.2. *The first-order approximation for emitter impedance*

An approximation to the emitter impedance z_e is obtained from equation (7.16) with the help of the expansion

$$\sinh sm \simeq s\left\{m + \frac{m^3(1+j\omega\tau)}{6}\right\} \tag{7.29}$$

$$\simeq s\left(1 + \frac{j\omega\tau m^2}{6}\right)\sinh m. \tag{7.30}$$

Division of (7.30) by (7.22) gives

$$\tanh sm \simeq \frac{s\tanh m}{1 + \frac{1}{3}j\omega\tau m^2} \tag{7.31}$$

and from (7.16)

$$z_e \simeq \frac{1/g'_{11}}{1 + \frac{1}{3}j\omega\tau m^2}. \tag{7.32}$$

Equation (7.32) can be represented by a resistance r_ϵ and a capacitance C_ϵ in parallel since the impedance of this combination has the form

$$z_e = \frac{1}{1/r_\epsilon + j\omega C_\epsilon} = \frac{r_\epsilon}{1 + j\omega C_\epsilon r_\epsilon}. \tag{7.33}$$

Comparing (7.32) and (7.33), using equation (6.27), we obtain

$$r_\epsilon = \frac{1}{g'_{11}} \simeq \frac{kT}{qI_e}, \tag{7.34}$$

$$C_\epsilon = \frac{\tau m^2}{3r_\epsilon} = \frac{qI_e\tau m^2}{3kT}, \tag{7.35}$$

or, using (7.27),
$$C_\epsilon = \frac{0 \cdot 81}{\omega_\alpha r_\epsilon} = \frac{0 \cdot 81 q I_e}{k T \omega_\alpha}. \qquad (7.36)$$

From equation (7.35) we see that C_ϵ is proportional to emitter current and to minority-carrier lifetime and is thus a diffusion capacitance of the type considered in Chapter IV. It is called the emitter diffusion capacitance.

7.3.3. *The first-order approximation for the feedback voltage*

The feedback-voltage generator μ has the same form as α and we may put
$$\mu = \frac{\mu_0}{1 + j(\omega/\omega_\alpha)}. \qquad (7.37)$$

7.3.4. *The first-order approximation for collector impedance*

The collector impedance z_c may also be represented (approximately) by a resistance r_c and a capacitance C_{dc} in parallel, where
$$r_c \simeq \frac{\coth^2 m}{g'_{22}} \simeq \frac{1}{m^2 g'_{22}}, \qquad (7.38)$$

$$C_{dc} \simeq \tau g'_{22} \tanh^2 m \simeq \tau m^2 g'_{22}. \qquad (7.39)$$

Substitution of (6.30) shows that C_{dc} is proportional to I_e. It is called the collector diffusion capacitance.

7.4. High-frequency equivalent circuits for the complete transistor

The equivalent circuit for the complete transistor, when the above approximations to the intrinsic elements are used, is shown in Fig. 7.5. Here $C_c \ (= C_{dc} + C_{tc})$ is the total collector capacitance.

Various modifications to Fig. 7.5 are possible. For example, equation (7.37) may be written in the form
$$\mu = \frac{\mu_0}{1 + j(\omega \tau m^2 / 2 \cdot 43)}. \qquad (7.40)$$

The imaginary term of this does not differ very much from that of (7.32). If we assume that the denominators of these two equations are equal we may replace $\mu v'_c$, which is in series with the emitter impedance, by the generator $\mu_0 v'_c$ in series with r_ϵ

only, as shown in Fig. 7.6. Also, we may take the frequency dependence of α into account by using the current generator $\alpha_0 i_1$ instead of αi_e.

At higher frequencies the reactance of C_c is considerably smaller than r_c which may therefore be omitted. In this same region, because of the short-circuiting effect of C_c, v'_c ($= v_{cb'}$) decreases from its low-frequency value while the feedback

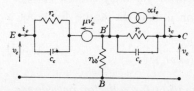

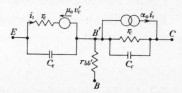

FIG. 7.5. *CB* high-frequency *T* equivalent circuit for the complete transistor.

FIG. 7.6. Another version of the *CB* high-frequency *T* equivalent circuit.

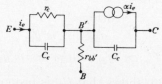

FIG. 7.7. Simplified version of Fig. 7.5, applicable at the higher end of the frequency range.

arising from the voltage drop across $r_{bb'}$ increases. The latter voltage is therefore large relative to $\mu v'_c$ and the generator may be omitted. The resulting equivalent circuit is shown in Fig. 7.7. The minimum frequency at which it is valid is determined by the conditions $\omega \gg 1/r_c C_c$ and $\mu_0 \ll j\omega C_c r_{bb'}$.

To give an exact frequency limit below which these circuits apply would require detailed consideration of the accuracy of the mathematical approximations used and of the variations between transistors of a given type. In practice they are often used at frequencies approaching f_α. The performance calculated from the equivalent circuit may then be in error by an amount similar to that which arises from variations between transistors. This is probably as good a criterion as can be found for determining the upper frequency limit.

The circuit of Fig. 7.6 may be transformed into the single-generator circuit of Fig. 7.8 by replacing $\mu_0 v'_c$ by the voltage drop across a resistor. The values of the new constants shown are $C_e = C_\epsilon$, $r''_b = \mu_0 r_c$, $r_e = r_\epsilon - (1-\alpha_0)\mu_0 r_c$. r_c and α_0 differ by negligible amounts from the corresponding elements of Fig. 7.6.

7.5. Lower-frequency approximations

The circuit of Fig. 7.8 is often simplified for use at lower frequencies by making the following approximations:

1. C_e, C_c and the frequency dependence of α are ignored. Fig. 7.8 then reduces to the low-frequency T-circuit of Chapter V with $r_b = r''_b + r_{bb'}$. Since r''_b may be several times as large as $r_{bb'}$

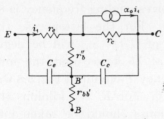

FIG. 7.8. Single generator CB high-frequency equivalent circuit.

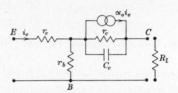

FIG. 7.9. CB low-frequency T-circuit with collector capacitance added.

we see that r_b, the base resistance in our intuitive derivation of Chapter V, is not even a fair approximation to $r_{bb'}$—although in some early equivalent circuits they were assumed to be identical.

2. C_e and the frequency dependence of α are ignored but C_c is taken into account. The usual form of the CB equivalent circuit in this case is shown in Fig. 7.9. However the CE connection is now almost invariably used in the frequency range for which this approximation is suitable. Its equivalent circuit, in which the collector capacity is increased by a factor $1/(1-\alpha_0)$, is shown in Fig. 7.10.

The circuit of Fig. 7.10 is sometimes used, for general-purpose transistors, at frequencies ranging up to about 15 kc/sec. Above this frequency some of the factors omitted—notably the shift of phase of α with frequency—become important. However, even in the range below 15 kc the usefulness of Fig. 7.10 is limited to applications in which the load resistance is relatively high. The output of the current generator divides between three paths containing $r_c(1-\alpha_0)$, $C_c/(1-\alpha_0)$, and (R_l+r_e) respectively. If R_l is low, most of the current passes through it and the effect of $C_c/(1-\alpha_0)$ is negligible. For the 2N369 for example, $C_c \simeq 33\,\mu\mu\mathrm{F}$ and $\alpha_0 = 0.982$ so that $C_c/(1-\alpha_0) \simeq 1,800\ \mu\mu\mathrm{F}$. The reactance of this is $10^6/2\pi f C_c = 87/f$ megohms. Thus the current and power gain will both be down by about 3 db when $R_l = 87/f$

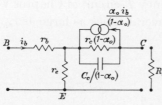

FIG. 7.10. *CE* version of Fig. 7.9.

megohms. If $R_l = 5$ kilohms the 3 db down point occurs at 17·4 kc/sec, while for $R_l = 1$ kilohm the corresponding frequency is 87 kc/sec. For the latter case the effect of $C_c/(1-\alpha_0)$ will be negligible at 15 kc/sec and the low-frequency T-circuit of Fig. 5.8 will be as accurate as that of Fig. 7.10. For $R_l \geqslant 5$ kilohms the effect of C_c on the frequency response should be taken into account and Fig. 7.10 should be used.

3. An attempt to increase the frequency range of the circuit of Fig. 7.10 is sometimes made by introducing the frequency dependence of α from equation (7.28)—the condenser C_e still being omitted. If the load resistance is high this is usually a satisfactory approximation up to and somewhat beyond the *CE* current gain cutoff frequency f_β. An approximation to f_β may be obtained with the help of equation (7.28). Thus

$$h_{fe} = \beta = \frac{\alpha}{1-\alpha} = \frac{\alpha_0}{1-\alpha_0+j(\omega/\omega_\alpha)}$$

or

$$h_{fe} = \beta = \frac{\left(\dfrac{\alpha_0}{1-\alpha_0}\right)}{1+j\dfrac{\omega}{(1-\alpha_0)\omega_\alpha}} = \frac{\beta_0}{1+j\dfrac{\omega}{\omega_\beta}}, \qquad (7.41)$$

where β_0 is the low-frequency value of β and $\omega_\beta = (1-\alpha_0)\omega_\alpha$ is the frequency at which β is 3 db down from its low-frequency value. The CE cutoff frequency $f_\beta = \omega_\beta/2\pi$ is thus much smaller than its CB counterpart. For the 2N369 for example, $\alpha_0 \simeq 0\cdot982$, $f_\alpha \simeq 1\cdot3$ Mc/sec, and $f_\beta \simeq 23$ kc/sec. At this frequency the collector capacitance $C_c/(1-\alpha)$ is important if R_l is large and the effect of C_e may then be ignored. The circuit of Fig. 7.10 is not normally used at frequencies beyond f_β because of complications introduced by the frequency dependence of $C_c/(1-\alpha)$.

The frequency dependence of the CC current gain is very similar to that of β, and the CC version of Fig. 7.10 may be obtained by placing $C_c/(1-\alpha)$ across $r_c(1-a)$ $(\simeq r_c(1-\alpha_0))$ of Fig. 5.9.

7.6. The CE hybrid-π equivalent circuit

With the exception of Fig. 7.10, the equivalent circuits so far considered have been for the CB connection. This is a result of our consideration of the physics of transistor processes. However, in small-signal circuit applications the CE connection is now almost invariably used because it supplies much higher gain. The CE connection may be preferable for this reason even beyond the CB cutoff frequency. For small-signal amplifiers the CB connection is therefore only used when the operating frequency is in the neighbourhood of f_α or when rather special input and output impedances are required.

The circuit of Fig. 7.10 has the serious disadvantage, referred to above, that some of its components are functions of frequency and this is true also of the CE versions of the more accurate circuits of Figs. 7.6, 7.7, and 7.8. Fortunately CE circuits whose elements and generators are independent of frequency do exist. The most generally useful of these is the CE hybrid-π equivalent circuit of Giacoletto. The development of this circuit is described in a very complete paper [3] which is recommended to students of the high-frequency operation of transistors. A development of the CE hybrid-π circuit from the CB high-frequency circuit of Fig. 7.7 is described by Jansson [4]. This description is part of a study in which the intrinsic transistor is represented by a transmission line containing resistive and capacity elements. This analysis, which contains many of the circuit transformations mentioned here, is an interesting alternative to the method of the present chapter.

The CE hybrid-π equivalent circuit is shown, with the usual symbols for its elements, in Fig. 7.11. These elements may be expressed in terms of those previously described, as follows:

$$g_{b'e} = (1-\alpha_0)/r_\epsilon, \qquad C_{b'e} = C_\epsilon = 0.81/r_\epsilon\,\omega_\alpha,$$
$$g_{b'c} = \mu_0(1-\alpha_0)/r_\epsilon, \qquad C_{b'c} = C_c,$$
$$g_{ce} = \mu_0/r_\epsilon, \qquad g_m = \alpha_0/r_\epsilon.$$

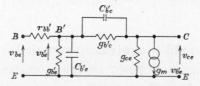

FIG. 7.11. CE hybrid-π equivalent circuit.

The dependence of these circuit constants on emitter current, collector voltage, and absolute temperature may be determined from formulae given in this and the preceding chapter. Experimental confirmation of these and other relations is given in Giacoletto's article. For conversion of published data from one operating condition to another the following relations are probably satisfactory:

$$g_{b'e} \propto I_e/T, \qquad C_{b'e} \propto I_e/T,$$
$$g_{b'c} \propto I_e/TV^{\frac{1}{2}}, \qquad C_{b'c} \propto 1/V^{\frac{1}{2}},$$
$$g_{ce} \propto I_e/TV^{\frac{1}{2}}, \qquad g_m \propto I_e/T.$$

Data in the above form are given, at the time of writing, by at least one manufacturer (R.C.A.). It is hoped that others will follow suit in the near future.

Using relations contained in this and the preceding chapter, it is theoretically possible to calculate the hybrid-π parameters when the low-frequency h-parameters, the collector capacitance, and f_α are given. In practice, however, errors ranging from 5 per cent to 15 per cent may occur in all parameters—with the exception of g_{ce} where the error may reach 60 per cent, due apparently to the fact that surface leakage has been neglected. Thus hybrid-π parameters should be determined by measurement if they are not obtainable from manufacturers' specifications.

The CE hybrid-π equivalent circuit has the following advantages:

1. Its elements are constant over the useful frequency range of the transistor.

2. The mechanism of feedback from output to input can be readily visualized and the values of external circuit elements required to compensate for it can be readily calculated. Such calculations are discussed in the next section.

7.7. Neutralization of internal feedback

The internal feedback mentioned above is one of the major problems in the design of high-frequency transistor amplifiers. If we use the h-representation equations

$$v_1 = h_i i_1 + h_r v_2, \tag{7.42}$$

$$i_2 = h_f i_1 + h_o v_2, \tag{7.43}$$

this feedback is represented by the parameter h_r which shows the extent to which the input voltage is influenced by voltage changes in the output circuit. (We note that the low-frequency h-equations can be used at high frequencies but that the h-parameters will then all be functions of frequency. In particular, h_r will depend on C_c and C_e as well as the resistive components.)

The internal feedback produces the following effects:

1. The properties of the amplifier vary with frequency in an undesirable manner.

2. At very high frequencies the feedback becomes positive and may cause oscillation.

3. The input and output impedances depend on each other to such an extent that proper matching of input to generator impedance and of output to load impedance is very difficult to attain. In a multistage amplifier, for example, any change in the generator or load impedance of one stage is reflected into all the other stages so that matching becomes an arduous and time-consuming process.

The internal feedback can be compensated for or 'neutralized' over a range of frequency which depends on the transistor connection. When this is done the input and output circuits are effectively isolated from each other and can be matched to the preceding and following stages without difficulty. Distortion of frequency response is also diminished and the range of frequency, over which amplification without oscillation can be attained, is extended.

With the help of an equivalent circuit representation it is possible to determine the elements of an external feedback circuit which will accomplish the required neutralization. Since the transistor is thereby made into a one-way device, in which an input signal can influence the output but the reverse is not true, the compensation process is often called 'unilateralization'. This term is rather unwieldy and we shall use the term 'neutralization' for this process. This does not correspond to the usual definition in which neutralization refers only to the removal of the reactive feedback term but in the present case no confusion is likely to arise.

7.7.1. *Admittance neutralization*

We now consider a general determination of the circuit constants required to neutralize a CB or CE amplifying stage and

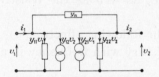

FIG. 7.12. Neutralization of the y-matrix equivalent circuit.

calculate the parameters of the neutralized circuit. The results we obtain will not be applied to the CC connection as this is rarely used in the neutralized condition. Neutralization is usually only worth while in the high-frequency region in which the combination of a capacitance load and complex equivalent-circuit parameters may be sufficient to produce a negative h_{ic} with a resulting tendency to oscillation.

The most common form of neutralization makes use of an external element such as y_n in Fig. 7.12. It is usually applied to the CE connection and, since the external element is most conveniently expressed in admittance form, the process is often called 'admittance neutralization'. In this section we shall determine the value of y_n and the properties of the neutralized circuit. For this purpose it is most convenient to use the y-representation of the transistor as shown in Fig. 7.12 and to express the properties of the neutralized circuit in terms of admittances Y_{12}, etc. Hence

$$i_1 = Y_{11}v_1 + Y_{12}v_2, \tag{7.44}$$

$$i_2 = Y_{21}v_1 + Y_{22}v_2. \tag{7.45}$$

To determine the Y-parameters we consider two conditions:

1. *Output short circuited* $(v_2 = 0)$.

Then

$$i_1 = (y_{11} + y_n)v_1 = Y_{11}v_1, \tag{7.46}$$

$$i_2 = (y_{21} - y_n)v_1 = Y_{21}v_1. \tag{7.47}$$

2. *Input short-circuited* $(v_1 = 0)$.

$$i_1 = (y_{12} - y_n)v_2 = Y_{12}v_2, \tag{7.48}$$

$$i_2 = (y_{22} + y_n)v_2 = Y_{22}v_2. \tag{7.49}$$

Neutralization of the feedback requires that

$$Y_{12} = 0 \tag{7.50}$$

so that $y_n = y_{12}$ and the other parameters become

$$Y_{11} = y_{11} + y_{12}, \tag{7.51}$$

$$Y_{21} = y_{21} - y_{12}, \tag{7.52}$$

$$Y_{22} = y_{22} + y_{12}. \tag{7.53}$$

With the help of these and Appendix VI we can determine the h-parameters of the neutralized circuit in terms of the original h-parameters. Thus

$$H_i = \frac{1}{Y_{11}} = \frac{1}{1/h_i - h_r/h_i} \simeq h_i, \tag{7.54}$$

$$H_f = \frac{Y_{21}}{Y_{11}} = \frac{h_f + h_r}{1 - h_r} \simeq h_f, \tag{7.55}$$

$$H_o = \frac{\Delta Y}{Y_{11}} = Y_{22} = \frac{\Delta h - h_r}{h_i}. \tag{7.56}$$

The approximate relations of equations (7.54) and (7.55) apply to the CB and CE connections. The exact expressions apply to all three connections but are of doubtful value in the CC case for the reason given above.

From Appendix VI we see that $y_n = y_{12} = -h_r/h_i$ and since h_r and h_i are positive for the CE and CB connections, y_{12} and y_n must be negative admittances. The fact that y_{12} is negative merely indicates that we have drawn the arrow representing the current $y_{12}v_2$ in Fig. 7.12 in the wrong direction. If we reverse it and use $y'_{12} = -y_{12}$ the above analysis gives $y_n = -y'_{12}$ so that y_n remains a negative admittance. In order to reverse

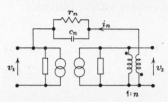

FIG. 7.13. Practical representation of the admittance neutralizing network.

the sign of y_n so that it can be represented by a normal admittance we must insert a transformer. This is usually connected as in Fig. 7.13. The positions of the dots associated with the primary and secondary windings indicate that their outputs are 180° out of phase.

The neutralizing network then consists of a condenser C_n and a resistance r_n in parallel since $-y_{12} = h_r/h_i$ is of this form. If the transformer ratio is $1:1$, r_n and C_n are equal to the components C_{12} and r_{12} that form $-y_{12}$. If the ratio is $n:1$ in the direction shown in Fig. 7.13 we must have $r_n = nr_{12}$ and $C_n = C_{12}/n$ since the neutralizing current i_n must remain unchanged. This fact enables us to choose convenient values of neutralizing components by altering the turns ratio although there is an optimum value $n = (R_o/R_i)^{\frac{1}{2}}$, where R_o and R_i are the output and input resistances of the transistor, which reduces the loss in the neutralizing network to a minimum [5].

7.7.2. Bridge neutralization

Admittance neutralization can be applied to both the CE and CB connections. For the latter, however, a different method, known as bridge neutralization, is more generally used. This may be described with the help of the high-frequency circuit of Fig. 7.5. For this purpose the small generator $\mu v'_c$ may usually be omitted since it has a negligible effect at the high frequencies at which CB neutralization is normally used. In this method the external elements R_n, R', and C_n are connected as shown in Fig. 7.14. They combine with $r_{bb'}$, r_c, and C_c to form a balanced bridge so that the output voltage v_2 produces equal and opposite voltage drops in R_n and $r_{bb'}$. The effect of feedback in the input circuit is thereby neutralized. This neutralization will be effective as long as the parameters of the transistor itself do not vary with frequency. Thus bridge neutralization of the CB connection should be independent of frequency in the region below f_α. When used above f_α the CB neutralized circuit has a limited frequency range because of transistor parameter variations but its bandwidth is normally greater than that of a CE-connected amplifier.

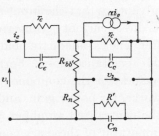

FIG. 7.14. Bridge neutralization of the CB connection.

The CE connection could, in principle, be neutralized by a bridge method but the form of the CE hybrid-π equivalent circuit indicates that admittance neutralization should be more suitable. It can in fact be demonstrated experimentally that admittance neutralization is effective over a broader range of frequencies than bridge neutralization [6]. Consequently, for the CE connection, admittance neutralization (or, in narrow-band amplifiers, a modification of it described below) is the common method.

7.7.3. *Neutralization of the CE hybrid-π equivalent circuit*

When the hybrid-π parameters are available the reverse transfer admittance y_{12} may be readily calculated at any frequency. (For frequencies above f_β, y_{12} will be a function of frequency because the shunting effect of $C_{b'e}$ reduces the current i_1 that flows in the input circuit when it is short-circuited.) It can be shown [5] that

$$y_n = y_{12} = -\frac{y_{b'c}y_{bb'}}{y_{b'e}+y_{bb'}+y_{b'c}}, \qquad (7.57)$$

where

$$y_{b'c} = g_{b'c}+j\omega C_{b'c},$$

$$y_{bb'} = 1/r_{bb'},$$

$$y_{b'e} = g_{b'e}+j\omega C_{b'e}.$$

The neutralizing network may take the form of the parallel arrangement of Fig. 7.13 (in which case equation (7.57) gives the values of the neutralizing components), or a resistance and a capacitance in series (impedance neutralization) may be used. In both cases the resistance and capacitance are functions of frequency but the gain of the admittance-neutralized amplifier is less affected by frequency than the impedance-neutralized version. On the other hand impedance neutralization has the advantage that the input and output circuits are isolated as far as direct current is concerned. In many cases, especially at high frequencies, adequate neutralization can be obtained by the use of capacitance alone. Formulae, in terms of the hybrid-π parameters, for the components of the impedance-neutralizing networks, for power gain, and for input and output admittance of the neutralized amplifier, are given by Jansson [5]. The more important of these are considered in Chapter XIV.

7.8. Calculation of properties in the region beyond cutoff

The circuits described in the preceding sections are useful, unless otherwise noted, at the α cutoff frequency and below. Most transistor applications are in this region. Transistors can, however, be applied at higher frequencies and in some cases their obvious advantages of small size, ruggedness, and low power consumption may outweigh disadvantages resulting from reduced gain in the region above α cutoff. In this section we shall consider briefly operation in this region and shall describe a method of determining circuit properties that is becoming increasingly popular.

Small-signal operation in the region beyond cutoff is usually confined to two types of amplifier:

1. The tuned band-pass type of amplifier.
2. The untuned wide-band or video amplifier.

The first of these finds the wider application at present. It will be discussed in some detail later. Its design requirements, which are similar to those of the preceding section, are:

1 a. To compensate for the internal feedback of the transistor at the design frequency.

1 b. To calculate the power gain and the input and output impedances of the stage.

The wide-band amplifier will probably increase in importance with experience in the design of transistor circuits. The design procedure in this case is:

2 a. To determine the power gain at the highest operating frequency.

2 b. To reduce the gain at lower frequencies by feedback and to maintain the gain at high frequencies by filter networks so that substantially constant gain over a wide band of frequencies is attained. Procedures for doing this are discussed briefly in Chapter XV.

Equivalent circuits for the region beyond cutoff have been developed [7]. They involve second-order approximations of some of the y-parameters and are considerably more complicated than any we have so far encountered. We shall not consider them further but shall outline an alternative approach to circuit design in this region which simplifies the user's problems although it increases the amount of data that the manufacturer must supply. At least two manufacturers have attacked the design of high-frequency amplifiers from this point of view and it is hoped that others will follow their example.

The method makes use of a low-frequency matrix equivalent circuit form, accepting the fact that the parameters vary with frequency. It may be demonstrated by considering the transducer gain in terms of the h-parameters. Thus, from equation (5.45), substituting for A_i and Z_i from Appendix X,

$$G_T = \frac{4|H_f|^2 R_g G_l}{|(H_i+Z_g)(H_o+Y_l)-H_r H_f|^2}, \qquad (7.58)$$

where the H-parameters are those of the conjugate matched (tuned) and neutralized circuit. Since $H_r/H_i = -Y_{12}$, neutralization removes the second term of the denominator. Conjugate matching makes $Z_g = R_i'-(1/j\omega C_i')$, where R_i' and C_i' are series components forming H_i, and $Y_l = G_o'-j\omega C_o'$, where G_o' and C_o' are parallel components forming H_o. Introduction of these relations into equation (7.58) gives

$$G_{mn} = \frac{|H_f|^2}{4 R_i' G_o'}, \tag{7.59}$$

where G_{mn} is the power gain in the conjugate matched and neutralized condition. Equations (7.58) and (7.59) may be used for CE or CB stages. Except at the very highest frequencies the CE has the higher gain and manufacturers' data of the type we are considering usually refer to the CE connection.

From equations (7.54) and (7.55) we see that R_i' may be replaced by the corresponding component of the original h-parameter and H_f may be replaced by h_f. Also equation (7.56) reduces to

$$H_o = h_o - \frac{h_r(1+h_f)}{h_i}. \tag{7.60}$$

Since h_{fe} is small in the region we are considering the second term of (7.60) may usually be neglected [8]. Hence we may put

$$G_{mn} \simeq \frac{|h_f|^2}{4 r_i g_o}, \tag{7.61}$$

where r_i and g_o are the real components of h_i and h_o. When the complex values h_f, h_i, and h_o are given at a certain frequency we may use equation (7.61) to determine the power gain per stage. Also, since the input impedance and output admittance are approximately h_i and h_o respectively, we may use these quantities to determine the ratios of the input and output transformers.

In many cases complex parameters of the type described here are not available from manufacturers and must be measured experimentally. A procedure for experimental matching involving inexpensive equipment is discussed later (Chapter XIV). If measurements are to be made over a range of frequencies for design purposes it is probably best to use admittance parameters [6].

7.9. Non-regenerative switching

Our discussions of transistor operation have so far been concerned with the amplification of small steady-state signals.

Other applications in which transistors are used to a considerable extent include the following:

1. Large-signal steady-state amplification.
2. Small-signal transient amplification.
3. The production or amplification of large transients.

The first two of these may be studied by means of the techniques and circuits that we have already described although some account must be taken of variations in parameters that result from large changes of current, voltage, or frequency. In a low-frequency power amplifier, for example, the variation of h_{fe} with emitter current is important, and in the amplification of small pulses with sharp leading and trailing edges the frequency range may be very broad. The important factors in such cases will be discussed in later chapters when circuit applications are considered.

The response of transistors to large transients introduces factors, such as carrier storage, that we have not considered in detail for transistors. An understanding of operation under such conditions requires a study of the physical processes involved. These will be considered in this section. We shall not attempt to describe equivalent circuits for this type of operation. Such circuits have been devised and are well described in the literature [9, 10, 11]. However, in most applications a few simple formulae, indicating how the shape of the output pulse varies with transistor and circuit parameters, are sufficient for preliminary designs provided the characteristics of a typical circuit are given by the transistor manufacturer. The present trend among manufacturers is to give this sort of information. Our chief concern in this section will therefore be to understand qualitatively how the above-mentioned formulae arise and to describe measures that may be taken to minimize distortion of the output waveform.

7.9.1. *The transistor as a switch*

The usefulness of the transistor as a producer of large pulses arises from the following properties:

1. It is an almost ideal switch, i.e. it can be easily changed

from an almost open-circuited condition in which, even with full-rated voltage across it, the current flowing through the device is very small, to an almost short-circuited condition in which the current flowing through it is large and the voltage drop across it is a small fraction of a volt.

2. The amount of driving power required to produce the transfer from one state to another may be a small fraction of the total power change.

3. The change from the closed to the open state or vice versa can in most cases be made so rapidly that the amount of power dissipated in the transistor is a small fraction of the total power change. Small devices may therefore be used to switch large amounts of power.

FIG. 7.15. Schematic representation of a *CE* switching stage.

These facts may be illustrated by consideration of a *CE* switching stage shown schematically in Fig. 7.15. In order to simplify the description of the physics of the process an *n-p-n* transistor has been chosen although most switching transistors are of the *p-n-p* alloy type. The latter type has a lower voltage drop, and thus lower losses when driven hard into the 'on' state. *n-p-n* grown-junction transistors are, however, used in some low-power switching applications such as those arising in computers. The collector characteristic of a commercial *n-p-n* germanium switching transistor (the GE 2N167) is shown in Fig. 7.16. The straight line passing through the battery-voltage point V_{cc} (= 12 volts in this case) has a slope $(-1/R_l)$ corresponding to the resistance R_l of the load and is called the load line. It is readily seen that the operating point, which indicates V_c, I_c, and I_b at the instant we are considering, must lie on this line. Only in this case will the sum of the voltages across R_l and the transistor equal the impressed voltage V_{cc}.

From Fig. 7.16 we see that, by varying the base current I_b, the operating point may be driven to the point A at which the collector current is reduced to a value slightly smaller than the reverse saturation current I_{c0}. At this point the transistor 'switch' is open. Application of a positive base current of 200 μA or larger moves the operating point to B and reduces the voltage across the transistor to a fraction of a volt. Almost the full source voltage V_{cc} is then applied across the load. This is the closed position of the transistor switch. A change in base current of about 200 μA which may be produced by a change

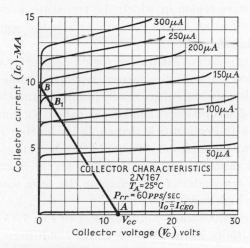

Fig. 7.16. Collector characteristics of the 2N167 *n-p-n* switching transistor.

in emitter-base potential of about 250 mV (and thus an input-power change of 60 μW) thus produces a change in load power of about 115 mW. Additional input power will, of course, be dissipated in the resistance of the input circuit but a power ratio of several hundred to one is probably not unreasonable. Further—and this is a very important point—the power consumed by the transistor in either the closed or open state is very small. Thus if the transition between A and B is made to occupy a small fraction of the time that the transistor is in the conducting or non-conducting states, the average power consumption will remain at a few milliwatts. A small transistor may thus switch a power equal to ten times its collector dissipation with ease. For larger transistors this factor may be increased to about twenty so that high efficiency of operation is possible.

7.9.2. *The switching process*

As implied above the transistor characteristic divides itself, for switching purposes, into three regions which may be described as follows:

1. The cutoff region corresponding to the open-switch position. This is defined by the point A of Fig. 7.16.

2. The active region in which the transistor performs in the usual manner as an active device. This is the region between points A and B.

3. The high-current saturation region defined by the point B. In this region the collector current reaches a value decided by the load resistance and substantially independent of base current. This type of saturation is sometimes called bottoming since it occurs when the collector is driven to its bottom position, i.e. very close to the emitter. It should not be confused with the low-current saturation which occurs when the transistor is cut off. In the remainder of this chapter the term saturation will refer to the high-current condition.

We now consider the n-p-n transistor of Fig. 7.15 and assume that it is initially in the open or cutoff condition. Application of a positive voltage to the point A causes the transistor to conduct heavily, so that the operating point moves into the active region to a position such as B_1 in Fig. 7.16 for non-saturated operation or B if the saturated condition is reached. It remains there as long as the input signal lasts. If, after some time, the applied voltage is removed the transistor eventually returns to the cutoff condition.

This switching process, in which the transistor remains in any state only for the length of time that an input signal or bias applied (except for delays characteristic of the type of operation) is called non-regenerative switching. If the operating point is driven into the saturation region the device is called a saturated switch. This mode of operation has the following advantages:

1. Because the voltage across the transistor is a fraction of a volt losses in the 'on' state are small.

2. Well-defined 'off' and 'on' levels are obtained with a minimum of components.

The chief disadvantage of operation in the saturation region is the time delay that occurs in switching off because of excessive minority carrier storage in the base region. This disadvantage can be largely removed by preventing the operating point from leaving the active region and thereby producing a non-saturated switch. When the maximum switching speed is required it is necessary to resort to this type of operation.

Because of its simplicity, saturated operation is used in most switching applications. The physical processes taking place in it and formulae for determining some of the delays involved will be considered in the next section. Non-saturated operation which involves the same processes except in the storage phase will be considered in § 7.9.4.

7.9.3. *Operation of the saturated switch*

We now consider the phases of operation of the saturated non-regenerative switch during a complete cycle in which a signal is applied and subsequently removed. The general equations governing this type of operation, which were first given by Ebers and Moll [9], are

$$I_e = -\frac{I_{e0}}{1-\alpha_N\alpha_I}\{\exp(qV_e'/kT)-1\}+\frac{\alpha_I I_{c0}}{1-\alpha_N\alpha_I}\{\exp(qV_c'/kT)-1\},$$

(7.62)

$$I_c = \frac{\alpha_N I_{e0}}{1-\alpha_N\alpha_I}\{\exp(qV_e'/kT)-1\}-\frac{I_{c0}}{1-\alpha_N\alpha_I}\{\exp(qV_c'/kT)-1\}.$$

(7.63)

Here V_e' and V_c' are the junction voltages which are positive when the p-type material is at the higher potential. α_N is the d.c. or large-signal CB current gain and α_I is the corresponding quantity when the emitter and collector are interchanged. I_{e0} is the emitter cutoff or leakage current which flows when the emitter is reverse-biased and the collector circuit is open. For a diffusion transistor, i.e. a transistor of the type so far described (cf. Chapter VIII), it can be shown that

$$\alpha_I I_{c0} = \alpha_N I_{e0}.$$

(7.64)

The conditions at cutoff and at saturation are determined from these equations. They will be used in the remainder of this section and in the descriptions of switching circuits in Chapter XVI.

7.9.3.1. *Cutoff*

This condition might be achieved by biasing the base to make the emitter current exactly zero. The current flowing would then be the cutoff or leakage current I_{c0} of the collector junction. A more convenient arrangement consists of applying a reverse bias to the E-B junction. The base is then negative with respect to the ground point of Fig. 7.15 and a current I_{b0} flows out of it. This current is the sum of the two components

$$I'_c = \frac{I_{c0}(1-\alpha_I)}{1-\alpha_N\alpha_I}, \tag{7.65}$$

$$I'_e = \frac{I_{e0}(1-\alpha_N)}{1-\alpha_N\alpha_I} \tag{7.66}$$

which are determined from equations (7.62), (7.63), and (7.64) when the exponential terms are negligible. Since $\alpha_I < \alpha_N$ and $\alpha_N \simeq 1$ we see that $I'_c < I_{c0}$ and $I'_e \ll I_{e0}$. The current

$$I_{b0} = (I'_c + I'_e)$$

is slightly larger than I_{c0}.

7.9.3.2. *Turn-on*

If the input voltage is suddenly increased, the base current reverses and assumes the value $I_{b1} \gg I_{b0}$ shown in Fig. 7.17. The transistor then attempts to produce a current $h_{FE}I_{b1}$ where $h_{FE} \simeq \alpha_N/(1-\alpha_N)$ is the CE d.c. or large-signal current gain applying at the chosen value of I_b and at a constant collector voltage. It is usually less than the manufacturer's specified value of h_{fe}. In general the collector current I_{c1} finally reached

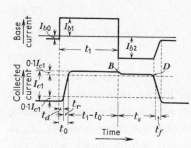

FIG. 7.17. Base-current and collector-current waveforms for the CE saturated switch.

will be less than $h_{FE}I_{b1}$ because of saturation or the use of some other method of limiting I_c. Also I_{c1} will not be reached immediately for the following reasons:

1. At the start of the pulse of Fig. 7.17 the voltage across the

emitter junction is changed from a quite large reverse value to a small forward value. This change appears across the emitter-transition region capacitance C_{te} which must be charged through the external-base resistance in series with $r_{bb'}$. This causes a delay in the build-up of the normal emitter current of the transistor.

2. When the emitter current is very low the transit time through the base is long and the recombination rate high (apparently owing to the presence of traps whose presence can be ignored at larger emitter currents) so that α and f_α are both small. These factors contribute to an additional delay in the build-up of emitter current.

3. A distribution of electrons (minority carriers) must be produced in the base sufficient to drive I_{c1} through the base by diffusion. The type of distribution required is shown by curve (1) of Fig. 7.18 b. The current flowing at any point in the base is $qD_n \, dn/dx$ where n is the density of electrons at that point and D_n is their

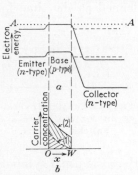

Fig. 7.18.   *CE* saturated switch characteristics. (*a*) Electron-energy diagram. (*b*) Schematic diagram of carrier distribution in the base.

diffusion coefficient. This distribution of electrons in the base, which is obtained by injection from the emitter, constitutes the charge stored in the emitter diffusion capacitance under large-signal conditions. In order to achieve it and maintain electrical neutrality in the base an equal number of positive holes must also be stored there. These positive holes form the major component of I_{b1} and the finite rate of flow decided by this current limits the rate at which I_c can rise when α and f_α have reached their normal values. It thus produces a further delay in the turn-on of the transistor.

4. The collector capacity must be charged up through the load resistance R_l and the time constant of this circuit makes a fourth contribution to turn-on time.

The delays (1) and (2) are usually assumed to form the 'delay time' t_d which is defined experimentally as the time for I_c to reach 10 per cent of its final value. It is difficult to calculate but can be reduced by decreasing the initial reverse bias on the emitter junction, by reducing the series base resistance, and by using a large value of I_b. The first of these procedures reduces the amount of charge that must be supplied to C_{te}, the second decreases the time constant of the charging process, while the third leads to both rapid charging of C_{te} and a rapid increase in α.

The delays (3) and (4) contribute to the rise time t_r which is defined as the time for the collector current to change from 10 per cent to 90 per cent of its final value. They may be expressed in terms of the time constant τ_e to charge up the emitter-diffusion capacitance and τ_c to charge the collector capacitance.

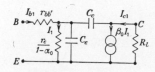

FIG. 7.19. Simplified hybrid-π circuit for the analysis of switching circuits.

These time constants may be determined quite readily from the hybrid-π circuit which is redrawn in Fig. 7.19. Here the usual symbols have been replaced by the equivalents mentioned in § 7.6 and the current generator has been expressed in terms of the current I_1. Thus

$$g_m V_{b'e} = \frac{\alpha_0}{r_\epsilon} I_1 \frac{r_\epsilon}{1-\alpha_0} \equiv \beta_0 I_1. \tag{7.67}$$

The conductances g_{ce} and $g_{b'c}$ which, in switching applications, are usually small compared with the load conductance, have been omitted.

The hybrid-π circuit is essentially a small-signal equivalent circuit and, when applied to high-level switching, its validity may be questioned. However, in this respect all transistor equivalent circuits are in the same category. The best that can be done in the development of an equivalent circuit for switching is to choose average values of the small circuit parameters and to assume that they apply over the active region. This procedure often leads to surprisingly accurate results and in most cases gives response times that are within a factor 3 of the true value.

If we assume that the rise time is decided chiefly by the

emitter-diffusion capacitance we may omit C_c in Fig. 7.19. For a high-impedance (current) drive the differential equations for I_{c1} $(= \beta_0 I_1)$ then becomes

$$\frac{dI_{c1}}{dt} + \frac{I_{c1}}{\tau_e} = \frac{\beta_0 I_{b1}}{\tau_e}, \qquad (7.68)$$

where I_{b1} is the applied sudden change (step) of base current and

$$\tau_e = \frac{C_\epsilon r_\epsilon}{1 - \alpha_0} \simeq \frac{0 \cdot 8}{\omega_\beta}. \qquad (7.69)$$

The latter relation may be obtained with the help of equations (7.27) and (7.35). The solution is

$$I_{c1} = \beta_0 I_{b1}(1 - e^{-t/\tau_e}). \qquad (7.70)$$

If the rise time is decided by the collector capacitance we may omit C_ϵ in Fig. 7.19. Equations (7.68) and (7.70) then apply with τ_e replaced by

$$\tau_c = \frac{C_c(r_\epsilon + R_l)}{(1 - \alpha_0)} \simeq (1 + \beta_0)C_c R_l. \qquad (7.71)$$

If τ_e and τ_c differ considerably in magnitude the rise time is thus given by

$$0 \cdot 9 I_{c1} \simeq \beta_0 I_{b1}\{1 - \exp(-t_r/\tau_{ec})\} \qquad (7.72)$$

or

$$t_r \simeq \tau_{ec} \ln \frac{1}{1 - 0 \cdot 9 I_{c1}/\beta_0 I_{b1}}, \qquad (7.73)$$

where τ_{ec} is the larger of the two time constants. Even when τ_e and τ_c are almost equal, equation (7.72) may be used to give an estimate of t_r that is accurate enough for most purposes.

Equations (7.72) and (7.73) with I_{e1} replacing I_{c1} may be used for the CC connection and, with ω_β, β_0, and I_{b1} replaced by ω_α, α_0, and I_{e1} respectively, for the CB connection.

Usually the base is overdriven (i.e. $\beta_0 I_b \gg I_{c1}$) in an attempt to reduce the turn-on time t_0 $(= t_d + t_r)$. The logarithm of the denominator of equation (7.73) may then be expanded and if $\beta_0 I_{b1} \geqslant 3(0 \cdot 9 I_{c1})$ the first term of the series may be used to give

$$t_r \simeq \frac{0 \cdot 9 I_{c1} \tau_{ec}}{\beta_0 I_{b1}}. \qquad (7.74)$$

With the above restriction on I_{b1}, this result is within 15 per cent of that given by equation (7.73).

For the 2N167, the design centre values of the required parameters are $\omega_\alpha = 55$ Mc/sec, $\beta_0 = 67$ and $C_c = 2\cdot5$ $\mu\mu$F. Hence with $I_{c1} = 8$ mA, $I_{b1} = 0\cdot8$ mA, $R_b = 6\cdot2$ kΩ and $R_l = 1\cdot2$ kΩ equation (7.74) gives $t_r \simeq 0\cdot2$ μsec. The manufacturer's quoted value for t_0 under these conditions is $0\cdot4$ μsec. Thus the calculated value of t_r is probably within 50 per cent of the experimental value. The overdrive factor $\beta_0 I_{b1}/I_{c1}$ is $6\cdot7$ in this case. For most transistors $t_d \sim t_r$ under such conditions so that t_r may be used to give a rough estimate of the turn-on time t_0.

Finally we emphasize that the above outline assumes a constant current or high-impedance drive. If a low-impedance (voltage) source is used I_{b1} may be very large initially, thus reducing the turn-on time. In most applications the source impedance is intermediate in value. The assumption of a constant current drive then leads to an overestimate of t_0 but the result is probably of the correct order and, in any event, the error is in the right direction.

7.9.3.3. *Storage*

At the completion of turn-on, when I_c has reached 90 per cent of its final value, an electron distribution of the form (1) of Fig. 7.18 *b* exists in the base. The concentration of electrons at W is very small as the reverse voltage remaining on the collector junction produces a field large enough to move them rapidly into the collector. If the transistor is driven sufficiently hard the collector current increases further until the operating point enters the saturation region. The potential across the transistor is then a fraction of a volt and the collector current is limited to a value I_{c1} which is slightly less than V_{cc}/R_l and considerably less than $h_{FE}I_{b1}$.

Base current continues to flow after the distribution (1) has been built up and storage of electrons and holes in the base continues. However I_{c1}, which is constant, is equal to $qD_n(dn/dx)$, and the slope of the electron distribution in Fig. 7.18 *b* must therefore remain approximately constant. The added carriers therefore raise the concentration to that represented schematically by curve (2) of the figure.

Since the concentration of electrons capable of flowing into the collector at W is now large, the collector current can be limited to I_{c1} only if the field in the transition region, and hence the potential step at W, is reduced. The boundaries of the collector energy bands therefore assume the positions indicated by the dashed lines of Fig. 7.18 a. This reduces the electron current which is driven from base to collector by the field in the collector transition region but this 'field' current remains larger than I_{c1}. However, the raising of the collector levels causes the concentration of electrons in the collector with energies above the dotted line AA to become larger than that in the base. A diffusion current of electrons therefore flows from collector to base and opposes the field current. The result is to make the net current crossing the collector junction equal to I_{c1}.

The flow of collector diffusion current (i.e. the injection of electrons into the base) can occur only if the height of the collector barrier is reduced below its equilibrium value—that is if the junction is forward-biased. Thus the collector junction of a saturated transistor is forward-biased even though the net current crossing it is in the reverse direction.

The following features of operation in the high-current saturation region should be noted:

(a) The diffusion current injected from collector to base increases very rapidly with V_{cb}. Once the forward-biased condition is reached, V_{cb} will therefore change very little, even though the concentration of minority carriers in the base continues to increase. In Fig. 7.16 this is illustrated by the fact that the curves for different base current are indistinguishable from each other when V_{ce} is small.

(b) The value of V'_{ce} at saturation may be determined [9] from equations (7.62) and (7.63), and the relation $I_c + I_b + I_c = 0$, to be

$$V'_{ces} = \pm(V'_c - V'_e) = \pm \frac{kT}{q} \ln \frac{\alpha_I[1 - I_c(1 - \alpha_N)/I_b \alpha_N]}{[1 + (I_c/I_b)(1 - \alpha_I)]}.$$

$$(7.75)$$

The positive sign applies to p-n-p transistors and the negative sign to n-p-n transistors. In addition to this junction voltage drop the true saturation voltage includes small voltage drops in the emitter and collector body material. However, the total does not exceed a fraction of a volt and it is usually lower for alloy-junction transistors than for grown or diffused types for the following reasons:

(b_1) Alloy junctions are better injectors than grown junctions.

(b_2) The saturation voltage of an unsymmetrical transistor, in which the collector is larger than the emitter, is smaller than that of a symmetrical junction [9]. Alloy junctions are asymmetrical while grown junctions and some diffused junctions are not.

(b_3) The collector body resistance of an alloy transistor is lower than that of the equivalent grown- or diffused-junction transistor. At large current densities the collector voltage drop is therefore smaller for the alloy-junction transistor.

(c) If the base current is maintained indefinitely the increase of charge in the base continues until the recombination rate there, resulting from the presence of large numbers of electrons and holes, is equal to the rate at which carriers enter. The base current may, however, be cut off before this steady state is reached thereby limiting the amount of stored charge. The excess carrier concentration or stored charge, due to the flow of base current after saturation is reached, is given by the difference between curves (1) and (2) of Fig. 7.18 b.

The current curves for saturated operation are shown in Fig. 7.17. Here the current I_{b1} is applied for the time interval t_1 and the interval during which excess storage takes place is approximately $t_1 - t_0$. The excess storage may reach a constant value or not depending on the magnitudes of I_{b1} and t_1.

7.9.3.4. *Turn-off from the saturated state*

In order to turn off the n-p-n transistor a negative potential V_2 is applied to the point A in Fig. 7.15 and a current I_{b2} (Fig. 7.17) flows out of the base. The following conditions then exist in the transistor:

1. For the reason mentioned above, the presence of large numbers of minority carriers in the base requires that both

emitter and collector junctions remain forward-biased and that
the voltage drops across them be small. The collector current
therefore remains close to the value V_{cc}/R_l until the distribution
of charge stored in the base has dropped from (2) to (1) in
Fig. 7.18 b.

2. The positive-hole current flowing out of the base is
$I_{b2} \simeq V_2/R_b$. If $V_2 = -V_1$, where V_1 is the voltage initially applied
to turn on the transistor, $I_{b2} \simeq I_{b1}$. Also, we must now have
$I_c - I_e = I_{b2}$ and the difference between the collector and emitter
currents represents a rate of removal of
electrons equal to the rate of removal of
holes via the ohmic base connection. The
neutrality of the base is thus preserved.

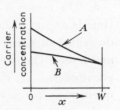

3. In order to satisfy the condition
$I_c > I_e$ the slope of the electron distribution at $x = W$ must exceed that at $x = 0$.
The distribution of electrons in the base
must alter from the concave curve A of
Fig. 7.20 to the convex curve B. This
requires the removal of the carriers in the

Fig. 7.20. Change of
carrier distribution in
the base immediately
following application of
the turn-off potential.

region between the curves and produces a slight reduction in
collector current. The small time interval during which the
above charge is being removed is indicated by the rounding
that occurs at the point B in the collector current curve of
Fig. 7.17.

4. Following the slight readjustment just mentioned the collector current cannot change appreciably until the excess charge
between curves (1) and (2) of Fig. 7.18 b has been removed
from the base. During this time t_s, which is called the storage
time, the collector remains forward-biased and the operating
point is in the saturation region. Upon removal of the excess
charge the concentration of electrons at W in Fig. 7.18 b becomes
very low and the collector acquires a reverse bias. The current
flowing through the load then starts to decrease.

In practice the storage time is usually assumed to last from
the time of application of the turn-off signal until the collector
current has dropped to 90 per cent of its maximum value. It

therefore includes an additional small delay during which the collector is transferring from the forward to the reverse condition. This delay includes the time required to change the amount of charge stored in the collector transition-region capacitance and to remove stored minority carriers (holes) from the part of the collector adjacent to the base. The latter contribute to the charge stored in the collector diffusion capacitance and are more important in grown and diffused transistors than in those of the alloy type.

5. The removal of charge from the base during the storage time is accomplished by two mechanisms—the flow of current described in paragraph 2, and the recombination of electrons and holes. The recombination rate is expressed in terms of four parameters, viz. the normal current gain α and its cutoff frequency ω_N ($= \omega_\alpha$) and the corresponding inverse parameters α_i, ω_I that are obtained when the functions of collector and emitter are reversed. For a symmetrical transistor in which the emitter and collector have the same area and similar body properties such as resistivity, α_i and α are approximately equal, while for an asymmetrical unit α may exceed α_i by 20 per cent or more. The CB cutoff frequencies are similarly related, i.e. $\omega_N \simeq \omega_I$ for a symmetrical transistor, while $\omega_N > \omega_I$ for an asymmetrical unit. In alloy transistors asymmetry occurs because of the difference in emitter and collector areas. Minority carriers injected by the outer part of the collector must travel greater distances to cross the base than those injected by the emitter. The quantity W_0/L ($= m$) in equations (6.43) and (7.27) is thus larger for the inverse current than for the normal transistor current and hence $\alpha_i < \alpha$ and $\omega_I < \omega_N$.

We can see fairly readily why the inverse characteristics are important when the transistor is saturated. The diffusion current I_{cf} that enters the base as a result of the forward bias on the collector junction produces an emitter current $\alpha_i I_{cf}$ and the number of electrons in I_{cf} that recombine in the base in unit time is $(1-\alpha_i)I_{cf}$. The rate of recombination increases with the transit time $1/\omega_i$ of this current.

When the two mechanisms of charge removal are taken into

account the storage time is found to be [9,10]

$$t_s = \frac{\omega_N + \omega_I}{\omega_N \omega_I (1 - \alpha_N \alpha_I)} \ln \frac{I_{b1} - I_{b2}}{\{I_{c1}(1 - \alpha_N)/\alpha_N\} - I_{b2}}. \qquad (7.76)$$

In this expression the small-signal parameters α and α_i have been replaced by the d.c. quantities α_N and α_I. This is not strictly correct but the d.c. parameters differ by relatively small amounts from α and α_i and the error in (7.76) is negligible. For switching transistors α_N and α_I are the parameters ordinarily given by manufacturers.

The first factor of (7.76) gives the effect of recombination on t_s while the logarithmic term shows how it is influenced by the base currents that flow before and after the turn-off pulse is applied. The recombination term is the same for all three connections. The logarithmic factors for the CB and CC connections are obtained by changing the sign of I_{c1} in the denominator and replacing I_b by $I_e(1 - \alpha_N)$ for the CB case and I_c by $\alpha_N I_e$ for the CC case [9, 10]. Incidentally, it should be noted that I_{b2} is negative and $I_{b1} > I_{c1}(1 - \alpha_N)/\alpha_N$ so that the logarithmic factor in (7.76) is always positive.

For a symmetric transistor the first factor of (7.76) is approximately equal to $1/\omega_N(1 - \alpha_N)$ while for a highly unsymmetrical one it is approximately equal to $1/\omega_I(1 - \alpha_I)$. The inverse parameters are therefore required for the calculation of the storage time of an alloy transistor. These are now provided by some manufacturers. For grown-junction transistors we may use $1/\omega_N(1 - \alpha_N)$ for the recombination factor. For the 2N167 with $I_{c1} = 8$ mA, $I_{b1} = -I_{b2} = 0.8$ mA we obtain $t_s \simeq 0.8$ μsec while the manufacturer gives the experimentally determined value of 0.7 μsec. Such good agreement is probably fortuitous but equation (7.76) does give a useful estimate of the storage time when I_{b2} is not too large.

An excellent description of the physical processes taking place during storage has been given by Cooke-Yarborough [12].

7.9.3.5. *Fall time*

Upon completion of the storage time t_s the collector acquires a reverse potential and the operating point moves into the active region of Fig. 7.16. The time to complete the turn-off process is then decided by the rate of removal of the charge distribution (1) of Fig. 7.18 b. It is defined by the fall time t_f which is the time required for the collector current to drop from 90 per cent to 10 per cent of its maximum value.

The process that determines the fall time is the reverse of that responsible for the rise time t_r and, like it, depends on the emitter and collector time constants. For the CE connection the equation determining t_f is

$$\frac{I_{c1}}{10} \simeq I_{c1}\exp(-t_f/\tau_{ec})+\beta I_{b2}\{1-\exp(t_f/\tau_{ec})\}, \qquad (7.77)$$

where τ_{ec} is the larger of τ_e and τ_c. The first term on the right-hand side of this equation shows the way in which I_c decays when the base current is zero. The second term indicates that there is a similar delay in the production of the collector current βI_{b2} which (since I_{b2} is negative) also reduces I_c.

Equation (7.77) gives the relation

$$t_f = \tau_{ec}\ln\frac{I_{c1}-\beta I_{b2}}{0\cdot1 I_{c1}-\beta I_{b2}} \qquad (7.78)$$

in which β may be replaced by h_{FE} if desired. The conditions under which this equation may be applied to the CC and CB connections are the same as those mentioned for equation (7.73).

The way in which I_c and I_b change during the fall time is shown in Fig. 7.17. Towards the end of the turn-off process the stored charge near the emitter drops to a very low value and the emitter voltage reverses. The base current then drops to the cutoff value I_{b0}.

7.9.4. *Operation of the non-saturated switch*

When very high-speed operation is desired it is often necessary, as mentioned earlier, to prevent the operating point from entering the saturation region. In order to do this and still retain a short turn-on time it is necessary to overdrive the transistor and to reduce the base or emitter current when the desired operating point is reached. The circuit modifications to accomplish this will be described in Chapter XVIII. In the present section we will discuss briefly the delays occurring in this type of operation.

The base and collector currents for non-saturated operation when the base circuit has a high resistance (constant-current drive) are shown in Fig. 7.21. Here the turn-on current I'_{b1} is reduced to I_{b1} when the desired operating point is reached. With the exception of t_{d2}, the times shown are defined in the same manner as for the saturated case. The turn-on delay time is now called t_{d1} instead of t_d. Also, there is no excess carrier storage and there is no storage time t_s. However, the two relatively short delays that occurred at the beginning and end of t_s—and were included in it—are still present and are combined to form the turn-off delay time t_{d2}. The first of these occurs because I_c must exceed I_e and is of the type discussed in connection with Fig. 7.20. The second results from the discharge of the

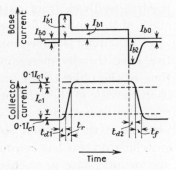

Fig. 7.21. Base-current and collector-current wave-forms for the *CE* non-saturated switch.

collector-diffusion and transition-region capacitance. The diffusion-capacitance effect is negligible in alloy transistors but for grown or diffused transistors (e.g. very fast 'mesa' switching transistors of the type described in Chapter VIII) it may be appreciable because of minority carrier storage in the collector. For some mesa transistors, when driven very hard using an emitter-clamping circuit (Chapter XVI), the delays t_{d1} and t_{d2} are approximately equal to t_r and t_f. At the time of writing minimum values for these times lie in the range from 3×10^{-9} to 10^{-8} seconds.

As in the saturated case, the turn-off current I_{b2} is decided by the (negative) cutoff bias voltage applied to the base. This voltage must be sufficient to turn off the transistor rapidly, but not so large that the delay time t_{d1} is increased.

The speed of operation of the non-saturated switch can be increased by using a low-impedance (voltage) drive. In this case the currents I'_{b1} and I_{b2} may reach considerably higher values than those obtainable with constant-current drive.

7.10. Regenerative switching

Our description of switching phenomena has so far been concerned with the behaviour of junction transistors with no regard to special circuit arrangements for enhancing speed. Many such arrangements, having two or more ordinary transistors, use positive feedback from output to input of the amplifier. The effect of this positive feedback or 'regeneration' is twofold:

1. The circuit is driven much harder than in the non-regenerative case, thereby increasing the switching speed. A turn-on time of the order of $1/f_\alpha$ can be obtained with a power gain characteristic of the CE connection.

2. The operation of the circuit becomes substantially independent of the size and shape of the input pulse. Once the switching process has commenced, it will continue until a final 'on' or 'off' state is reached and the output will depend only on the properties of the initial and final states, and the switching rate.

For transistor circuits the regenerative process can be described most easily in terms of current gain, which must exceed unity and should be as large as possible consistent with other requirements such as large f_α and low capacitance. In the type of circuit mentioned above large current gain is usually obtained by using the CE connection. Because of the signal reversal that occurs in a single CE stage, positive feedback can only be obtained by using two stages. In CC stages there is a large current gain and no signal reversal, but the feedback, which is inherent in the connection itself, is again negative. In the CB connection the feedback is positive but the current gain is less than unity. However, in certain devices, such as point-contact transistors and avalanche transistors, the combination of large current gain and positive feedback can be obtained in a single stage if the circuit arrangement is suitable. With other avalanche devices, regeneration occurs internally and no special feedback arrangement is necessary. Some of these devices, which make

possible simplifications and economies in circuit design, will be
described in the next chapter.

All regenerative switching circuits, consisting of one or more
devices, have *I-V* characteristics that may be represented
schematically [13] by the curves of Figs. 7.22 and 7.23. The
first of these, which is exemplified by the four-layer diode
described in the next chapter, is said to be open-circuit stable
since it can be brought to a stable state by placing a sufficiently

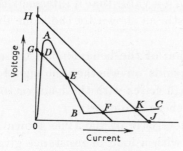

FIG. 7.22. Characteristic of an
open-circuit-stable regenerative
switching device or circuit.

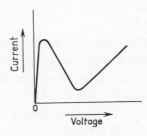

FIG. 7.23. Characteristic of
a short-circuit-stable regenerative switching device
or circuit.

large resistance in series with it. The device or combination of
devices whose characteristic is shown in Fig. 7.23 can always
be stabilized by connecting a sufficiently small resistance in
parallel with it and is therefore said to be short-circuit stable.
The best-known example of this type of device is the tunnel
diode which is also described in Chapter VIII.

We shall describe regenerative switching by considering the
operation of the open-circuit-stable arrangement of Fig. 7.22.
The analogous procedure in the application of short-circuit-stable
combinations will be obvious. The characteristic of Fig. 7.22
consists of three sections *OA*, *AB*, *BC* which may be curved or
may consist of smaller sections of somewhat different slope;
these are details which do not affect the general description.
The section *OA*, in which the current is small even for quite
large values of voltage across the device (or across the output
stage if there is more than one stage), represents the 'off' region.

The section BC, which has a low resistance, is the 'on' region. The section AB, through which the device passes in going from the 'off' to the 'on' position, is produced by regenerative action and appears as a region of negative resistance. A positive-load resistance in series with the device is represented by a line which intersects the axes at points whose signs are the same and thus has a negative slope as shown, for example, by $GDEF$. If two stable switch positions (the 'on' and 'off' positions) are to exist, the load resistance must be of such a value that it intersects the three sections of the characteristic as shown by the same line $GDEF$.

From this point the description of the behaviour of the re-generative device or circuit depends on whether the signal is applied across the device itself (in series with the load) or to a control electrode. We consider these two cases:

1. If a diode having a characteristic of the type shown in Fig. 7.22 is connected in series with a load of resistance given by the line $GDEF$ and the applied voltage is OG, the operating point will be at D and the current flowing will be small. If the applied voltage is now increased to OH the load line will assume a position HKJ. The operating point will move to the point of intersection K of the load line and the diode characteristic, because only then will the sum of load and diode voltages equal the applied voltage. In moving from D to K the operating point passes rapidly through the negative-resistance section AB since in this region any increase in current lowers the voltage across the diode and the excess potential available increases the current still further. Stabilization of the operating point can only occur when the positive-resistance region BC is reached.

If the applied voltage is now reduced to its original value OG the operating point returns along CB to the point F. Thus after the passage of a voltage pulse sufficient to drive the load line beyond A the diode has switched from its open position D to its closed position F at which most of the applied voltage appears across the load. To return the circuit to the open condition it is necessary to reduce the applied voltage so that the load line falls below B. The inverse of the above process then takes place and, upon restoration of the initial conditions, the operating point will be at D.

2. If the device is a regenerative triode, or a pair of non-regenerative triodes in a regenerative connection, the control signal will usually be applied to a low-power electrode—e.g. the base of a CE-connected transistor. Its effect will be to lower the peak OAB and, perhaps, to shift it along the current axis. If the point A drops below the load line $GDEF$ the device will 'trigger' and, after passage of the control pulse, will remain in the 'on' position F. It may be turned off by a pulse which raises the point B to a position above the load line or moves it along BC beyond the point F.

This brief outline is probably sufficient to describe the general behaviour of regenerative devices or circuits. In the next chapter we shall describe briefly some of the methods by which regeneration is obtained in single devices. In a later chapter some regenerative circuits using ordinary junction transistors will be considered.

HIGH-FREQUENCY TRANSISTORS, SWITCHING DEVICES, AND POWER TRANSISTORS

8.1. Introduction

A study of the circuits of the preceding chapter shows the value of minimizing certain factors such as base spreading-resistance, minority carrier transit time, and collector capacitance in transistors designed for operation at high frequencies. The methods by which this is done in practical transistors are varied and lead to many modifications of the basic transistor structure. In this chapter we shall describe briefly some of the more successful high-frequency transistors, particularly those that are being produced commercially. Following this we shall consider solid-state amplifying devices that do not depend on transistor action and switching devices in which regenerative amplification can be produced by means of a single device. The chapter closes with a brief outline of factors affecting the design and application of power transistors. The descriptions of this large number of subjects are necessarily restricted and further details may be obtained from the extensive list of references for this chapter.

8.2. The high-frequency figure of merit

A common criterion for assessing the usefulness of a transistor at high frequencies is the product

$$K \equiv \text{(available power gain)}^{\frac{1}{2}} \times \text{(bandwidth)}. \qquad (8.1)$$

This is often called the 'figure of merit'. Its magnitude may be determined by using the low-frequency available (i.e. conjugate-matched) power gain and assuming that the bandwidth extends from zero frequency to the frequency at which this power gain (when matching has been carried out at this new frequency) has dropped by 3 db. This figure of merit also represents approximately the maximum frequency at which the device will oscillate

since at this frequency the available power gain will have dropped
to unity. The maximum frequency of oscillation f_0 is therefore
used instead of the figure of merit K in some manufacturers'
specifications.

For alloy transistors in the CE connection an approximation
to K may be determined quite readily with the help of the
hybrid-π equivalent circuit [1]. Thus

$$f_0 \simeq K = \frac{1}{4\pi}\left[\frac{g_m}{r_{bb'}\,C_{b'c}\,C_{b'e}}\right]^{\frac{1}{2}}. \qquad (8.2)$$

Substituting for g_m, $C_{b'e}$, and $C_{b'c}$ from the relations contained in
Chapter VII, we have

$$K = \frac{1}{4\pi}\left[\frac{1\cdot 2\omega_\alpha}{r_{bb'}\,C_c}\right]^{\frac{1}{2}}. \qquad (8.3)$$

Expressions of this form have been given by several writers
[1, 2, 3]. The most accurate version is probably that of Pritchard
[3] whose numerical factor is smaller than that of equation
(8.3) by 17 per cent.

For grown-junction transistors the figure of merit is of somewhat different form. An approximate value for the maximum
frequency of oscillation in this case may be derived from Pritchard's results. It is

$$f_0 \simeq 0\cdot 054\left[\frac{\omega_\alpha}{C_c^2 r_{bb'}\,r_\epsilon}\right]^{\frac{1}{3}}. \qquad (8.4)$$

The presence of r_ϵ indicates that, in contrast to the alloy-
transistor case, f_0 increases with emitter current. We emphasize
that this expression is approximate. A more accurate and considerably more complicated version may be obtained from
Pritchard's paper [3].

Equations (8.3) and (8.4) make possible a comparison of
different transistors for high-frequency amplifiers. They also
indicate clearly the factors that must be altered by transistor
designers if improved high-frequency response is to be obtained.
In the discussion of these factors we will make use of the alloy-
transistor equation (8.3). The results will, however, apply
qualitatively to grown- and diffused-junction transistors also.

Substituting in equation (8.3) the expression (7.27) for ω_α, we obtain

$$K = \frac{1}{4\pi}\left[\frac{3D}{W_0^2 r_{bb'} C_c}\right]^{\frac{1}{2}}, \qquad (8.5)$$

where D is the diffusion coefficient and W_0 is the base thickness. Equation (8.5) shows that the frequency response may be improved by decreasing one or more of W_0, $r_{bb'}$, and C_c. Unfortunately these quantities are interdependent to a large extent. An attempt to decrease base thickness, for example, will lead to an increase in base spreading-resistance although there will be a net gain in frequency response. However, the extent to which W_0 can be decreased is limited by unavoidable variations in base thickness. These become more important as the base thickness is decreased and increase the probability of punch-through. To prevent punch-through the device may be operated at low collector voltage but this increases the collector transition-region capacitance. To minimize C_c the collector area should be made small, thus decreasing the current rating.

The base spreading-resistance $r_{bb'}$ may be reduced by decreasing the resistivity of the base layer but the improvement attainable in this way is limited by the decrease in emitter injection-efficiency and by the fact that the collector voltage must be lowered to counteract the increased probability of avalanche breakdown. (It can be seen from equation (A4.21) that the field strength in the collector transition region increases as the base conductivity increases.)

Because of these factors, high-frequency transistors of the type so far described in this book tend to be small low-power devices. They are now usually described as 'diffusion' transistors to distinguish them from other high-frequency devices, to be described later, in which an electric field is produced in the base region.

In spite of the objections mentioned it is possible to obtain considerable improvement in the frequency response of diffusion transistors by the above measures and by ingenious schemes to minimize detrimental effects that arise when a parameter is altered. Examples of such methods are given in the next section.

8.3. Modifications of diffusion transistors to improve high-frequency response

The following are practical methods by which the frequency response of diffusion transistors may be improved:

1. *Use of a thick base in the spreading region* [4, 5]. In this method, which is applied to alloy-junction transistors, the base is made very thin to take advantage of the effect of a small W_0, but immediately outside the active region the base thickness

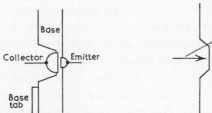

FIG. 8.1. Modified alloy-junction transistor for use at high frequencies.

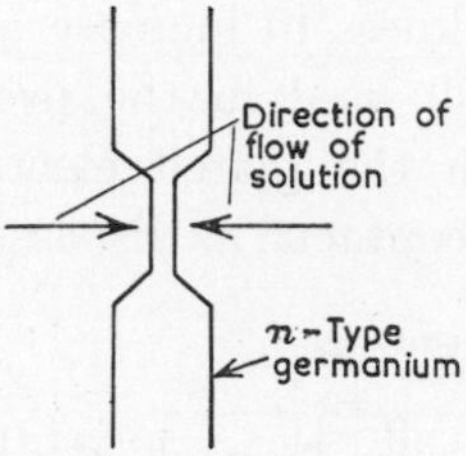

FIG. 8.2. Formation of emitter and collector depressions for the surface-barrier transistor.

increases abruptly to a large value so that the change in $r_{bb'}$ is not proportional to the change in W_0. The resistivity of the base is also made as small as possible, consistent with reasonably efficient injection from the emitter and avoidance of avalanche breakdown. A sketch of the junction geometry is shown in Fig. 8.1. The base connection is sometimes made in the form of a ring, concentric with the collector and the emitter, to reduce $r_{bb'}$ further. The collector diameter is made as small as possible in order to reduce both C_c and $r_{bb'}$.

2. *Control of base thickness and electrode geometry by electrolytic etching and plating.* This procedure was adopted in the manufacture of the surface-barrier transistor [6] which may be described with the aid of Fig. 8.2. In the production of a germanium transistor, jets of electrolytic solution, usually indium chlorate or sulphate, are directed at a wafer of n-type germanium as shown by the arrows and a current is passed through the solution to cause electrolytic etching of the surface. When a sufficiently thin base layer has been produced the

polarity of the current is reversed and its magnitude altered so that deposition of indium takes place to form metal electrodes. The contacts thus formed behave as p-n junctions and a p-n-p transistor is produced. In early units, which had α cutoff frequencies of about 40 Mc/sec, a collector diameter of about 0·004 inch, an emitter diameter of about 0·002 inch, and a base thickness of about 0·0002 inch were used.

It is apparent that this electrochemical technique makes possible very close control of transistor geometry and also allows the thickness to increase appreciably in the spreading region. It is still used in the preparation of blanks for transistors, although the plated electrodes have now been replaced by alloyed contacts, as discussed below.

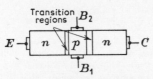

FIG. 8.3. Schematic diagram of the junction tetrode.

3. *Addition of a second base connection to form a junction tetrode* [7]. This device, which apparently is normally made from a grown-junction transistor or a transistor of similar geometry, is shown schematically in Fig. 8.3. A second base electrode B_2 is placed opposite the normal base B_1 and biased so as to drive minority carriers towards B_1—i.e. negatively in an n-p-n transistor. A large fraction of the emitter-junction area is therefore biased in the reverse direction and the current of minority carriers in the base is made to occupy a small area in the neighbourhood of B_1. The base spreading-resistance $r_{bb'}$ and the collector capacitance C_c are therefore reduced. There is an accompanying reduction of α because of reduced injection efficiency and increased recombination in the base layer but the net effect is an improvement in high-frequency properties.

There are other methods that can be used for improving the frequency response of diffusion transistors but these have found their main applications in a special class of high-frequency transistors known as graded-base transistors. Before outlining the methods we shall describe this type of transistor. Later, when the methods are considered, it will be evident that some of them could be applied to diffusion transistors if desired.

8.4. Graded-base transistors

The theory of graded-base transistors may be introduced by again considering equation (8.3), concentrating for the moment on the parameter C_c. The main component of this is the collector transition-region capacitance C_{tc}. In order that C_{tc} may be small, the collector transition region should be thick and this in turn requires that the base resistivity in the neighbourhood of the collector be very high. On the other hand, $r_{bb'}$ should be as small as possible and this requires that part of the base region at least should have a low resistivity. It is apparent, therefore, that a transistor whose base resistivity is graded from a low value near the emitter to a high value near the collector should have a better figure of merit than one whose base resistivity is constant. Analysis of such a structure discloses an extra dividend from the grading in the form of an electric field in the base region which drives carriers from emitter to collector, thus decreasing the transit time of minority carriers across the base and increasing ω_α. It is worth noting also that grading of the base diminishes the influence of the collector voltage on currents flowing through the transistor, thus decreasing both the output admittance and the internal feedback.

One important inaccuracy results from the application of equation (8.3) to graded-base transistors. In the derivations of equations (8.2) and (8.3) it was assumed that the emitter capacitance $C_{b'e}$ consisted purely of a diffusion capacitance. For diffusion transistors and some graded-base transistors this approximation is satisfactory. However, for very high-frequency graded-base transistors the chief component of the emitter capacitance is not the diffusion capacitance (which is proportional to the transit time) but the emitter transition-region capacitance C_{te}. Because of the high density of impurity centres near the emitter, the emitter transition region is very thin and its capacitance is correspondingly large. This causes a reduction in the figure of merit that is not apparent from equation (8.2). For these transistors a more appropriate figure of merit is obtained by replacing $C_{b'e}$ in equation (8.2) by C_{te}. Then, substituting for g_m and $C_{b'c}$, we obtain

$$K = \frac{1}{4\pi}\left[\frac{\alpha_0 I_e}{r_{bb'} C_c C_{te}} \cdot \frac{q}{kT}\right]^{\frac{1}{2}}. \qquad (8.6)$$

From this expression we see that, for best frequency response, the emitter current of a graded-base transistor, like that of a grown-junction transistor, should be large.

The net effect of all the factors discussed is to make the figure of merit of graded-base transistors larger than that of diffusion transistors of the same dimensions by a factor of about ten.

The exact form of the distribution of impurities in a graded-base transistor has a pronounced effect on the parameters of the device. Cases in which the distribution of impurities from emitter to collector decreases according to several different mathematical functions have been analysed by Moll and Ross [8]. These distributions are obtained by the method of solid-state diffusion described in Chapter III. An excellent review article discussing the mathematics of the diffusion process and techniques of obtaining the required impurity distributions has been written by Smits [9].

The methods of producing graded-base transistors are quite varied and may probably best be illustrated by considering the following examples of developmental and commercial types.

8.4.1. *The drift transistor*

This is apparently the first proposed graded-base transistor design. It was described by Kroemer in the German literature [10,11] and later in English [12]. In Kroemer's analysis the impurity distribution in the base is assumed to decrease exponentially from a density of approximately 10^{17}/c.c. near the emitter to a negligible density in the region of the collector. The positive-hole potential-energy diagram for this device is shown schematically in Fig. 8.4. A constant field exists throughout the base region. The minority-carrier velocity due to this field is much greater than that arising from diffusion.

It is relatively simple to make a drift transistor by alloying emitter and collector electrodes to a previously prepared base [13] and all commercial drift transistors seem to be made by this process. The base is prepared by the diffusion of an n-type impurity into an n-type semiconductor whose resistivity is so high as to be almost intrinsic. The resulting distribution of impurities is believed to be of complementary error-function form rather than the exponential form considered by Kroemer.

In common with other alloy transistors, drift transistors can be represented by the hybrid-π equivalent circuit and the major manufacturer of them (Radio Corporation of America) presents parameters in this form. At the time of writing the highest-frequency drift transistor available commercially (the R.C.A. 2N384) has a maximum oscillation frequency of 250 Mc/sec and an f_α of 100 Mc/sec.

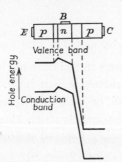

FIG. 8.4. Positive-hole energy diagram of the drift transistor.

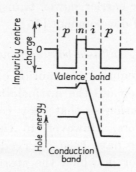

FIG. 8.5. Impurity distribution and positive-hole energy diagram of a p-n-i-p intrinsic-barrier transistor.

8.4.2. *The intrinsic-barrier transistor*

In this device, described by Early [14], the density of impurities in the base changes suddenly from a large value (10^{16}/c.c. to 10^{17}/c.c.) near the emitter to a very small value near the collector. The region near the collector is practically intrinsic and under proper operating conditions the transition region (depletion region) of the collector barrier occupies the whole of it. For this reason the device is called an 'intrinsic-barrier transistor'. The impurity distribution and the positive-hole energy diagram of an intrinsic-barrier transistor of the p-n-i-p type (in which i denotes the intrinsic layer) is shown in Fig. 8.5. In this case positive holes entering the base from the emitter must travel a short distance by diffusion before reaching the large field of the intrinsic barrier. However, because of the presence of the relatively thick intrinsic layer, the high-conductivity base region can be made very thin without danger of breakdown due to inhomogeneities. The other advantages of the graded-base transistor, viz. low base spreading-resistance and small collector capacitance, are also obtained. The developmental intrinsic-barrier transistor described by Early has $f_0 \simeq 100$ Mc/sec and $f_\alpha \simeq 25$ Mc/sec.

Base layers for intrinsic-barrier transistors have been made by grown-junction methods, by alloying and by diffusion. The devices are apparently not yet available commercially although intrinsic-barrier power transistors have reached an advanced stage of development [15].

8.4.3. *Diffused-base and mesa transistors*

The required distribution of impurities in the base of the drift transistor and the intrinsic-barrier transistor can be obtained by diffusion so that they could both be called diffused-base transistors. However, in the transistor literature this term seems to have been reserved for another type of graded-base transistor in which the starting material forms the collector rather than the base. Thus for a *p-n-p* graded-base transistor the starting material is of *p*-type rather than *n*-type as in the above cases. The graded base and the collector junction are formed simultaneously by the diffusion of an *n*-type impurity into the starting material. A thin *n*-type layer is thus created on the surface and the concentration of *n*-type impurity diminishes with penetration into the *p*-type material as shown in Fig. 8.6. The net impurity concentration, indicated by the shaded area, changes gradually from *n*-type to *p*-type forming both a graded-base layer and a diffused collector junction. The emitter junction is formed by

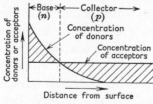

FIG. 8.6. Concentrations of impurities in the diffused-base transistor.

alloying p-type material to the n-type surface layer. The proto-
type of such devices is Lee's germanium p-n-p transistor [16]
mentioned in Chapter III.

The diffusion process as applied by Lee can be readily adapted
to the production of large numbers of transistors since a relatively large sheet of germanium can be used and subsequently
sliced into a large number of small area pieces. Lee introduced
the following additional procedures that further improve the
high-frequency response and contribute to ease of manufacture:

1. The emitter and base connections were formed by evaporating small closely spaced rectangular electrodes of aluminium (for

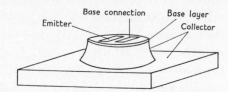

FIG. 8.7. Basic elements of the mesa transistor.

the emitter) and gold-antimony alloy (for the ohmic base connection) on to the surface of the base layer. These were subsequently alloyed into the base by heat treatment.

2. Following construction of the device the germanium surrounding the electrodes was etched away to form the table-like
area or 'mesa' shown in Fig. 8.7.

Typical emitter and base-electrode dimensions for Lee's
devices were $0{\cdot}001$ inch $\times 0{\cdot}002$ inch and typical spacing between
them $0{\cdot}0005$ to $0{\cdot}001$ inch. The base-layer thickness was about
6×10^{-5} inch.

The effect of the geometry of this type of transistor on its
figure of merit has been discussed by Early [2]. He has pointed
out that the important part of the collector capacity is that of
the region immediately below the emitter. The remaining collector capacity has negligible loss associated with it and thus
has a relatively small effect on the figure of merit. It does,
however, cause feedback from collector to base and should
therefore be kept as small as possible. This is one reason for

reducing collector area by the formation of a mesa. A further advantage is the reduction of surface leakage from collector to base.

For an idealized device in which the emitter width is s and the spacing between emitter and base is $s/2$ the figure of merit is inversely proportional to s. It is, however, substantially independent of the length of the electrodes since the product $r_{bb'}C_c$ is independent of length.

This type of diffused-base transistor in which the emitter and base electrodes are closely spaced rectangles and the collector area is reduced by etching is now generally referred to as a 'mesa' transistor. Examples of it, now available commercially in the U.S.A., are the Motorola 2N700 for which $\alpha_0 = 0{\cdot}96$, $f_\alpha = 400$ Mc/sec, and collector dissipation is 50 mW, and the more recent Texas Instruments 2N1141 for which $\alpha_0 = 0{\cdot}97$, $f_\alpha = 750$ Mc/sec, and collector dissipation is 0·75 watts. An article describing constructional details and giving data on the Motorola 2N695 and 2N700 has been published by Knowles [17].

8.5. Transistors combining the above-described techniques

There are many devices that combine base grading with one of the other techniques mentioned above for the production of high-frequency transistors. We consider three examples.

8.5.1. *Micro-alloy diffused (MADT) transistors*

These transistors are made by the Philco Corporation and their licensees by the following procedure [18]:

1. An n-type impurity is diffused into a plate of high resistivity n-type germanium to form an exponentially-graded base layer of depth ranging from 5×10^{-5} to 25×10^{-5} inch depending on the frequency rating of the device.

2. Emitter and collector depressions are made on opposite sides of the plate by the electrolytic etching technique previously described. The emitter depression is made very shallow so that the emitter will be in contact with low-resistivity base material.

3. Electrodes are plated into these pits and subsequently

alloyed. The 'micro-alloying' process used allows control of electrode depth to less than 10^{-5} inch. Typical electrode diameters are 0·0075 inch for the collector and 0·0045 inch for the emitter. The total base width varies from 10^{-4} to 4×10^{-4} inch.

4. The part of the surface which is etched away to form the emitter depression has a very low resistivity so that, upon completion of the device, the surface of the germanium on the emitter side has a low-resistivity layer that extends almost to the emitter. This helps to lower the base-spreading resistance and also cuts down surface recombination by preventing the flow of injected holes to the surface.

MADT transistors are built for both steady-state amplification and switching. Units of substantially the dimensions mentioned above, with heat dissipators attached, are capable of dissipating surprising amounts of power—up to approximately $\frac{1}{2}$ watt. One of these 'high-power' versions [18] has a figure of merit of 600 Mc/sec and an h_{fe} of 15. It can operate as an amplifier at 70 Mc/sec with an efficiency of 70 to 80 per cent.

8.5.2. Grown-diffused tetrode transistors

In the manufacture of this type of device [19] the n-type collector is grown by the usual method but growth is stopped for a period during which base and emitter impurities are added together. A further section of crystal is then grown. Because of the different impurity densities and the different rates of diffusion the first part of this section is of graded p-type material while the remainder is n-type. An n-p-n graded-base transistor is therefore formed. Emitter and collector electrodes and two base electrodes are subsequently added to form a tetrode. The device described in the above reference (the Texas Instruments 3N35) is a 125 mW silicon tetrode for which $h_{fe} = 8$ and $f_{\alpha} = 100$ Mc/sec. In the CE connection useful gain can be obtained from it at frequencies up to 70 Mc/sec. A germanium transistor made by the same process is the 3N25 tetrode which has a collector dissipation of 25 mW, $h_{fe} = 65$, $f_{\alpha} = 200$ Mc/sec, and a figure of merit of 250 Mc/sec.

8.5.3. *Diffused-meltback transistors* [9]

The method of making these devices is a modification of the meltback process mentioned in Chapter III in which a crystal containing two or three impurities is grown and meltback is used to produce a sudden change in impurity density. The distribution coefficients and diffusion coefficients of the impurities are such that graded-base transistors are produced during a subsequent heat treatment. Silicon n-p-n transistors or germanium p-n-p transistors can be made by this method. At the time of writing they do not seem to be available commercially. Germanium n-p-n tetrodes made by the meltback process described in Chapter III are, however, manufactured for use at high frequencies. An example is the G.E. 3N37 which has a dissipation of 30 mW and $f_\alpha = 90$ Mc/sec.

8.6. Unipolar and field-effect transistors

It has been shown earlier that the junction transistor, which makes use of two types of current carrier, is inherently different from the vacuum tube which has one type only. Shockley [20, 21] has called them bipolar and unipolar devices respectively and has pointed out that it is possible, in principle, to make two types of unipolar semiconductor devices. These should have the advantages over the 'diffusion' junction transistor of higher input impedances and better figures of merit. As discussed below, they do not have better figures of merit than graded-base transistors. These devices, which are known as analogue transistors and field-effect transistors, will now be described briefly.

8.6.1. *The analogue transistor*

This device was probably suggested to demonstrate a principle rather than as a practical amplifier. A cross-section of one version, in which the current is carried by electrons is shown schematically in Fig. 8.8. The strongly n-type (n^+-type) material S corresponds to the cathode of a vacuum tube. It is called the 'source'. The n^+-type material D corresponds to the anode of a vacuum tube and is called the 'drain'. The p^+-type sections are connected together to form the 'grid' to which a negative potential is applied. The material between the electrodes, which corresponds to the vacuum in a vacuum tube, is intrinsic. A space-charge region analogous to that in a vacuum tube can be developed in it and the flow of electrons through the space-charge region can be controlled by the grid which, being biased in reverse, has a high input resistance. This high input resistance and the high-frequency response characteristic of majority-carrier flow are the advantages predicted for the analogue transistor. A compensating disadvantage is the appreciable

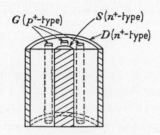

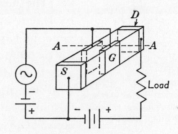

FIG. 8.8. Schematic diagram of the analogue transistor.

FIG. 8.9. Schematic diagram of the field-effect transistor.

voltage drop across the space-charge region with its accompanying loss of power.

A version of the analogue transistor in which the current is carried by positive holes can also be imagined. The bias potentials applied to it would be the reverse of those of the vacuum tube. It is for this reason that the terms source and drain rather than cathode and anode are used for the analogue transistor.

8.6.2. *The field-effect transistor*

The construction of a device of this type, in which the carriers are electrons, is shown schematically in Fig. 8.9. The source and drain, which have the same functions as in the analogue transistor, are ohmic electrodes attached to the n-type body of the device. The third electrode, which is commonly called the gate, is of p^+-type material. In the present case it consists of two sections joined together electrically and biased in the reverse direction with respect to the adjoining n-type material. The depletion layers of these p-n junctions extend into the n-type material as shown in Fig. 8.10. Since these depletion layers are denuded of conduction-band electrons the material in them is an insulator. They therefore cut down the area available to electrons flowing from source to drain. The widths of the depletion layers vary with gate voltage and the gate can be used as a high-impedance electrode to control the flow of electrons (majority carriers) through the device. By proper design considerable amplification at quite high frequencies may be obtained.

Depletion layers

FIG. 8.10. Cross-section in a vertical plane passing through the line AA of Fig. 8.9.

Following Shockley's original suggestion [21] the field-effect transistor was developed by Dacey and Ross [22, 23] who have made versions capable of oscillating at frequencies up to 50 Mc/sec.

A field-effect transistor called the 'Tecnetron' has now been announced [24, 25]. The design is similar to that of Fig. 8.9. The body consists of a filament of n-type germanium, of 5 to 10 ohm cm resistivity, 2 mm long. The central section is etched electrolytically to form a neck of 6 to 8×10^{-3} cm diameter around which a ring of indium is deposited to form a p-n junction with the underlying material. The device can apparently be manufactured quite readily and has the other advantages outlined above. An early sample [24] has a mutual conductance of 750 μmhos at 305 Mc/sec but 200 μmhos at frequencies of a few hundred Mc/sec seems to be more typical [25]. A figure of merit of 500 Mc/sec is estimated for this device.

The future of unipolar transistors is rather uncertain. Early's idealized analysis [2] has indicated that the graded-base mesa transistor should have a figure of merit exceeding that of the field-effect transistor by a factor of about ten. The mesa transistor should also be competitive as far as power-handling capability and ease of fabrication are concerned. This leaves only the high input-impedance of the unipolar transistor as a compensating advantage.

8.7. Depletion-layer transistors

Other attempts to develop a high input impedance high-frequency solid-state amplifier have produced 'depletion-layer transistors' in which carriers are injected into the depletion region of a reverse-biased *p-n* junction. The latest theoretical and experimental developments along these lines are described in references [26] and [27]. A version of one device of this type, the 'spacistor tetrode' is shown in Fig. 8.11. The *p-n* junction is biased in the reverse direction and contacts *A* and *B* are mounted on its depletion layer (transition region) *D*. *A* is an *n*-type electron-injecting contact biased in the forward direction

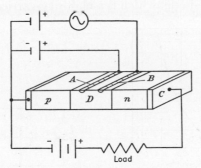

FIG. 8.11. Schematic diagram of the spacistor tetrode.

with respect to the underlying material and *B* is a *p*-type modulating contact biased in the reverse direction. Electrons injected into the depletion layer are swept rapidly towards the ohmic contact at *C*. The amount of injection at *A* is controlled by the electrode *B* which functions similarly to the grid of a vacuum tube. This control is made possible by the fact that the transition region of the junction is an insulator so that the electrostatic field produced by *B* extends to *A* and controls its emission.

The spacistor can have input and output impedances of the order of tens of megohms and the coupling between input and output terminals is almost purely capacitive (provided surface effects can be avoided). Its characteristic is therefore similar to that of a vacuum pentode. Present values of its mutual conductance are small ($\sim$ 100 micromhos) and information on the maximum operating frequency of developmental units has not been given. The depletion-layer transistor concept is very ingenious but a considerable amount of developmental work is apparently necessary before it can compete with more conventional high-frequency transistors.

8.8. The tunnel diode

Thus far in this chapter we have considered minority and majority carrier devices for the amplification of continuous signals at high frequencies. Before leaving this subject we consider the tunnel diode, which is a majority-carrier device having

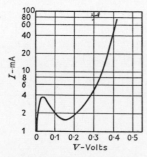

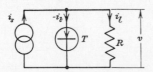

FIG. 8.12. Characteristic of one of Esaki's diodes taken at room temperature.

FIG. 8.13. Demonstrating the use of negative resistance to obtain amplification.

great possibilities as a high-frequency amplifier, oscillator, or switch.

The tunnel diode, which was discovered by Esaki [28], is a p-n alloy junction in which both regions are very heavily doped. Germanium was the first material to be used but gallium arsenide, which has a larger energy gap and a higher electron mobility, is superior to germanium in most respects (e.g. current, voltage, and temperature range, and frequency response). Tunnel diodes of both materials are now manufactured.

The characteristic of one of Esaki's units taken at room temperature in the forward direction is shown in Fig. 8.12. The region from 0·03 to 0·15 volts represents a negative resistance whose mean value is about 45 ohms. This negative-resistance region makes it possible to use the device as a regenerative switch, oscillator, or amplifier. The method of operation as a regenerative switch is analogous to that described in § 7.10. Operation as an amplifier may be described in an elementary way with the help of Fig. 8.13. Here the signal current i_s supplied by a current generator is the sum of a positive current i_l and a negative current $-i_t$. (Since an increase of voltage in the negative-resistance region produces a decrease of current, the incremental or signal current must be negative.) Hence $i_s < i_l$ and current amplification is obtained. Also since the same voltage v exists across generator and load there is a power amplification.

If the load resistance is made larger than the maximum negative resistance of the tunnel diode, i_s becomes negative and the device can be used as a relaxation or sinusoidal oscillator whose frequency is controlled by parallel inductance and capacitance in addition to the capacitance of the tunnel diode itself.

The reason for the negative resistance characteristic may be determined from a study of the distribution of electrons over the energy states in the materials forming the p-n junction. We first note that, because the concentration of impurity centres in both n- and p-type materials is very high (of the order of 10^{19} per c.c.), the Fermi level is in the conduction band of the n-type material and in the valence band of the p-type material (cf. § 1.3). The electron-energy diagram of the

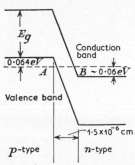

Fig. 8.14. Electron-energy diagram of the tunnel diode whose characteristic is given in Fig. 8.12.

p-n junction is therefore of the form shown in Fig. 8.14 (which represents the unit whose electrical characteristic is given in Fig. 8.12). The built-in potential energy step is therefore larger than the energy gap.

Because of the high impurity concentrations, the transition region of the junction is very thin and the field correspondingly high. The distance between points A and B of Fig. 8.14 is therefore so small that tunnelling across the energy gap (Zener effect) occurs even with no potential applied to the device.

In order to understand the effect of an applied potential we consider the flow of electrons across the gap AB. In equilibrium most of the states above the Fermi level in the valence band of the p-type material are empty and most of the states below the Fermi level in the conduction band of the n-type material are full. The number of states per unit energy per c.c. in a band is zero at the edge of the band and increases with energy separation from the band edge as shown by the dashed lines in Fig. 8.15.

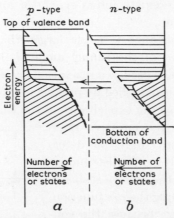

FIG. 8.15. Schematic diagram of the numbers of states and electrons in the two regions of a tunnel diode. Horizontal shading indicates empty states and diagonal shading indicates states containing electrons.

(For an ideal material we have $N(E) \propto E^{\frac{1}{2}}$ where $N(E)$ is the density of states of energy E. The expression applying to germanium differs somewhat from this but the difference need not concern us here.) The number of states per c.c. occupied by electrons in the valence band of the p-type material and in the conduction band of the n-type material are indicated by the diagonally shaded areas of Fig. 8.15 while empty states are indicated by horizontal shading. The numbers of electrons or states are plotted in opposite directions for the p-type and the n-type regions purely as a matter of convenience so that states in one region available to electrons from the other may be shown quite readily. The horizontal spacing between the two sections a and b of Fig. 8.15 is not intended to indicate the distance separating the two groups of electrons. This distance is AB of Fig. 8.14.

In equilibrium the relative positions of the energy levels in the two materials are as shown in Fig. 8.15. A small number of electrons in the n-type material is then opposite (i.e. at the same energy as) empty states in the p-type material and vice versa. Electron currents therefore flow as a result of horizontal transitions indicated by the arrows in Fig. 8.15. With no voltage applied these currents are equal and relatively small.

When a reverse voltage is applied, the potential step of Fig. 8.14 is increased and diagram a of Fig. 8.15 moves upward relative to diagram b. The flow of electrons from left to right increases rapidly because electrons in the p-type material reach positions opposite a large number of empty states. The flow of electrons from right to left diminishes owing to a reduction in the number of states in the p-type material available to electrons from the n-type material. There is thus a large net flow of electrons from left to right and a tunnel diode biased in the conventional reverse direction of a p-n junction has a low resistance. The decrease in the distance AB (Fig. 8.14) that occurs when a reverse voltage is applied also contributes to the rapid increase in current since the probability of tunnelling increases rapidly as AB is reduced.

When a forward bias is applied, diagram a of Fig. 8.15 moves down relative to diagram b. The following conditions then occur:

1. The flow of electrons from left to right drops rapidly to a very small value as the applied potential is increased. For potentials greater than about 0·13 volt the electrons in the valence band of the p-type material are opposite the forbidden region in the n-type material and the flow of electrons in this direction is negligible.

2. The flow of electrons from right to left increases initially because the conduction-band electrons find themselves opposite a large number of empty states in the p-type material. However, a further increase of applied potential causes this flow of electrons to diminish again as electrons in the upper part of the n-type

distribution reach positions opposite the forbidden region in the
p-type material. When the applied potential reaches 0·13 volt
this flow of electrons drops to a negligible amount. The flow in
this direction is also diminished slightly because the distance AB
of Fig. 8.14 increases with forward bias. However, for the small
potentials with which we are concerned here, this decrease in
electron current is not very important.

The net current flowing in the forward direction therefore
increases initially and then decreases as the applied potential is
increased, thus producing the initial rapid rise of current and the
negative resistance region of Fig. 8.12.

3. If the applied potential is increased beyond 0·13 volt the
normal forward current of the junction, due to the injection of
minority carriers into the two regions of the crystal, becomes
dominant and the device behaves as a conventional forward-
biased p-n junction.

The outstanding property of the tunnel diode is its ability to
perform as an active device at very high frequencies. This
property arises from the fact that the current flowing in the
negative-resistance region consists almost entirely of majority
carriers. The conduction band in the n-type material and the
valence band in the p-type material both contain large numbers
of electrons and the electric disturbance produced by an applied
potential moves through them at speeds decided by very short
dielectric relaxation times (§ 2.2); it does not depend on the
carrier drift velocity. The chief frequency limitation therefore
arises from the time constant produced by the junction capacitance C (which may approach 100 $\mu\mu$F) and the internal resistance r. This time constant may be as low as 5×10^{-11} second.
The resulting high-frequency properties cannot be exploited
completely because of the abnormally low high-frequency impedance resulting from the presence of the capacitance C, but
it is nevertheless possible to operate above the frequency range
of most other semiconducting devices. In a comprehensive
article on the application of tunnel diodes [29] Sommers men-
tions units capable of oscillating at $1·4 \times 10^9$ c/sec and switching
in 2×10^{-9} sec.

8.9. The point-contact transistor

The significance of the discovery of the point-contact transistor [30] has been noted in Chapter I. The junction transistor
[31] which followed it has so many advantages (e.g. in repro-
ducibility, power capability, freedom from electrical noise,
better frequency response) that the point-contact transistor is
rapidly falling into disuse, although it is still used in certain
switching applications. However, a description of it is worth
while for historical reasons and as an introduction to devices
having inherent current multiplication.

The point-contact transistor, which is
shown schematically in Fig. 8.16 consists,
in its most usual form, of a block of high
resistivity (5 to 10 ohm cm) n-type germanium upon which two chisel-pointed small
diameter wires or 'whiskers' of springy
material (e.g. tungsten or phosphor bronze)
are placed in close proximity. The diameter
of the wire used is usually about 0·005 inch

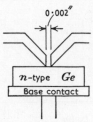

FIG. 8.16. Schematic
diagram of the point-
contact transistor.

and the spacing between them 0·002 inch. The whiskers form
rectifying contacts, of the type described in Chapter III, with
the n-type semiconductor. One of them is biased in the forward
direction to form the emitter of the transistor. The other is
reverse-biased and forms the collector. It is given a special
heat treatment called 'forming' which consists of passing a large
current through it in the reverse direction for a short time. In
order to produce the reverse breakdown that permits passage of
this large current a relatively high reverse voltage must be
applied. This heat treatment apparently produces an n-n^+
junction in the semiconductor immediately below the collector
wire [32]. The base electrode consists of a large-area ohmic
contact to the semiconductor surface opposite to that on which
the whiskers are placed.

The electrode potentials of the point-contact transistor are
the same as those of a p-n-p junction transistor and transistor
action arises from the injection of holes into the n-type material.

However, it differs from the junction transistor in that its CB short-circuit current gain α is greater than unity and usually lies between 2 and 3 in germanium transistors. For reasons discussed in the next section this makes the point-contact transistor inherently unstable under certain conditions and makes possible the construction of simple pulse-amplifying or trigger circuits.

The most important mechanism producing current gain may

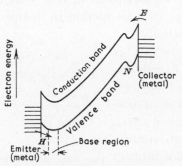

FIG. 8.17. Electron-energy diagram of the point-contact transistor.

be described with the help of the energy diagram of Fig. 8.17 —ignoring for the moment the small barrier at the point N. Holes injected at the emitter as shown by the arrow at H move rapidly towards the collector electrode. When they reach the part of the germanium adjacent to the collector, their charge lowers the effective height of the barrier there. There is a copious supply of electrons on the metal side of this barrier and some of these enter the semiconductor at E in an attempt to neutralize the positive charge of the holes. These electrons pass through the body of the semiconductor and out of the ohmic base electrode, thus contributing to the collector current but not to the emitter current. If electrons and holes had the same mobility the resulting current multiplication from emitter to collector would be two. However, $\mu_e = b\mu_h$ with $b \simeq 2$ and, since the numbers of injected holes and electrons entering to neutralize them are approximately equal, the current carried by electrons is approximately double that carried by holes. The total effect of this neutralization process is therefore to make $\alpha \simeq 3$.

If the holes are slowed down as they approach the collector and the electrons maintain their normal velocity the ratio of electron current to hole current will increase. Thus in some transistors α may exceed 3. Values greater than 10 have been reported.

Two possible explanations of this decrease of positive-hole velocity have been suggested. The first assumes the presence of a small barrier to holes, near the collector, produced by a change in conductivity. Such a barrier between n-type and n^+-type material near the collector is shown schematically at N in Fig. 8.17. It has been discussed in detail by Gunn [32]. Its presence causes an accumulation of holes and for small emitter currents the electron current from the collector may therefore be considerably larger than in the above case. For large emitter currents the gain approaches the value ($\simeq 3$) mentioned above.

The second mechanism of accounting for large current gains requires the presence near the collector of a large number of centres that act as traps for positive holes but not for electrons. Since the holes spend a certain fraction of their transit time in the traps their effective mobility is reduced while that of electrons is unchanged from its normal value. The factor b again exceeds 2 and α is correspondingly increased.

It is possible that both mechanisms play a part in practical transistors although present evidence seems to favour the presence of an n-n^+ barrier as the main reason for large current gains.

We note finally that the point-contact transistor is inherently a low power (~ 100 mW) device and that most of its characteristics are poorer than those of junction transistors. However, because the dimensions of its active region are so small and there is a drift field in the body of the semiconductor f_α is relatively large ($\simeq 10$ Mc/sec).

8.10. Explanation of the instability occurring when α exceeds unity

The reason for the tendency towards instability when $\alpha > 1$ can be seen quite readily by considering the CB circuit of Fig. 8.18. If a signal is applied to make the emitter positive with respect to the base, the currents flowing are shown by the small arrows and the relations $i_c \simeq \alpha i_e$, $i_b \simeq (\alpha - 1)i_e$ apply. The flow of the base current through the internal base resistance

r_b makes the base negative and thus produces positive feedback in the input circuit. If r_b is sufficiently large, or there is sufficient external resistance in the base circuit, instability may result.

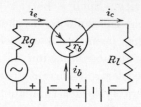

FIG. 8.18. *CB* circuit illustrating the effect of current gain greater than unity.

Stability criteria for all three transistor connections have been given by Ryder and Kircher [33]. Their analysis is based on the voltage-generator equivalent circuit of Fig. 5.4. For all three connections the condition for stability reduces to

$$\alpha \simeq \frac{r_m}{R_c} < 1 + \frac{R_e}{R_c} + \frac{R_e}{R_b}, \qquad (8.7)$$

where the capital letters indicate that the quantities concerned include external resistances in series with r_e, r_b, r_c, etc. Thus, for the *CB* and *CE* connections $R_c = r_c + R_l$ while for the *CE* and *CC* connections $R_b = r_b + R_g$. (Note that r_c not $r_c(1-a)$ is used for the internal collector resistance for the *CE* and *CC* connections.) The approximation $\alpha \simeq r_m/R_c$ is quite good for point-contact transistors and very good for junction transistors.

It can be seen from equation (8.7) that the *CB* will be the most stable and the *CE* the least stable of the three connections. In the *CB* connection the external emitter resistance must be large for linear operation and the r.h.s. is usually greater than three. For linear operation of the *CE* connection R_b must be large and the r.h.s. approaches unity. The same is true of the *CC* connection except when the load resistance, which forms part of R_e, is very large.

In the application of point-contact transistors to multistage linear amplifiers R_g or R_l may be decided by a preceding or a succeeding stage. When *CE* and *CC* stages are used one or both of these quantities may be negative, thereby increasing the chance of instability. It is chiefly for this reason that point-contact transistors are rarely used for linear amplifiers except in the CB connection.

Equation (8.7) may be applied to junction transistors of the avalanche type (§ 8.12.3) in which α is increased by carrier multiplication at high collector voltages. Miller [34] has shown that the low voltage α of a transistor operated in this manner is multiplied by a factor

$$M = \frac{1}{1-(V/V_B)^n},\tag{8.8}$$

where V is the voltage applied to the collector junction and V_B its breakdown voltage. The factor n depends on the type of conduction and on the resistivity on the high-resistivity side of the junction. It is approximately 3 for high-frequency p-n-p alloy transistors. The high voltage α can therefore be appreciably greater than unity for voltages well below V_B.

In the usual CB arrangement ($R_e \gg R_b$) α must exceed unity by a considerable amount before the circuit becomes unstable and it is usually assumed that the condition for instability is $V \simeq V_B$, i.e. the current gain is infinite. In the CE and CC connections instability occurs at the lower collector voltage for which $\alpha \simeq 1$. However, the current gain in these connections is proportional to $1/(1-\alpha)$ so that the condition for instability in all three cases is expressed by the statement that the current gain must approach infinity.

These stability considerations apply to any other transistor in which there is current multiplication between emitter and collector or to any diode in which current multiplication takes place. When any of these devices is operated in the unstable region, regeneration of the type described in § 7.10 is obtained.

8.11. The hook-collector transistor

In an attempt to explain the operation of the point-contact transistor Shockley devised the junction transistor with p-n hook collector [35]. This has not been applied commercially but it is frequently mentioned in transistor literature, especially in connection with avalanche devices, and a brief description of it seems desirable. The CB connection of one form of it is shown, with its electron-energy diagram, in Fig. 8.19. It consists of a p-n-p transistor to which an extra n-type section has been added. The junction which this section forms with the collector is forward-biased and produces a small step in the collector energy diagram at D. Positive holes arriving at the collector tend to accumulate at this step and under steady d.c. current

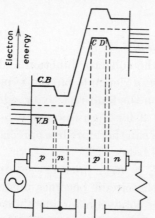

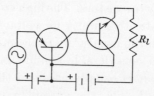

FIG. 8.19. Electron-energy diagram   FIG. 8.20. Circuit diagram of
of the hook-collector transistor.   the hook-collector transistor.

conditions there is an excess of positive charge in the region CD. This produces a forward bias which increases the flow of electrons across the junction at D. Values of α considerably in excess of unity can thus be produced.

The hook at D in Fig. 8.19 is similar to that in Fig. 8.17 so that the behaviour of the hook-collector transistor is similar to that of the point-contact transistor and the p-n hook might be considered as an alternative to the n-n^+ junction described earlier. However, it is found experimentally that the presence of donor impurities in the collector whisker is necessary for good forming action. This fact favours the n-n^+ junction as the cause of large current gains.

The arrangement of Fig. 8.19 can also be considered as a combination of a CB connected p-n-p transistor and a CC connected n-p-n transistor as shown in Fig. 8.20. The two inner regions of the crystal are common to both transistors. The current multiplication and the switching speed are decided largely by the CC connection of the second transistor.

8.12. Other regenerative switching devices

Within the past two or three years the development of regenerative switching devices has become quite intense. Some of these are now available commercially although at the time of writing their prices are rather high. This condition will no doubt be rectified shortly. It is also possible by careful selection to find ordinary transistors that will function in the same way as some of the devices to be described (e.g. as avalanche transistors). It therefore seems worth while to give a brief summary of developments in this field.

These devices, which are all of the type described in § 7.10, may be classified in the following groups:

1. Non-avalanching regenerative triodes.
2. Avalanche diodes.
3. Avalanche triodes.
4. The unijunction transistor.

8.12.1. *Non-avalanching regenerative triodes*

The first group includes the point-contact transistor and the hook-collector transistor. Recent additions to it consist of germanium p-n-p-m transistors in which the last symbol m denotes a metal containing a p-type impurity such as indium. At least two devices of this type have been described recently [36, 37]. Their electron-energy diagrams are apparently of the form shown in Fig. 8.21 in which the p^+ layer is formed by penetration of indium from the metal electrode into the germanium. The mechanism of current multiplication has not yet been discussed in detail in the literature but from the form of the energy diagram near the p^+-metal contact it may be similar to that of the point-contact transistor. Accumulation of positive holes in the region DE would lower the barrier to the entry of electrons from the metal thus providing current multiplication.

We note that the procedure for producing an electron-injecting contact at the collector electrode is similar to that described in Chapter III for the production of ohmic contacts. If the proposed mechanism is correct, the treatment of the germanium surface must be such as to remove electron-trapping levels and the penetration of p-type impurity from the metal must be insufficient to remove the metal-semiconductor barrier completely.

These devices show promise as solid state 'thyratrons' or con-

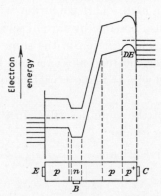

FIG. 8.21. Suggested electron-energy diagram for p-n-p-m devices.

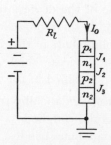

FIG. 8.22. Schematic diagram of the four-layer avalanche diode.

trolled rectifiers. Their resistance in the 'on' position is low and they can carry large currents. They have the advantage over grid-controlled gas-tube rectifiers that they can be turned off more readily. Their turn-on time is of the same order as that of high-speed gas tubes but their turn-off time is considerably shorter.

8.12.2. *Avalanche diodes*

The second type of device is a multijunction (four-layer) switching diode that makes use of avalanche breakdown to generate large current gains at high speed. Apparently it was first suggested by Shockley and has been described by Moll *et al.* [38] and by Shockley and Gibbons [39]. It is shown schematically in Fig. 8.22.

When a voltage is applied as shown in the figure the junctions

J_1 and J_3 are forward-biased and act as emitters. The junction J_2 is reverse-biased and acts as a collector. The hole current I_0 flowing through p_1 is injected into n_1 and a current $\alpha_1 I_0$ arrives at the collector J_2. Similarly a fraction $\alpha_2 I_0$ of the electron current I_0 injected into p_2 from n_2 reaches J_2 which acts as a collector in this case also. The total current crossing J_2 is therefore

$$I_0 = \alpha_1 I_0 + \alpha_2 I_0 + I_{c0}. \tag{8.9}$$

Equation (8.9) merely expresses the current-density relation. From it we see that

$$I_0 = \frac{I_{c0}}{1-(\alpha_1+\alpha_2)}. \tag{8.10}$$

If $(\alpha_1+\alpha_2)$ is appreciably less than unity the current flowing through the device is of the order of I_{c0}, but if $(\alpha_1+\alpha_2) > 1$ the current given by equation (8.10) is negative and operation becomes unstable. A useful switch can be made if $(\alpha_1+\alpha_2)$ is small at low voltages and increases with voltage—especially if the increase becomes very rapid at some definite value of voltage.

As mentioned earlier (Chapter V) the current gain of silicon transistors is very low for small currents but increases rapidly with current so that a device in which $(\alpha_1+\alpha_2) \ll 1$ in the ordinary range can be made quite readily from silicon. Its characteristic in this region is represented by the line OA of Fig. 8.23. It is

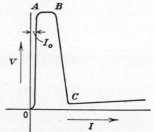

FIG. 8.23. Characteristic of the four-layer avalanche diode.

decided largely by the reverse characteristic of junction J_2, across which almost all of the diode voltage appears, i.e. $I_0 \simeq I_{c0}$ as may be confirmed from equation (8.10). When the breakdown voltage of J_2 is approached, both the electron and hole currents crossing it are multiplied by the avalanche process as outlined in § 8.10. The current flowing through the device therefore becomes

$$I = \frac{I_{c0}}{1-(M_1\alpha_1+M_2\alpha_2)}, \tag{8.11}$$

where M_1 and M_2 are the multiplication factors for holes and electrons respectively. The resulting increase in current increases both α_1 and α_2.

In the region AB, α_1 and α_2 are increasing while M_1 and M_2 are decreasing slightly because the increase in current increases the voltage across junctions J_1 and J_3 and the body resistance thus reducing slightly the voltage across J_2. At the point B, $(\alpha_1 + \alpha_2) = 1$ and, for currents larger than this, a regenerative condition can be maintained even with M_1 and M_2 each equal to unity. There follows a region BC of high negative resistance in which the voltage across J_2 drops to a low value. At the point C the junction J_2 is biased in the forward direction and is no longer a collector so that equation (8.11) does not hold. The condition here is similar to that of a saturated transistor and can be analysed in the same way. The total resistance of the device is low and positive.

The characteristic of Fig. 8.23 is of the same general form as that of Fig. 7.22, and the avalanche diode can be used as a regenerative switch of the type described in Chapter VII. Developmental units have operated in relaxation oscillators at frequencies as high as 2 Mc/sec indicating a switching time of a microsecond or less [38]. Switching times considerably shorter than this ($\simeq 10^{-8}$ sec) can be obtained in one direction [39].

8.12.3. *Avalanche triodes*

Several devices in which current gain is obtained by avalanching, and in which switching can be controlled by a third electrode, have been discussed in the literature. We will describe three of them briefly.

1. The first is a p-n-p or n-p-n transistor which is operated at a collector voltage large enough to produce instability [40]. Multiplication at the collector junction produces a CB current gain greater than unity and characteristics similar to those of the point-contact transistor or the hook-collector transistor. The condition for instability is given by equation (8.7).

This type of avalanche transistor has an f_α of the same order as that of a similarly constructed non-avalanching transistor. This is in contrast to the hook-collector transistor whose f_α

approaches the CC cutoff frequency of an ordinary transistor of similar dimensions. The avalanche transistor has the additional advantage that minority-carrier storage (which occurs in both point-contact and hook-collector transistors) is eliminated since the collector voltage never reaches the saturation region.

2. The second type of avalanching triode [41] is obtained by connecting a base lead to either the n_1 or p_2 sections of the diode in Fig. 8.22. We consider the case in which a base current

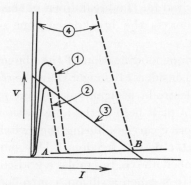

FIG. 8.24. Characteristic of the four-
layer avalanche triode.

flows into p_2 thus increasing the current crossing the junction J_3. This increases α_2, the current gain of this section, so that the regenerative condition is reached for a lower collector voltage than in the diode case. The effect on the characteristic of the device is shown schematically in Fig. 8.24. The curve (1) represents the characteristic when no base current is applied, and curve (2) is obtained when a base current flows into p_2 ($I_b > 0$). No attempt is made to show the exact form of the negative-resistance sections of the characteristics, which are therefore represented by broken lines. It is seen that increasing I_b lowers the breakdown voltage and decreases the resistance in the 'off' condition. The latter effect is usually not serious. The value to which the current drops before switch-off takes place is also lower.

A load line (3) which just intersects curve (2) is also drawn in Fig. 8.24. When the base current is increased from the value

$I_b = 0$ to that for curve (2), the device will switch on. In order to switch it off it is necessary to apply a negative base current sufficient to produce curve (4) which intersects the line AB just beyond B. We note from this curve that the device may be held in the 'off' position even when the collector voltage is large enough to produce a large current multiplication. This is of course due to the fact that α_1 and α_2 are then so small that the overall current gain remains less than unity.

The time required for the breakdown of this type of triode is of the same order as the breakdown time of the four-layer avalanche diode.

3. A high-current modification of the above triode, in which the section n_1 is considerably longer than the remaining sections and the base electrode is again placed on p_2, has also been described [42]. A drift field in the long section apparently aids the flow of minority carriers during the switch-on process and also allows greater design freedom. This device, in common with those described above, resembles a grid-controlled gas tube or 'thyratron'. It is called a silicon 'controlled rectifier'.

4. Another type of regenerative action involving both avalanche breakdown and punch-through in selected alloy transistors has been studied [43]. A device to be used in this manner must have a punch-through voltage somewhat above the voltage at which α becomes unity due to avalanching. When the latter voltage is reached breakdown occurs extremely rapidly. Switch-on times are an order of magnitude shorter than would be expected from the ordinary high-frequency properties of the transistor. The improvement apparently arises from the reduction in transit time across the base when the punch-through condition is approached.

8.12.4. *The unijunction transistor*

A device whose regenerative property is obtained in a somewhat different manner from those so far considered is the unijunction transistor or double-based diode [44]. In the commercially available form this consists of a small rod of n-type silicon having ohmic contacts at both ends and a p-n alloy junction near its centre as shown schematically in Fig. 8.25. Voltages are applied as shown in the figure, their magnitudes being such that the junction E (called the emitter) is initially reverse-biased with respect to the material immediately beneath it at D. The resistance of the emitter junction is then very high. Application of a positive voltage of suitable magnitude between emitter and base B_1 causes the emitter to inject positive holes. These, and the electrons that enter to neutralize them, increase the conductivity of the region DB_1—a process

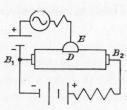

known as conductivity modulation. The decreased voltage drop across DB_1 allows more of the applied voltage to appear across the emitter junction, thus increasing the injected current and further increasing the conductivity of $B_1 D$. The process is cumulative and produces a negative emitter resistance.

Fig. 8.25. Schematic diagram of the unijunction transistor.

It continues until the resistances of the emitter junction and the base contact at B_1 are dominant. The device then has a low positive resistance and a characteristic similar to that described in § 7.10. It can be used in the same manner as the other regenerative diodes described above. It can also be used as a solid-state thyratron by applying the control voltage between bases B_1 and B_2, but the control-circuit resistance in this case is very low. It has the additional disadvantage that the voltage drop across it in the 'on' position is quite high (about two volts) and its maximum current is therefore limited to relatively low values.

8.13. Power transistors

We close this chapter with a brief outline of the factors influencing the design and construction of power transistors. This is based on a review article by Clark [45] to which the reader is referred for further details and references.

8.13.1. *Power ratings*

Transistors may be classified very roughly, according to their power-handling ability, into the following three groups:

1. General purpose or low-power transistors having maximum power dissipations in the range from 10 to 100 milliwatts.

2. Medium-power transistors having maximum dissipations in the range from 100 mW to 1 watt.

3. Power transistors whose maximum dissipations are, at present, in the range from 1 to 80 watts. However, the upper limit is climbing rapidly and units of several hundred watts dissipation will undoubtedly be available shortly.

The nominal maximum dissipation mentioned in these definitions is the total power that can be consumed in the transistor when its case temperature is held at 25° C. As mentioned in § 12.2 the practical maximum dissipation may be considerably smaller (e.g. by a factor 4) than this nominal rating. In power stages designed for linear amplification of alternating currents the power delivered to the load may range from approximately one-third the practical maximum transistor dissipation to almost three times that figure, depending on the type of connection used (cf. Chapter XII). In switching circuits, as pointed out in Chapter VII, the ratio of load power to transistor dissipation may be much larger.

The dissipation rating of a power transistor depends on the maximum temperature at which it can be operated and on the rate at which heat can be removed from it. Since most of the heat is generated at the collector junction the transistor is usually constructed so that heat can be conducted rapidly from collector to case. The case is so shaped that it can make good thermal contact to a large metal plate which transfers heat rapidly to the surroundings and forms a 'heat sink'. Most transistors having nominal dissipations above 200 mW are rated on the assumption that an infinite heat sink will be provided. The relation of the thermal characteristics of power transistors to the design of power stages will be considered in Chapter XII.

8.13.2. *Factors influencing power-transistor design*

The factors influencing the design of power transistors are probably best expressed by the following figures of merit [45]:

1. The power-gain power-output product. For a class A

stage, in which the d.c. collector (bias) current is approximately one-half of the maximum attainable collector current (cf. Chapter XII),

$$G_p P_0 = \left(\frac{\alpha}{1-\alpha}\right)^2 \frac{V_m^2}{8r_{bb'}}, \tag{8.12}$$

where G_p is the operating power gain and P_0 the power output. V_m is the maximum allowable collector voltage and $r_{bb'}$ the base-spreading resistance.

2. The high-power high-frequency figure of merit. For a class A stage this is

$$G_p P_0 f^2 = \alpha^2 f_\alpha^2 \frac{V_m^2}{8r_{bb'}}. \tag{8.13}$$

Equation (8.13) is derived on the assumption that the frequency response is governed by f_α rather than by the collector and emitter capacitances. Since power transistors operate under low-impedance conditions this assumption is justified except in the case of some recently developed high-frequency high-power transistors of diffused emitter and base (mesa) types [15]. For these the high-frequency figure of merit discussed earlier is more suitable.

It is apparent from equations (8.12) and (8.13) that most of the factors that are important in general-purpose high-frequency transistors are also important in power transistors and it is unnecessary to discuss them in detail. We merely note the following:

(a) Alloy transistors are favoured over grown-junction transistors for the following reasons:

(a.1) The geometry of alloy transistors is more suitable for the production of low $r_{bb'}$ values.

(a.2) Attempts to lower $r_{bb'}$ by lowering the base resistivity may be carried further in the case of alloy transistors without lowering appreciably the emitter efficiency and the current gain. This is, of course, due to the fact that the emitter resistivity of alloy transistors is considerably lower than that of grown-junction transistors.

(a.3) The lower emitter and collector body resistivities in alloy-junction transistors help to minimize parasitic losses in these parts of the transistor at high current densities. Such losses are considerably larger in grown-junction transistors.

(*b*) In most low-frequency ($f_\alpha \simeq 300$ kc/sec) germanium power transistors, V_m is apparently limited by surface breakdown—present maximum values being about 100 volts. For higher-frequency power transistors of the grown or alloy type, other limitations such as punch-through and avalanching may decide the voltage rating.

(*c*) The range of current over which a power transistor

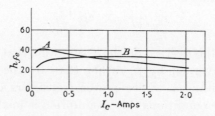

FIG. 8.26. *CE* current gain of power transistor as a function of collector current. (*A*) For a commercial transistor (2N235A). (*B*) For a power tetrode (schematic).

operates usually extends from approximately zero to something approaching its maximum allowable current (e.g. 3 to 5 amperes in a 25-watt transistor). The decrease of α at large values of emitter current, discussed in Chapter V, therefore plays a very important part in power-transistor applications. This effect is best demonstrated by considering a plot of β ($= h_{fe}$) against collector current as shown for a 25-watt transistor (Bendix 2N235A) in curve *A*, Fig. 8.26. Because of the larger current densities and larger areas of power transistors this phenomenon is more complicated than in general-purpose transistors. In power transistors the transverse voltage drop due to the flow of base current through the base resistance lowers the voltage across the emitter junction as the distance from the base connection is increased and this leads to a concentration of emitter current near the base contact. This exaggerates the change of β with emitter or collector current. Also, in many power transistors the base thickness varies at different parts of the cross-section and this, combined with the above effect, leads to a decrease of f_α with emitter current. Since large-area junctions are required, the production of uniform base thicknesses is a difficult problem which has not been completely solved in commercial alloy transistors. The most promising method of producing uniform base layers is the solid-state diffusion process mentioned in § 8.4. This has the added advantage that very thin base layers and grading of impurities in the base can be obtained. The effect of these factors in improving the power gain and frequency response of power transistors is similar to that in low-power high-frequency transistors.

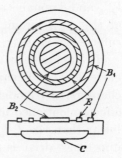

An attempt to decrease the variation of current gain with emitter or collector current in alloy transistors is made in the tetrode power transistor [46]. The construction of this device is shown schematically in Fig. 8.27. A ring-shaped alloyed

FIG. 8.27. Electrode arrangement in the power tetrode.

emitter E is placed on one surface of an n-type germanium disk and a conventional alloyed collector on the opposite side. Two base connections in the form of a ring B_1 and a circle B_2 are placed concentrically with the emitter and are thus on opposite sides of the narrow base region that lies beneath the emitter. One of these, B_1, forms the usual base connection while the other, B_2, may be used in the following two ways [47]:

(c.1) It may be biased negatively with respect to the main base connection. The forward voltage across the junction EB_2 is then larger than that across EB_1. The biasing effect of the base resistance is thus reduced and the emitter current is spread more uniformly over the emitter surface. The rise in current gain at low emitter currents, due to the field produced by majority carriers in the base (see Chapter V), is thus reduced because the densities of the minority carriers and the majority carriers that neutralize them are lower than in a triode carrying the same emitter current. The drop in emitter efficiency that results from the large density of carriers in the base at large emitter currents is likewise reduced. The $\beta\text{-}I_c$ curve is therefore of the form B in Fig. 8.26.

(c.2) In the second method of biasing, B_2 is made positive with respect to the emitter to such an extent that no emitter current flows until V_{B_1E} has exceeded a certain threshold value. Once this threshold has been passed the active area of the emitter apparently increases approximately in proportion to V_{B_1E} and β remains substantially constant. The input resistance of the $B_1 E$ circuit is also approximately constant if V_{B_2E} is sufficiently large ($\simeq 5$ volts).

(d) For low-level transistors in the CE connection the collector current varies linearly with base current as discussed in earlier chapters. In modern alloy power transistors, because of the effects mentioned under (c) above, the plot of I_c vs. V_{be} is more linear than the $I_c\text{-}I_b$ characteristic, thus indicating that a low-impedance drive is required for minimum distortion. This has the advantage that the amount of power lost in the driving circuit is small, but, unless negative feedback is used, requires that the power stage be driven from either a low-impedance transformer or a common collector stage.

TRANSISTOR BIAS CIRCUITS

9.1. Introduction

THE preceding chapters have been concerned with descriptions of the physical processes taking place in p-n junction rectifiers and transistors, and with small-signal equivalent circuits derived from them. In order to use these equivalent circuits, or to use transistors in large-signal applications of the type described in Chapter VII, we must be certain that the d.c. (bias) values of current and voltage do not alter sufficiently under any conceivable condition of operation to cause distortion of the signal voltage or current. In many cases such distortion is bound to occur unless the d.c. values are stabilized by careful design. Indeed, in some applications the operating point may shift to such a large extent that the transistor either ceases to operate as an active device or, in an extreme case, destroys itself.

The need for stabilization arises chiefly from two factors:

1. The effect of temperature on transistor parameters.
2. Variations in characteristics between different units of the same type.

Temperature fluctuations may result from ambient temperature changes or from losses in the transistor itself. Their effect is very important in the application of germanium transistors. For these devices some attempt to minimize the effects of changes in temperature is almost always necessary. For silicon transistors, operating at low-power levels and ordinary temperatures, the effects of temperature changes are considerably smaller but at high-power levels or at the high ambient temperatures that may be encountered in some military applications, stabilization may be necessary for these devices also.

Variations between units of the same type are important for transistors made from both materials but, at the present stage of development, are probably somewhat greater for silicon devices. In general these variations are important only when large numbers of a given circuit are to be built or when rapid replacement of a transistor without realignment of the circuit is necessary. Since this book is intended primarily for experimentalists who are concerned with small numbers of stages and can take the time to readjust the operating point following circuit changes, we shall not consider item (2) further in the derivation of our stabilization formulae. Later we will describe a way of taking these variations, and the tolerances of resistors used in the bias circuits, into account experimentally. For those concerned with the design of circuits to be produced in large numbers, more complete methods, taking all conceivable fluctuations into account in the circuit design, are available [1, 2, 3].

9.2. Characteristics affected by changes of temperature

9.2.1. *The collector cutoff current*

The most important temperature-dependent property of transistors is the collector cutoff current I_{co} that flows when the collector junction is biased in the normal (reverse) direction and the emitter current is zero. For germanium transistors, as mentioned in Chapter IV, it has a temperature dependence similar to that of the reverse saturation current I_s of the collector junction. The change of this quantity with temperature may be estimated from equation (4.9) written in the form

$$\ln I_s = \text{constant} + 2\ln T - \frac{E'_g}{kT}, \tag{9.1}$$

in which ln represents a natural logarithm. When the variation of E'_g with temperature is taken into account as in § 4.5 and the second term, which varies slowly with temperature, is omitted we obtain the expression

$$\ln I_s = \text{constant} - \frac{E_g}{kT}. \tag{9.2}$$

Differentiation of (9.2) gives

$$\frac{\Delta I_s}{I_s} = \frac{E_g}{kT}\frac{\Delta T}{T}. \tag{9.3}$$

When E_g has been determined equation (9.3) may be used to estimate the change of I_{co} for changes of temperature less than 10° C. For larger changes equation (9.4) below is more accurate.

The plot of $\ln I_{co}$ vs. T for the 2N369 (Fig. A11.11), when fitted to equation (9.2) gives $E_g \simeq 0.55$ eV. The difference between this and the theoretical value (0.25 eV) is probably due to the presence of surface impurities. Fig. A11.1 also shows that, in this case, I_{co} doubles for each rise in temperature of 10° C, or

$$\frac{I_{co}(T+10)}{I_{co}(T)} \simeq 2. \tag{9.4}$$

This useful relation applies to most low-frequency germanium transistors at temperatures above 50° C. At temperatures near 25° C the factor on the r.h.s. is about 2.5 in most cases (e.g. for the 0C71) indicating the existence of a slight curvature, as would be expected from equation (9.2), in the $\ln I_{co}$ vs. T characteristic.

The change of I_{co} given by these equations is very large. Thus the design centre value of I_{co} given by Fig. A11.11 increases from 5 μA at 25° C to 60 μA at the conservative operating temperature of 60° C.

For silicon transistors the magnitude of I_{co} is several orders of magnitude larger than the expected value of I_s and it doubles for each rise in temperature of approximately 15° C rather than the 5° C predicted by equation (9.2). Current components generated at impurities on the surface, or in the collector transition layer, apparently dominate the cutoff current in these devices.

The influence of I_{co} on transistor operation depends markedly on the transistor connection as may be seen from the following:

(a) For the CB connection the external base resistance is very small and all of the collector cutoff current flows out of the base. The variation in I_c arising from changes in temperature is then equal to I_{co} and rarely exceeds 100 μA for a low-power transistor under normal operating conditions. The changes in collector voltage and dissipation produced by the flow of this current through the load resistance are usually small.

(b) For the CE connection the external base resistance is

usually high and the effect of I_{co} is more pronounced. This may be seen by considering a p-n-p transistor whose base is open-circuited. The applied d.c. collector voltage causes holes and electrons to flow in the directions shown by the arrows in Fig. 9.1 and negative charge tends to accumulate in the base. Since the base is open-circuited the negative charge cannot be removed by a flow of electrons out of the ohmic base connection.

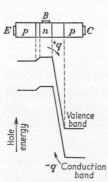

FIG. 9.1. Flow of carriers forming the collector cutoff current in a p-n-p transistor.

Also, because the emitter-base junction is a high-efficiency hole injector, very few electrons are removed via the emitter. The base is therefore biased negatively with respect to the emitter, i.e. the forward bias on the emitter junction is increased. The resulting increase in the flow of holes from the emitter tends to neutralize the negative charge in the base. However, a fraction α_N of these holes (where α_N is the d.c. current gain defined in Chapter VII) passes through the base into the collector and only a fraction $(1-\alpha_N)$ is effective in neutralizing the negative charge in the base arising from I_{co}. Hence we must have $(1-\alpha_N)I_{e1} = I_{co}$, where I_{e1} is the emitter current arising from the effect of I_{co}. I_{e1} produces a collector current $\alpha_N I_{e1}$ so that, as a result of the neutralization process, a collector current $\alpha_N I_{co}/(1-\alpha_N)$ flows. The total collector current flowing when the base is open, is thus

$$I_0 = I_{co} + \frac{\alpha_N I_{co}}{(1-\alpha_N)} = \frac{I_{co}}{1-\alpha_N} = (1+h_{FE})I_{co}. \qquad (9.5)$$

This current I_0, which flows when the external base resistance is infinite and the external emitter resistance is zero, represents the maximum effect that I_{co} can have on the collector current in the CE connection. It can be quite large if the variation in temperature is appreciable. For the 2N369 in the temperature range considered above, $\Delta I_{co} = 55$ μA. The corresponding change in I_0 is $\Delta I_0 = 55$ μA/$(1-0.982) = 3$ mA. The effect of this may be seen by considering the load line AB on the CE

characteristic of Fig. A11.3. The collector supply potential in this case is $V_{cc} = 12$ volts and the collector bias resistance is 3 kilohms. A convenient operating point O is obtained with a base bias current of 20 μA. The corresponding collector current is 1·8 mA. If I_c were to attempt to increase by the above ΔI_0 the operating point would move up the load line until the transistor saturated and no longer functioned as an amplifier. A change in I_c of 3 mA could just be accommodated if the operating point at 25° C were placed at $V_{co} \simeq 10$ volts, $I_o \simeq 0\cdot7$ mA corresponding to $I_b \simeq -5$ μA but in this case the signal that could be amplified without distortion would be very small.

If the collector bias resistance is small, as in an amplifier with transformer-coupled output, this change in V_{ce} will not take place but the increased collector dissipation $\Delta I_0 V_{ce}$ may lead to thermal runaway and destruction of the transistor as described in § 9.5.

(c) The mechanism responsible for the large effect of I_{co} in the CE connection also applies to the CC connection.

9.2.2. The base-emitter voltage

The temperature dependence of the base-emitter voltage V_{be} also affects the transistor operating point to some extent. It is less important than I_{co}, but can be dominant in a CB circuit having low external emitter resistance or in a CE circuit that has been well compensated for I_{co} effects. It arises from the change in resistance of the emitter junction with temperature and can be estimated from the formula for the V-I characteristic of a forward-biased junction rectifier, if the emitter current is assumed to be constant. As indicated by equation (4.21), $\Delta V_{be}/\Delta T$ is about 2·3 mV/°C for germanium and silicon.

9.2.3. The short-circuit current gain

As mentioned in Chapter VI the temperature dependence of α is small and is not important for the CB connection. For the CE and CC connections for which $h_{fe} = \beta = \alpha/(1-\alpha)$ and $h_{fc} = -1/(1-\alpha)$, variations in α are amplified and for a high-gain transistor the variation with temperature of h_{fe} and h_{fc} may be appreciable. A similar remark applies to the d.c.

parameters h_{FE} and h_{FC}. For the 2N369 these current gains increase by about 25 per cent when the temperature is raised from 25° C to 60° C. Although it does not approach the magnitude of the I_{co} effect, this change in α with temperature may sometimes produce an appreciable shift of the operating point.

9.3. Methods of compensating for temperature effects in low-level stages

In this section we consider, for the CE connection, methods of compensating for variations of the parameters mentioned in § 9.2. The methods to be described may also be used for the other connections. For the CB connection as normally used the methods are needed only when the temperature variations are rather large, and, in view of the relatively small number of applications of this connection, we will not consider it further. Mention of applications to the CC connection will be made as we proceed.

9.3.1. *The unstabilized circuit*

Before describing the methods by which the operating point of a low-level transistor stage may be stabilized we shall obtain expressions for the dependence of collector current on the three parameters mentioned in § 9.2, when the simplest possible nonstabilized bias circuit is used. These expressions will confirm the

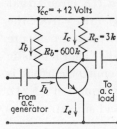

FIG. 9.2. Unstabilized *CE* amplifier.

reasoning of § 9.2 and the method used in obtaining them will serve as an introduction to the more complicated procedures to be outlined later.

The circuit of the unstabilized CE amplifier, whose circuit characteristics are described in § 9.2.1, is shown in Fig. 9.2. The base bias current is obtained from the power supply by means of resistor R_b. For convenience in analysis the currents are drawn in the directions characteristic of an n-p-n transistor. The equations for this arrangement are

$$I_c = I_0 + h_{FE} I_b + h_{oe} V_{ce}, \tag{9.6}$$
$$V_{cc} = I_b (R_b + r_{bb'}) + V_{be} = I_c R_c + V_{ce}. \tag{9.7}$$

Equation (9.6) is obtained by inspection of Fig. A11.3. The last term takes account of the slope of the characteristics. It may be omitted for low-gain transistors since

$$h_{oe} = h_{ob}/(1+h_{fb}) = (1+\beta)h_{ob}$$

is then small. The slope of I_0, the collector characteristic for $I_b = 0$, has been ignored since its effect is usually negligible. The internal base resistance $r_{bb'}$ acts, for these d.c. currents, in the same manner as an external resistance and has therefore been added to R_b.

The expression for I_c obtained from these equations is

$$I_c = \frac{1}{1+h_{oe}R_c}\left[\frac{h_{FE}(V_{cc}-V_{be})}{R_b+r_{bb'}}+h_{oe}V_{cc}+I_0\right] \qquad (9.8)$$

and by partial differentiation we obtain

$$\Delta I_c(I_{co}) = \frac{\Delta I_0}{1+h_{oe}R_c} = \frac{1+h_{FE}}{1+h_{oe}R_c}\Delta I_{co}, \qquad (9.9)$$

where equation (9.5) has been used. Also

$$\Delta I_c(V_{be}) = \frac{-h_{FE}}{(R_b+r_{bb'})(1+h_{oe}R_c)}\Delta V_{be}, \qquad (9.10)$$

$$\Delta I_c(h_{FE}) = \frac{V_{cc}-V_{be}}{(R_b+r_{bb'})(1+h_{oe}R_c)}\Delta h_{FE}. \qquad (9.11)$$

Here the bracketed quantity following ΔI_c is the independent variable concerned.

For the 2N369, $h_{oe} \simeq 20\ \mu$mhos so that, for the above example, $h_{oe}R_c = 0.06$. Omission of this factor would alter the expressions (9.9) to (9.11) by 6 per cent—a negligible amount when the variations of parameters from one transistor to another are taken into account. Equation (9.9) thus gives practically the same result as equation (9.5), indicating that this method of biasing does not compensate for changes in I_{co}. The effects of ΔV_{be} and Δh_{FE} are, however, drastically reduced because of the large magnitude of R_b.

The large value of $\Delta I_c/\Delta I_{co}$ eliminates this simple biasing method as far as germanium transistors are concerned. For silicon transistors the disadvantage is not as great but even here one of the types of stabilization described below is worth while, especially when advantage is taken of the higher allow-able operating temperature.

9.3.2. *Feedback stabilization*

The simplest biasing arrangement that produces some d.c. stabilization uses a resistor R_b between collector and base as

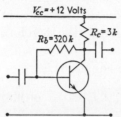

$V_{cc} = +12$ Volts

$R_b = 320k$ $R_c = 3k$

FIG. 9.3. *CE* amplifier stabilized by feedback from collector to base.

shown, for approximately the same room-temperature operating point as in § 9.3.1, in Fig. 9.3. Because of the signal inversion inherent in the *CE* connection the arrangement produces negative feedback from output to input. Thus for any fluctuation in output, produced by a change of temperature, a signal opposing the fluctuation is transmitted to the input of the amplifier.

Solution of the equations for this case and subsequent differentiation leads to the following results:

$$\Delta I_c(I_{co}) = K\Delta I_0, \tag{9.12}$$

$$\Delta I_c(V_{be}) \simeq -K\frac{h_{FE}\Delta V_{be}}{R_c+R_b}, \tag{9.13}$$

$$\frac{\Delta I_c(h_{FE})}{I_c} \simeq K\left(1-\frac{I_0}{I_c}\right)\frac{\Delta h_{FE}}{h_{FE}}, \tag{9.14}$$

where
$$K = \frac{1}{1+\{R_c(h_{FE}+h_{oe}R_b)/(R_c+R_b)\}} \tag{9.15}$$

and $r_{bb'}$, which is small compared with R_b, has been neglected. The factor K thus indicates the extent to which variations in I_c are reduced by feedback. In using it we are following the practice of Johnson and Vermes [1, 2] in their excellent analysis of stabilization.

For the 2N369 connected as in Fig. 9.3, $K \simeq 0.66$ so that the effect of ΔI_{co} has been decreased by only one-third. This result can be improved somewhat by increasing R_c and decreasing R_b. The first procedure requires an increase in V_{cc} and the second produces an increase in the magnitudes of I_b and I_c. The power dissipated in R_c is therefore increased.

The effects of ΔV_{be} and Δh_{FE} on I_c are small compared with that of I_{co} and these factors need not be considered further for this method of stabilization.

This method of stabilizing transistor circuits has the following disadvantages:

1. The amount of stabilization that can be obtained without going to rather wasteful arrangements is limited.

2. The operating point and the amount of stabilization are not independent of each other.

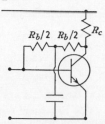

FIG. 9.4. Feedback-stabilized CE amplifier with a.c. degeneration removed.

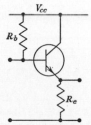

FIG. 9.5. CC amplifier stabilized by feedback.

3. In addition to the reduction in stage gain, which is often not serious, the negative feedback lowers the input resistance and raises the output resistance by the factor K. The last two effects are often disadvantageous. All three effects can, however, be eliminated for a.c. signals, while still retaining feedback for d.c. stabilization, by filtering the a.c. component from the feedback current. A capacitor connected as in Fig. 9.4 may be used for this purpose. It should not, strictly speaking, be connected to the exact centre of R_b but this arrangement is usually satisfactory.

In spite of the above disadvantages the feedback stabilization circuit is often used when the amplified signal is small and considerable shift of the operating point can be tolerated without introducing distortion. Its main advantage is that it requires few components. It is especially useful at very low frequencies where the better methods discussed below require very large emitter by-pass capacitors.

The CC version of Fig. 9.3 is shown in Fig. 9.5. The formulae for this case are obtained from equations (9.12) to (9.15) by replacing R_c by R_e.

9.3.3. *Emitter resistor stabilization*

A second method of reducing temperature-dependent variations in I_c uses negative current-feedback introduced by a resistor in series with the emitter. The most generally useful bias stabilization circuit is of this type. It is shown, for a resistance-capacitance coupled amplifier, in Fig. 9.6. Here the

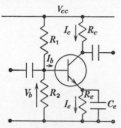

FIG. 9.6. Emitter resistor stabilization of a resistance-capacitance coupled amplifier.

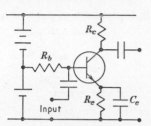

FIG. 9.7. Emitter resistor stabilization when a tapped supply is available.

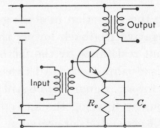

FIG. 9.8. Emitter resistor stabilization of a transformer-coupled amplifier.

resistors R_1 and R_2 form a potentiometer which adjusts the potential of the base to take account of the voltage drop across R_e. These resistors also make it possible to control the external base resistance and have a pronounced effect on the degree of stabilization. If two power supplies (or a single tapped supply) are available, the base level may be established by the method of Fig. 9.7. In this case R_b is required to prevent short-circuiting of the a.c. input by the battery.

For transformer-coupled amplifiers the arrangement of Fig. 9.8 may be used. We note, incidentally, that this method of stabilization is the only suitable linear feedback method for low-level transformer-coupled amplifiers. The collector feedback method of the preceding sections is ineffective because of the small resistance of the output transformer winding.

With a reasonable amount of stabilization an intolerable amount of a.c. negative feedback (degeneration) is introduced by R_e and this component is usually by-passed by a capacitor C_e as shown in Figs. 9.6 to 9.8.

For d.c. stabilization purposes the circuits of Figs. 9.6 to 9.8 may be analysed by the same method provided we put

$$R_b = R_1 R_2 / (R_1 + R_2),$$

since the effective external base resistance in Fig. 9.6 is that of R_1 and R_2 in parallel. For the directions of the variables indicated in Fig. 9.6 we have the following equations:

$$V_b = I_b(R_b + r_{bb'}) + V_{be} + I_e R_e, \qquad (9.16)$$

$$I_c = h_{FE} I_b + I_0, \qquad (9.17)$$

$$I_b + I_c - I_e = 0. \qquad (9.18)$$

In writing these equations we have assumed that R_c is small and, in view of the results of the preceding section, we have neglected the slopes of the V_c–I_c characteristics. We have also ignored the small internal emitter resistance r_e. The analysis, which applies in almost all practical cases, then leads to the following results:

$$K = \frac{1}{1 + h_{FE} R_e / (R_b + r_{bb'} + R_e)}, \qquad (9.19)$$

$$\Delta I_c(I_{co}) = K \Delta I_0 = K(h_{FE} + 1)\Delta I_{co}, \qquad (9.20)$$

$$\Delta I_c(V_{be}) = -\frac{(1 - K)}{R_e} \Delta V_{be}, \qquad (9.21)$$

$$\frac{\Delta I_c(h_{FE})}{I_c - I_{co}} = K \frac{\Delta h_{FE}}{h_{FE}}. \qquad (9.22)$$

Equations (9.19) to (9.22) may be used in the design of bias circuits. However, different procedures are required for high- and low-power outputs—the design method for small-signal (low-power) applications being generally much simpler. A useful criterion for deciding in which group a given transistor design belongs may be obtained from the following analysis given by L. B. Johnsonh [2]:

Neglecting the effect of I_{co}, the collector dissipation is

$$P_c = I_c V_{ce} = I_c[V_{cc} - I_c(R_e + R_c)], \qquad (9.23)$$

where V_{cc} is the collector power-supply voltage. The effect of I_{co} is to change I_c by an amount ΔI_c and P_c by

$$\Delta P_c = \Delta I_c[V_{cc} - 2I_c(R_c + R_e)],$$

or $$\Delta P_c = \Delta I_c(2V_{ce} - V_{cc}). \qquad (9.24)$$

This equation shows that the effect of ΔI_c will be to increase the collector dissipation if $V_{ce} > V_{cc}/2$ and to decrease it if $V_{ce} < V_{cc}/2$. In the first case the increase in dissipation produces an increase in temperature which further increases I_{co}, etc. There is thus a positive feedback effect which may produce a large shift of the operating point if $(R_c + R_e)$ is small and the circuit is not well stabilized. In extreme cases this positive feedback may lead to a catastrophic increase in temperature—a phenomenon commonly called 'thermal runaway'. In the second case ($V_{ce} < V_{cc}/2$) the feedback is negative and the operating point moves a relatively small amount. This is the low-power case which we shall consider in the remainder of this section. The high-power case will be discussed in the final section of this chapter.

For the low-power case ($V_{ce} < V_{cc}/2$) the writers have found the following rules to be useful in the design of bias circuits:

1. Choose a d.c. load line and an operating point on it so that the operating point remains well within the linear part of the transistor characteristic for the required output current swing ($\pm i_c \sqrt{2}$, where i_c is the r.m.s. output signal current). The point at which the d.c. load line intersects the V_c axis is the power-supply voltage V_{cc}, and the slope of the line is the resistance $(R_c + R_e)$.

In many cases V_{cc} may be decided by other considerations. The position of one end of the load line is then fixed and its slope should be chosen to give a suitable operating point.

The following factors have an important bearing on the choice of operating point:

(a) Increase of temperature will tend to move the operating point towards the (high-current) saturated condition.

(b) The minimum value of I_c may now drop almost to I_{co}

since the presence of R_e makes it possible to drive the emitter-base junction voltage to a very low value and to remove almost all of the excess charge from the base via the ohmic base connection. This is in contrast to the feedback stabilization case in which I_c cannot be reduced below I_0.

The effect of these two factors is to make it desirable to place the operating point at a lower current than would be decided by room-temperature conditions.

2. Assume that $I_c R_e \simeq V_{cc}/4$, where I_c is the current at the operating point. R_e should range between 500 and 2,000 ohms for low-power transistors. A larger value will give a more stable circuit. The values of R_e and R_c are then known.

3. Choose R_2 (Fig. 9.6) within the limits $5R_e \leqslant R_2 \leqslant 10R_e$. A value in this range will normally provide adequate stabilization and will not load the preceding stage too heavily.

4. Determine R_1 from the relations:

$$R_1 = \frac{V_{cc}-V_b}{(V_b/R_2)+I_b}, \qquad V_b = I_c R_e+0\cdot 2, \qquad (9.25)$$

where V_b and I_b are the d.c. base variables. The number $0\cdot 2$ is the d.c. base-emitter voltage for a germanium transistor as normally operated. For silicon transistors this quantity is about $0\cdot 6$ volt.

5. Calculate K and hence determine the shift of the operating point with the maximum anticipated rise in ambient temperature, taking account of the additional rise produced by the collector dissipation $V_c I_c$. The latter may be determined from the thermal resistance R_t given in the transistor manufacturer's data, e.g. for the 2N369 in free air, R_t is $0\cdot 5°$ C per mW dissipation.

In determining the effect of I_{co} it is probably best to use the maximum value given by the manufacturer for the collector voltage concerned. If a curve of I_{co} vs. temperature is not given equations (9.3) and (9.4) may be used to estimate the value of I_{c0} at the operating temperature. The design centre value of h_{FE} may be used in the calculation of K and in the determination of $\Delta I_c(I_{co})$ and $\Delta I_c(h_{FE})$.

6. Confirm that the operating point has not shifted enough

to cause distortion of the output current. If distortion occurs a new operating point, and possibly a different load line, must be chosen and the process repeated.

7. Determine experimentally if the room-temperature operating point is close to the designed position. A deviation from this position is probably due to deviations of the bias resistances from their nominal values. Minor adjustments may be made by increasing R_e or R_c.

The above procedure gives the maximum output current swing regardless of the impedance of the a.c. load—which may, for example, be the input impedance of a following stage connected to the collector of the present stage through a capacitor. The total a.c. load will then consist of this impedance in parallel with R_c. The circuit design in such cases, including consideration of the size of the by-pass capacitor C_e, is illustrated by an example in Chapter XI.

To conclude this section we summarize the advantages of emitter-resistor stabilization as follows:

1. This bias circuit may be designed, and its performance calculated, in a relatively straightforward manner.

2. Almost any desired degree of stabilization can be obtained.

3. Because the emitter-base bias can be driven almost to zero the collector current swing may be considerably larger than that attainable with the simple feedback connection.

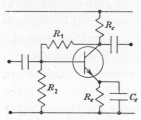

FIG. 9.9. Combination stabilization of a resistance-capacitance coupled amplifier.

9.3.4. *Combination stabilization*

A third biasing method which is a combination of the first two is shown in Fig. 9.9. It has the advantage over the simple feedback stabilization method that the amount of feedback can be made independent of the bias. To obtain this independence resistors R_2 and R_e are added, thus furnishing, in addition, control of the external base resistance and the emitter current.

For the usual transistor application this combination method does not have sufficient advantage over the emitter resistor method to justify the additional design complications that it introduces. It is, however, particularly useful when transistors are used in conjunction with vacuum tubes and thus are fed from a relatively high-voltage supply, or when feedback from collector to base is required to reduce input impedance or to raise output impedance. If a.c. voltage feedback is not required the midpoint of R_1 may be by-passed to earth as outlined earlier.

The following are the design formulae for this combination bias circuit:

$$K = \frac{1}{1 + \dfrac{h_{FE}\left(R_e + \dfrac{R_c R_2}{R_c + R_1 + R_2}\right)}{R_e + R_b + r_{bb'}}}, \qquad (9.26)$$

where $R_b = \dfrac{(R_c + R_1)R_2}{R_c + R_1 + R_2}$ is the resistance of $(R_c + R_1)$ in parallel with R_2. The second factor in the bracket of (9.26) indicates that the feedback voltage from R_c is reduced by the potentiometer ratio $R_2/(R_c + R_1 + R_2)$ before being returned to the transistor input.

$$\Delta I_c(I_{co}) = K(h_{FE} + 1)\Delta I_{co}, \qquad (9.27)$$

$$\Delta I_c(V_{be}) = -\frac{1}{R_e}\left[(1 - K) - \frac{R_c}{R_1}\{(h_{FE} + 1)K - 1\}\right]V_{be}, \qquad (9.28)$$

$$\frac{\Delta I_c(h_{FE})}{I_c - I_{co}} = \frac{\Delta h_{FE}}{h_{FE}}. \qquad (9.29)$$

9.4. Other biasing methods

9.4.1. *Negative d.c. feedback over several stages*

The above-described methods of biasing are really d.c. feedback amplifiers in which variations in collector voltage or emitter current are returned to the input in such a way as to reduce themselves. Such d.c. feedback can also be applied over two or more stages, thus reducing the changes in output variables to a much greater extent than is possible with single-stage feedback. The direct coupling required between stages for this type of circuit can be obtained easily with transistors because of their ability to operate at very low collector voltages. A very attractive arrangement from the point of view of temperature stability, lack of distortion, and economy is thus obtained. One such scheme is shown in Fig. 9.10. The base bias current for $T1$ is taken from the emitter of $T2$, while $T2$ draws base bias through the collector bias resistor of $T1$. This is a negative feedback loop in which the overall gain is approximately that of the CE stage $T1$ multiplied by the gain of $T2$

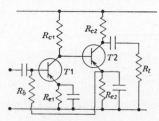

FIG. 9.10. Stabilization of a direct-coupled amplifier by negative feedback over two stages.

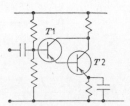

FIG. 9.11. CE form of the Darlington compound connection.

as a CC stage. A small increase in the emitter current of $T2$ tends to raise the base current of $T1$. Corresponding to this there is an increase in the collector current of $T1$ which diverts current from the base of $T2$, thereby resisting the original action. The result is an extremely well-stabilized amplifier [4].

Another very useful direct-coupled amplifier is the Darlington compound connection [5, 6] illustrated in its CE form in Fig. 9.11. The current gain of this circuit is approximately equal to the product of the CE gains of the individual transistors. The arrangement has the high input resistance of $T1$ operated as a CC stage. The transistor $T2$ usually has a higher power rating than $T1$ since its base current is the emitter current of $T1$. The latter will carry an appreciable fraction of the load current only when the current flowing through $T2$ is large enough to reduce the current gain of $T2$ appreciably.

When stabilized by the emitter resistor or combination method this circuit is affected very little by temperature fluctuations. The excellent stability arises chiefly from the following facts:

(a) The emitter resistance external to $T1$ approaches the

input resistance of $T2$ considered as a CC stage and is thus very high.

(b) The external base resistance of $T2$ is equal to the CC output resistance of $T1$ and is therefore very low.

9.4.2. Non-linear stabilization methods

In some cases d.c. stabilization is obtained by the introduction of resistive elements, external to the transistor, whose resistance values are functions of temperature. In one such scheme the resistor R_2 of Fig. 9.6 is replaced by a reverse-biased diode and a battery [6, 7]. A diode whose reverse current is equal to the I_{co} of the transistor, and varies in approximately the same manner with temperature, can compensate for the change in I_{co} over a wide range of temperature. The effect of V_{be} is reduced by R_e as before.

In CE power stages the base is usually fed from a source having a low d.c. resistance (e.g. a trans- former) and the effect of variations in I_{co} is negligible. The most important tempera- ture dependent quantity is then V_{be}. In many such applications the power loss in R_e cannot be tolerated and the circuit of Fig. 9.8 is then replaced by that of Fig. 9.12 [6, 7, 8]. The voltage across the forward-biased diode D compensates for that across the base-emitter junction of the transistor over quite a large temperature

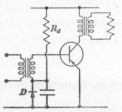

Fig. 9.12. Stabilization of a transformer- coupled power stage by means of a forward- biased diode.

range. The diode D is sometimes replaced by a thermistor (i.e. a circuit element whose resistance decreases with increase of temperature). The characteristic of the thermistor is matched, over a moderate temperature range, to that of the base-emitter junction by the adjustment of R_d and another resistor in parallel with the thermistor. Another method of compensating for the change of V_{be} makes use of a small resistor R_e having a positive temperature coefficient [9].

The above brief descriptions will suffice to indicate the basic methods of compensating for the effects of temperature on transistors by the use of devices whose characteristics vary with temperature in a non-linear manner. Such devices find their chief application in a.c. power stages although they have been used in attempts to build transistor d.c. amplifiers. The drift problem in the d.c. amplifier case is especially severe since it is necessary to ensure not only that the operating point remains on a linear part of the amplifier characteristic, but also that its quiescent (i.e. zero-signal) position, in the output stage at least, remains fixed under all conditions of operation. The use of non-linear devices, with their attendant problems of adjustment for the chosen operating conditions by the addition of series or parallel resistors (padding), then becomes imperative. In general, transistors should not be regarded as candidates for d.c. amplifier applications. If d.c. signals are to be amplified by transistors they should be converted to a.c. signals, amplified in an a.c. amplifier and rectified to give a d.c. output. Because of their excellent switching characteristics, transistors make particularly good 'choppers' for d.c. to a.c. conversion. Examples of this type of circuit will be considered later.

9.5. Operating-point shift and thermal runaway

In many power stages, transistors are driven very hard and external losses are kept as small as possible in order that maximum efficiency may be obtained. The condition $2V_{ce} > V_{cc}$ then applies and it is usually necessary to stabilize the stage exceptionally well to prevent a large shift of the operating point or the thermal runaway condition mentioned in § 9.3.3.

The conditions for avoiding thermal runaway may readily be derived for stages in which R_c and R_e are small, i.e. $V_{ce} \simeq V_{cc}$. Most high-power stages are in this class and in the determination of the condition for thermal runaway we shall assume that $V_{ce} = V_{cc}$. Any error introduced thereby is in the right direction since the predicted shift of the operating point is larger than the true shift.

An increase of temperature ΔT produces a change in collector current ΔI_c. The increased dissipation $\Delta I_c V_{ce}$ arising from the change produces a further rise in temperature,

$$\Delta T_1 = \Delta I_c V_{ce} R_t. \tag{9.30}$$

If ΔT_1 exceeds ΔT the collector current will increase until the transistor either saturates or is destroyed. The condition for avoiding thermal runaway is therefore

$$\frac{\Delta T_1}{\Delta T} = \frac{\Delta I_c V_{ce} R_t}{\Delta T} < 1. \tag{9.31}$$

For germanium transistors at high operating temperatures the predominant component of ΔI_c arises from the change of collector cutoff current. We therefore put

$$\frac{\Delta I_c}{\Delta T} = \frac{\Delta I_c}{\Delta I_{co}} \frac{\Delta I_{co}}{\Delta T}. \tag{9.32}$$

With the help of equations (9.3) or (9.37) below and (9.12) or (9.20) the condition (9.31) then becomes

$$\frac{\Delta T_1}{\Delta T} = \gamma \simeq \frac{K(1+h_{FE})I_{co}V_{ce}R_t}{13} < 1, \tag{9.33}$$

where I_{co} is determined at the maximum temperature that will be reached in practice. This maximum temperature is the sum of the ambient temperature and the rise produced by collector dissipation. The latter may be estimated as follows:

If there were no I_{co} the collector dissipation would produce a temperature rise $\Delta_d T$. The effect of I_{co} is to produce a further rise of temperature which further increases I_{co}, etc. This is the positive feedback mentioned earlier. When the circuit has settled down to a steady temperature rise $\Delta_2 T$ we must have

$$\Delta_d T + \gamma \Delta_2 T = \Delta_2 T. \tag{9.34}$$

The second term on the l.h.s. is the feedback term arising from $\Delta_2 T$. Hence

$$\Delta_2 T = \frac{\Delta_d T}{1-\gamma}. \tag{9.35}$$

Thus if γ is not much smaller than unity the temperature rise is much larger than $\Delta_d T$. γ must then be determined by an iterative process of the type described below. The value of $\Delta_2 T$ must also be taken into account, when the operating point is chosen. The arguments for making $\gamma \ll 1$ are thus quite strong.

In some high-power applications the assumption $V_{ce} = V_{cc}$ is not accurate. If relatively large values of γ cannot be avoided, the procedure for determining the operating point then becomes quite complicated. This complication arises because I_{co}, as a function of temperature, cannot readily be introduced into the mathematics of the process and also because variations of V_{be} and h_{FE} often cannot be ignored. The following iterative procedure is therefore necessary:

1. Determine $\Delta_d T$ from the relation

$$\Delta_d T = R_t V_{ce} I_c, \tag{9.36}$$

where V_{ce} and I_c are the operating-point coordinates determined from the amplifier design without taking account of I_{co}.

2. Add $\Delta_d T$ to the maximum expected ambient temperature and determine the maximum possible I_{co} from a curve such as Fig. A11.11 or from the equation

$$\ln I_{co} = \ln I_{co0} + \frac{T - T_0}{13}, \tag{9.37}$$

where I_{co0} is the value of I_{co} at a standard temperature T_0. In most transistor specifications $T_0 = 25°$ C. Equation (9.37) is obtained by subtracting equations of the form (9.2) corresponding to temperatures T and T_0, assuming that $E_g \simeq 0.55$ eV. (It is also assumed that we may put $T \simeq T_0$ except when the temperature difference is required.) If desired, equation (9.37) can be expressed in exponential form.

3. Choose K so that the value of γ given by equation (9.33) is less than unity and preferably about 0.2.

4. Determine $\Delta I_c(I_{co})$, $\Delta I_c(V_{be})$ and $\Delta I_c(h_{FE})$ from equations (9.20) to (9.22). These are added to give ΔI_c, and V'_{ce} is determined from the relation $V'_{ce} = V_{cc} - (I_c + \Delta I_c)(R_c + R_e)$.

5. Repeat the process using V'_{ce} and $I'_c \; (= I_c + \Delta I_c)$ in equation (9.36) until the difference between successive values of $\Delta_d T$ is less than $2°$ C.

The number of iterations required usually will not exceed one or two unless the transistor is operated at a high-power level and γ is greater than 0.5. In extreme cases, however, $\Delta_2 T$ may be so large that the initially chosen position of the operating point will have to be changed.

As an example of this iterative procedure, consider a 2N369 for which $V_{cc} = 28$ V, $R_c = 2{\cdot}7$ kΩ, $R_e = 470$ ohms, the initially chosen operating-point coordinates are $V_{ce} = 16{\cdot}9$ V, $I_c = 3{\cdot}5$ mA, and the maximum ambient temperature is 35° C. Assuming operation in free air without a heat sink, $R_t = 0{\cdot}5$ °C/mW and $\Delta_d T = 29{\cdot}5°$ C. The maximum junction temperature is therefore 64·5° C and the maximum I_{co}, obtained by extrapolation from Fig. A11.11 is about 150 μA. (This assumes that, at high temperature, the I_{co} values are approximately the same at $V_{ce} = 5$ V and at $V_{ce} = 15$ V. This assumption is probably justified since the component of I_{co} that depends on collector voltage increases slowly with temperature.)

From equation (9.33) we have

$$\gamma = \frac{56 \times 0{\cdot}150 \times 16{\cdot}9 \times 0{\cdot}5}{13} K = 5{\cdot}5\,K.$$

Hence to prevent thermal runaway K must not exceed 0·18. We tentatively put $K = 0{\cdot}07$ in order to allow the use of reasonably large base-potentiometer resistors. Then from equation (9.20) $\Delta I_c(I_{co})$ is $0{\cdot}07 \times 56 \times 150 = 590$ μA and from equation (9.21), $\Delta I_c(V_{be})$, for a temperature rise from 25° C to 65° C, is about $(40 \times 2{\cdot}3)/470 = 196$ μA. From Fig. A11.8 the value of Δh_{FE} (where $h_{FE} \simeq 1/(1+h_{21})$) for the same temperature range is $(56/0{\cdot}72) - 56 \simeq 22$ and from equation (9.22) $\Delta I_c(h_{FE}) \simeq 0{\cdot}07 \times 3{\cdot}5 \times 22/56 \simeq 96$ μA. Hence $\Delta I_c = 0{\cdot}90$ mA. Hence $I'_c = 4{\cdot}4$ mA, $V'_{ce} = 14{\cdot}1$ V, and $\Delta'_d T = 31{\cdot}0°$ C. This differs from $\Delta_d T$ by 1·5° C. The reader may confirm by a repeat of the procedure that $\Delta'_d T$ is an excellent approximation to the true value. At 20° C a similar calculation (omitting $\Delta I_c(V_{be})$ and $\Delta I_c(h_{FE})$ which are negligible) gives $V_{ce} = 16{\cdot}2$ V and $I_c = 3{\cdot}7$ mA. The shift due to the rise in ambient temperature is thus relatively small and can be tolerated for peak-to-peak output-current swings of about 7 mA.

This example shows that even for a relatively heavily loaded resistance-coupled stage operating over a reasonably large range of ambient temperature the iterative process usually need not be carried beyond the first stage. For a transformer-coupled stage in which non-linear compensation for V_{be} is carried out by means of one of the non-linear methods of § 9.4.2, several iterations may be necessary but the procedure is identical to that just outlined.

This completes our outline of biasing methods for low-level stages and for single-transistor high-level amplifiers. Many high-level stages consist of two transistors whose input signals are in phase opposition. The special biasing problems associated with these 'push-pull' circuits will be considered, with the design of such stages, in a later chapter.

NOISE IN TRANSISTORS

10.1. Introduction

AN important factor in applications of transistors, as in many vacuum-tube applications, is the presence of unwanted signals due to spontaneous fluctuations of current and voltage. These fluctuations may occur in passive circuit components (e.g. resistors and diodes) as well as in the transistors themselves. When amplified and applied to a loudspeaker such fluctuations produce objectionable hissing or 'frying' noise. For this reason the electrical signals themselves are usually referred to as noise.

In this chapter we shall discuss briefly the sources of noise in passive circuit components and in transistors, and describe the methods by which the noise characteristics of amplifying stages are specified. We shall also indicate how manufacturers' specified noise figures may be applied in practical amplifiers.

10.2. Types of noise

Several types of noise, which are quite different functions of circuit conditions, occur in both passive and active circuit elements. In this section we consider these briefly, presenting analytical expressions for them where possible. However, before proceeding, a remark concerning the electrical representation of noise is necessary. Noise is a random phenomenon which may be represented as a superposition of alternating currents or voltages of different frequencies. Its average value, taken over a long period of time, is therefore zero. As in the case of all alternating variables, we must represent its magnitude by its root mean square (r.m.s.) value. Thus the noise produced in a circuit element may be represented by a voltage generator in series with it whose output is $\sqrt{(\overline{v^2})}$ where v is the instantaneous voltage and $\overline{v^2}$ is the average of v^2. Similarly the noise may be represented by a current generator $\sqrt{(\overline{i^2})}$ in parallel with the circuit element.

The following types of noise are important in junction diode and transistor circuits:

  1. Thermal or Johnson noise.
  2. Shot noise.
  3. Flicker or modulation noise.

We now consider these in turn.

10.2.1. *Thermal noise*

This noise, which was first considered in detail by Johnson [1], occurs in any component having electrical resistance. It is due to the fact that electricity is carried by discrete particles (electrons or positive holes) which move about in a random manner because of thermal excitation. Any motion of a charged particle produces an electric current and the sum of the r.m.s. values of these currents produces the thermal noise. This noise thus occurs whether external electrical excitation is present or not and, as would be expected from the manner of its production, increases with temperature. It cannot be eliminated but can be reduced by operation at very low temperatures.

The theoretical expression for thermal noise, first derived by Nyquist [2], is

$$P = \frac{1}{4}\frac{\overline{v^2}}{R} = \frac{1}{4}\overline{i^2}R = kTp(f)\Delta f, \qquad (10.1)$$

where P is the available noise power, in a frequency interval Δf, obtainable from a resistor of R ohms (i.e. the noise power entering a circuit matched to the resistor), k is Boltzmann's constant ($= 1{\cdot}38 \times 10^{-23}$ watt sec/°K), T is the absolute temperature and

$$p(f) = \frac{hf}{kT}\frac{1}{e^{hf/kT}-1}, \qquad (10.2)$$

where h is Planck's constant $= 6{\cdot}62 \times 10^{-27}$ erg sec. For ordinary temperatures, and frequencies up to 3×10^{10} c/sec (wavelength $= 1$ cm), $p(f) \simeq 1$ and we may put

$$P = \frac{1}{4}\frac{\overline{v^2}}{R} = \frac{1}{4}\overline{i^2}R = kT\Delta f. \qquad (10.3)$$

From this we see that the noise per cycle is independent of the frequency, i.e. the spectrum of the noise is flat. Such noise is often said to be 'white', thus implying that all frequencies are equally represented in it. An equivalent statement is that the noise is proportional to the frequency band under consideration. The amount of noise in a narrow-band amplifier will thus be much smaller than in a broad-band amplifier operating under the same conditions.

It is interesting to consider the magnitude of the output of one of the noise generators represented by equation (10.3). For example, if the resistor were matched to a gramophone amplifier capable of passing a frequency band of 30 to 12,000 c/sec the noise power entering the amplifier at room temperature ($T = 300°$ K) would be

$$P \simeq 1 \cdot 38 \times 10^{-23} \times 300 \times 12000 \simeq 5 \cdot 0 \times 10^{-17} \text{ watts.}$$

Thus if $R = 10$ ohms, $\overline{v^2} = 4RP = 20 \times 10^{-16}$ or $\sqrt{(\overline{v^2})} = 4 \cdot 4 \times 10^{-8}$ volts, and if $R = 1$ megohm, $\sqrt{(\overline{v^2})} = 14 \ \mu\text{V}$.

When the resistance R is the series resistance of an impedance element, the expression for available noise becomes

$$P_n = \frac{\overline{i^2}}{4g}, \tag{10.4}$$

where $g = R/(R^2 + X^2)$ is the conductance of the element.

10.2.2. Shot noise

In addition to thermal noise, which arises from fluctuations in *motion* of the current carriers, many circuit elements exhibit noise due to random fluctuations in the *number* of current carriers in some part of the element. When the carriers are in an electric field these fluctuations in numbers produce fluctuations in current which are called 'shot noise'. Since it depends on a fundamental effect, the fluctuation in the density of carriers, shot noise, like thermal noise, is inevitable.

In metals and in semiconductors of the resistivity used in transistors, the density of carriers is relatively large and the shot noise in the body of the material is negligible [3, 4]. However in junction diodes and transistors, shot noise is generated whenever a carrier crosses the space-charge region between p-type and n-type material [5]. Some of these crossings arise from the externally impressed current but others occur whether there is current flow through the device or not. For junction diodes the shot noise may be represented by a current generator, in parallel with the junction, whose output is $\sqrt{(\overline{i^2})}$ where

$$\overline{i^2} = (4kTG-2qI)\Delta f, \tag{10.5}$$

and the current I flowing through the diode is positive for forward bias and negative for reverse bias. G is the conductance of the diode; its low-frequency value is

$$G_0 = \frac{q(I+I_s)}{kT}, \tag{10.6}$$

where I_s is the magnitude of the reverse saturation current. Thus, for low frequencies,

$$\overline{i^2} = [2q(I+I_s)+2qI_s]\Delta f. \tag{10.7}$$

For large reverse voltages $I = -I_s$ and $\overline{i^2} = 2qI_s\Delta f$. For zero applied voltage $I = 0$ and $i^2 = 4qI_s\Delta f$. This corresponds to the picture presented in Chapter IV where it is assumed that, in the unbiased condition, currents of magnitude I_s flow in opposite directions across the junction so that the net current is zero. However, both components contribute to the shot noise, which is therefore twice as large as for large reverse voltages.

When the frequency dependence of G is taken into account equation (10.5) apparently gives reasonably good agreement with experiment [5]. Equations of the form (10.5) also hold for the emitter and collector junctions of transistors with the proviso that $G = 0$ for the collector junctions. Shot effects in transistors can therefore be represented by two current generators in parallel with the emitter and collector internal impedances respectively. However, these generators are not independent of each other since most of the current crossing the emitter junction also crosses the collector junction.

Shot noise is the most important noise component in modern transistors in the frequency region above a few kilocycles per second. The method of estimating it will be discussed below.

The noise arising from fluctuations in the components of the emitter current flowing into the collector and into the base is sometimes called 'partition' noise. However, this is really contained in the expression for general shot noise [5] and in present practice it is not referred to separately.

10.2.3. *Flicker or modulation noise*

A third type of noise which occurs in semiconductors, junction diodes, and transistors, is flicker or modulation noise. It also occurs in carbon resistors, in some thin metal layers, and in vacuum tubes. In early transistor work it was usually called excess noise but we shall follow the more usual present day practice and call it flicker noise.

The fluctuations occurring in this type of noise are larger than those occurring in thermal and shot noise. Flicker noise may be represented by a current [3]

$$\overline{i^2} = \frac{KI^a}{f^b}\Delta f, \tag{10.8}$$

where I is the d.c. current flowing through the material and K is a constant. The indices a and b are usually assumed equal to unity for transistors—the value of b being responsible for the term '$1/f$ noise' that is often applied to this component. However, as will be seen later, experimental values of b obtained on commercial transistors range from 1 to 1·6.

This type of noise is apparently due to the following surface effects [4, 5]:

1. A fluctuation in the number of majority carriers trapped at certain states, called 'slow states', on the surface of the material. The number of such trapped carriers varies with the electrical or thermal gradients in the surface layer and the times involved in the capture and release of carriers are quite long. Fluctuations in surface charge, thus produced, influence the generation and recombination of electrons and holes at other states (called 'fast states') at the surface. The fluctuations connected with both types of state modulate the conductivity of the bulk material thus producing a noise component, commonly called 'surface noise'. The variation of this component

with frequency is decided by the slow states and follows an approximate $1/f$ law. This type of noise occurs in many resistors, as well as in junction devices. It increases rapidly with current and is most important in forward-biased junctions.

2. Leakage due to the presence of a thin conducting film in parallel with a p-n junction. This is negligible under forward bias or reverse bias of a few volts but it increases with reverse voltage and can be quite large when the reverse voltage is large. A low-frequency noise component which follows the $1/f$ law arises from spontaneous fluctuations in the leakage current.

3. Channel effect due to the presence of a surface layer of conductivity opposite to that of the bulk material. Fluctuations in the channel currents could produce noise in p-n junctions and transistors.

The flicker noise in a reverse-biased p-n junction could thus arise from items 2 or 3 or a combination of both. Fonger [6] who has done much of the pioneer work on flicker noise favours 1 and 2 as the chief causes of this type of noise in junction diodes and transistors.

From the above description we see that flicker noise has not the 'fundamental' quality of thermal and shot noise and reductions in it may be expected as manufacturing techniques improve. Considerable progress in this direction has already been made.

10.3. Equivalent circuits for noise

The thermal, shot, and flicker noise of junction diodes and transistors can be represented by equivalent circuits which make possible reasonably accurate calculations of noise characteristics from the lowest frequencies normally used (a few cycles per second) to the frequencies at which transit-time and storage effects become important. This covers the useful range of junction diode operation and the operation of transistors to f_α, the CB cutoff frequency. For flicker noise such equivalent circuits have been given by Fonger [6]. Equivalent circuits for thermal and shot noise combined have been given by many workers. The most complete are those of Guggenbuehl and Strutt [7] and van der Ziel. Their results and those of most other investigators in this field have been summarized in the review article [5] mentioned above. Nielsen [8] used a simplified version of van der Ziel's equivalent circuit to derive equations from which the values of circuit parameters for low-noise operation of transistors may be determined. We shall summarize the results of these investigators which are most useful in the design of low-noise circuits. We shall not present equivalent circuits for noise since the noise parameters required in them are rarely given by transistor manufacturers. Readers who are interested in determining noise generators experimentally may consult the relevant references in van der Ziel's article [5].

10.4. The practical definition of noise—noise figure

In most applications of amplifying devices we are interested in the ratio of signal power to noise power (the signal-to-noise ratio which we identify by the symbol S) obtainable from the device. Thus if S_i and S_o are the input and output values of S, the effect of the noise produced in the amplifier will be to make S_o smaller than S_i. The extent of this reduction at a frequency f_s is given by the 'spot noise figure' or 'spot noise factor' F which is defined by

$$F = \frac{P_{on}}{P_{or}}, \tag{10.9}$$

where P_{on} is the total output noise power in the frequency interval Δf at frequency f_s and P_{or} is the output power in the same frequency interval resulting from the thermal noise in R_g, the resistance of the source or generator. If G is the operating power gain of the amplifier $P_{or} = GP_{in}$, where P_{in} is the thermal noise power entering the amplifier from R_g. Since, by definition, $G = P_o/P_i$, where P_o and P_i are the signal powers at output and input respectively, we obtain

$$F = \frac{P_{on}}{GP_{in}} = \frac{P_i/P_{in}}{P_o/P_{on}} = \frac{S_i(\Delta f)}{S_o(\Delta f)}, \tag{10.10}$$

i.e. F is equal to the signal-to-noise ratio at the input divided by that at the output where both are defined for a frequency interval Δf at frequency f_s.

In most transistor manufacturers' data, F is given for a bandwidth Δf of one cycle/sec at a frequency f_s of 1,000 cycles/sec.

In many applications the bandwidth cannot be expressed as a small interval Δf and the average noise figure F' over a larger bandwidth is required. This is defined as

$$F' = \frac{\int\limits_{f_1}^{f_2} F(f)\,G(f)\,df}{\int\limits_{f_1}^{f_2} G(f)\,df}, \qquad (10.11)$$

where f_1 and f_2 are the lower and upper frequencies of the band under consideration. In the general case F and G are both functions of frequency. If the gain is constant over the bandwidth (f_2-f_1) and drops sharply outside it we may use the equation

$$F' = \frac{1}{(f_2-f_1)} \int\limits_{f_1}^{f_2} F(f)\,df. \qquad (10.12)$$

Equations (10.11) and (10.12) indicate that the variation of F with frequency is required for a calculation of the total or average noise introduced by a transistor operating over a given bandwidth. For flicker noise, equation (10.8) with $a = b = 1$ is accurate enough for all practical purposes. For shot noise a more complicated expression, discussed below, is used.

When an amplifier contains several stages whose individual noise figures are F_a, F_b, F_c, etc., the overall noise figure is given by

$$F = F_a + \frac{F_b-1}{G_a} + \frac{F_c-1}{G_a\,G_b}, \quad \text{etc.,} \qquad (10.13)$$

where the first stage has gain G_a, the second G_b, etc. [9]. The importance of the stage noise figure thus diminishes rapidly for the second and subsequent stages. In most applications the gain of the first stage is sufficiently large that the noise figures of the remaining stages can be ignored.

10.5. Noise characteristics of transistors

In this section we outline briefly the noise characteristics of modern general-purpose junction transistors and consider the extent to which manufacturers' data may be used in determining the suitability of a certain transistor for a given application. We shall not discuss further the noise of junction diodes since these devices are not normally used in the earlier stages of transistor amplifiers except in rather special cases. Consequently transistor noise is much more important in most applications. Readers requiring data on diode noise will find equivalent circuits and many references in van der Ziel's review article [5].

The noise characteristic of a junction transistor, which applies to all three connections for frequencies up to f_α, has the general form shown in Fig. 10.1. It is divided into three sections which may be described as follows:

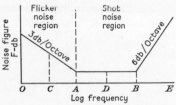

FIG. 10.1. Schematic diagram of the noise characteristic of a transistor.

1. The flicker-noise section OA in which the noise varies approximately as $1/f$. The noise figure expressed in decibels therefore drops linearly with the logarithm of the frequency at a rate of about 3 db per octave (i.e. for each increase of frequency by a factor 2). Fig. 10.2, which shows the flicker-noise characteristics of some commercial transistors under normal operating conditions, indicates that this rate varies between 3 and 5 db so that the power of f varies between -1 and -1.6. The $1/f$ law is thus only a fair approximation but is satisfactory for estimates of noise for circuit design.

The point A, at which the flicker noise is negligible relative to shot and thermal noise is usually stated to be below 1 kc/sec for modern transistors. However, under the usual conditions of operation, the deviations from this frequency may be quite large, as Fig. 10.2 shows. Here the break corresponding to point A in Fig. 10.1 occurs at a frequency above 1 kc/sec in all cases. Under different conditions—especially for smaller values of I_e— this break shifts to the left. The work of Montgomery and Clark [10] suggests that in many cases it will occur below 1 kc/sec when the optimum value of I_e (considered below) is chosen, but it will usually occur at larger frequencies for the currents

commonly mentioned in transistor specifications, viz. 0·5 mA
and 1·0 mA.

When considering the curves of Fig. 10.2, the following
factors should also be taken into account:

(*a*) None of the transistors mentioned is claimed to have

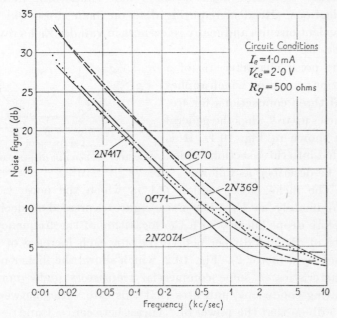

FIG. 10.2. Noise characteristics of some commercial transistors.

exceptionally low noise characteristics although several of them
are recommended for small-signal audio operation. The group
of European transistors, whose characteristics were measured
by Guggenbuehl and Strutt [7] apparently contains two low-
noise transistors (the TF65 and OC604). The relatively low
noise characteristic of the OC71 obtained by them is confirmed
by Fig. 10.2.

(*b*) The position of the point *A* (Fig. 10.1) depends on the
relative magnitudes of flicker and shot noise. Thus, an improvement in the shot-noise characteristic shifts *A* to the right. Such
an improvement in recent years might account for the fact that

A is still, on the average, above 1 kc/sec although the spot-noise figure at that frequency has been reduced.

2. In the second section of Fig. 10.1, shot and thermal noise (the latter chiefly in $r_{bb'}$, the base-spreading resistance) are dominant. The noise figure remains approximately constant from the point A to the point B at which

$$f \simeq f_\alpha \sqrt{(1-\alpha_0)} = \sqrt{(f_\alpha f_\beta)}.$$

3. In the region beyond B the noise is still due to shot and thermal effects and is thus constant with frequency but the noise figure rises because of the decrease in the gain of the amplifier, i.e. reduction in signal-to-noise ratio at the output. This is a consequence of the fact that most of the noise is produced in the collector circuit and hence is unaffected by the gain of the amplifier, while the signal is reduced because of transit-time effects. In this region beyond B the noise figure increases as $(f/f_\alpha)^2$ or at a rate of 6 db per octave as shown below.

10.6. The specification of noise in manufacturers' data

In order to estimate the importance of noise in a given transistor circuit an approximation to the curve of Fig. 10.1 is required for the transistor used in the first stage at least. An accurate enough approximation to this curve for most design purposes could probably be obtained if the maximum and minimum spot-noise figures were given, for the same bias conditions, at two points such as C and D in Fig. 10.1. The frequency f_C of the point C should be well within the flicker-noise region so that the contribution of shot noise there can be ignored. Similarly the frequency f_D should be in the shot-noise 'plateau'. On making the assumptions that the slope in the region OA is 3 db per octave and in region BE is 6 db per octave and using the relation $f_B = \sqrt{(f_\alpha f_\beta)}$ it would then be possible to draw curves of the form shown in Fig. 10.1 that would be accurate enough for design purposes. Then, using equation (10.11) or (10.12) it would be easy to calculate the average noise figure for an amplifier of any chosen bandwidth. With the help of the gain of the amplifier and equation (10.3) the equivalent noise power, voltage, or current, at input or output could also be determined.

Unfortunately data of the type just described have not yet been given for any commercial transistor. Usually one of the following procedures is followed:

(*a*) A spot-noise figure at 1,000 c/sec for a bandwidth of 1 c/sec may be given. If this is large by modern standards (> 10 db) it can be assumed that it is due chiefly to flicker noise and (provided the bias conditions are specified) thus fulfils the requirements for point *C* in Fig. 10.1. If it is small (≃ 7 db or less) about all we know is that it represents some combination of flicker noise and shot noise. In neither case is an accurate shot-noise figure obtainable. However, one can obtain a rough estimate of the shot-noise figure from Nielsen's formula which is given below. Thus for a transistor having a relatively high $1/f$ component an approximation to Fig. 10.1 can be obtained. The information obtainable from the spot-noise figure for a low-noise transistor is less useful.

(*b*) An average noise figure for a specified bandwidth is sometimes given by a manufacturer. Examples of this are the 'noise figures' given by Philco Corp. for their low-noise audio transistors. These compare the transistor output noise voltage with an equivalent input noise of 1 μV over a band extending from 0·3 to 3 kc/sec. On the other hand R.C.A. noise figures are given for a bandwidth extending from 7 c/sec to 12·3 kc/sec. From this information it is difficult to obtain a curve of the form of Fig. 10.1 except by a rather exhaustive trial-and-error process. However, the R.C.A. noise figure may be used directly in some audio amplifier applications.

10.7. Circuit conditions for minimum-noise operation

If it were possible to calculate noise figures from theoretical expressions involving other transistor parameters, information of the type described in the preceding paragraph would not be required. For shot noise this condition may not be too far away since, as shown below, fairly manageable expressions for shot-noise figures that are correct to within about 2 db may be obtained already. With the help of such expressions optimum values of R_g and I_e, which are sufficiently accurate for practical purposes, may be obtained. Flicker noise, which depends on surface conditions, is much less amenable to calculation. However, even in this case, the *form* of the expression for the noise is known and it may be used to estimate the optimum operating conditions. In this section we will give approximate expressions for both types of noise, from which the optimum operating conditions may be determined. The error in these expressions may in some cases amount to about 30 per cent but, in view of the noise variations between transistors, this is accurate enough for practical purposes.

10.7.1. *Effect of source impedance on the criterion for minimum noise*

Before presenting the equations which enable us to determine the best operating point we note that the criterion for minimum noise depends on the source impedance. We consider three cases in which:

1. The source impedance can be controlled, e.g. by the use of a matching transformer. The best value of R_g can then be chosen and the best criterion for low-noise operation is the noise figure of the transistor.

2. The source impedance is very low. The best transistor is then that having the lowest equivalent noise resistance R_n where R_n is defined, with the help of equation (10.3), by the expression

$$\overline{v_t^2} = 4kT\,R_n\,\Delta f, \tag{10.14}$$

where v_t is an e.m.f., in series with the source resistance R_g, which represents the noise produced by the transistor. The input noise power due to the transistor is therefore

$$\overline{v_t^2}\,R_i/(R_g+R_i)^2,$$

where R_i is the input resistance of the stage. The input noise power due to the source, is similarly, $\overline{v_g^2}\,R_i/(R_g+R_i)^2$, where v_g is the thermal-noise voltage of R_g. The noise figure may now be determined by an equation of the form (10.9) in which the noise powers are referred to the input rather than the output, i.e.

$$F = \frac{\overline{v_t^2}}{\overline{v_g^2}} = \frac{R_n}{R_g}. \tag{10.15}$$

The noise introduced by the transistor is therefore a minimum when FR_g is a minimum.

3. The source impedance is very high. The best transistor is then that having the highest equivalent input noise resistance, or, as it is usually expressed, the lowest input equivalent saturated diode current I_n. I_n is defined by the expression

$$\overline{i_t^2} = 2q\,I_n\,\Delta f, \tag{10.16}$$

where i_t is an equivalent noise current generator in parallel with the source resistance R_g. As in the above case it is readily seen that

$$F = \frac{\overline{i_t^2}}{\overline{i_g^2}} = \frac{2q\,I_n\,\Delta f}{4kT\,\Delta f/R_g} = \frac{q}{2kT}I_n\,R_g, \tag{10.17}$$

where equation (10.3) has been used for $\overline{i_g^2}$. The noise introduced by the transistor is therefore a minimum when F/R_g is a minimum.

10.7.2. *Optimum operating conditions for flicker noise*

In order to estimate the optimum operating conditions for flicker noise we make use of the following expression [5]

$$\overline{i_n^2} = \frac{\text{const}}{f}I_e\alpha_0(1-\alpha_0)\,\Delta f. \tag{10.18}$$

Here $\sqrt{(\overline{i_n^2})}$ is a current generator in parallel with the internal collector resistance. The output flicker-noise power is proportional to $\overline{i_n^2}$ when the transistor input is open ($R_g = \infty$).

The presence of the factor $(1-\alpha_0)$ in equation (10.18) implies that flicker noise is related to the rate of recombination in the base and supports the contention that this type of noise arises from the modulation of processes in the body of the base by those taking place at its surface.

The generator $\sqrt{(\overline{i_n^2})}$ may be used in the low-frequency T equivalent circuit for the calculation of output noise for other values of R_g. Thus, for the CE connection (Fig. 10.3) assuming $r_c(1-\alpha) \gg R_l$, we have

$$i_n + \beta i_b = i_c, \tag{10.19}$$

$$i_b(r_b + R_g) = -i_e r_e = -(i_c + i_b)r_e, \tag{10.20}$$

whence

$$i_b = \frac{-i_c r_e}{r_b + R_g + r_e} \quad \text{and} \quad i_c = \frac{i_n(r_b + R_g + r_e)}{r_b + R_g + (1+\beta)r_e}. \tag{10.21}$$

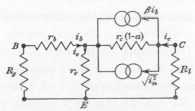

FIG. 10.3. CE low-frequency T-circuit containing a flicker-noise generator in the collector arm.

The output noise power is therefore

$$P_o = \overline{i_c^2} R_l = \frac{\overline{i_n^2}(r_b + R_g + r_e)^2 R_l}{[r_b + R_g + (1+\beta)r_e]^2}. \tag{10.22}$$

The noise figure is

$$F = \frac{P_g G + P_o}{P_g G} = 1 + \frac{P_o}{P_g G}, \tag{10.23}$$

where P_g is the noise power entering the transistor from R_g and G is the operating power gain. Thus

$$P_g = \frac{\overline{v_g^2} R_i}{(R_g + R_i)^2} = 4kT \, \Delta f \frac{R_g R_i}{(R_g + R_i)^2}. \tag{10.24}$$

The right-hand expression is obtained by applying equation (10.3). Also

$$G \simeq \left(\frac{\alpha_0}{1 - \alpha_0}\right)^2 \frac{R_l}{R_i}. \tag{10.25}$$

Substitution of equations (10.18), (10.22), (10.24), and (10.25) in (10.23) leads to the following expression for flicker-noise figure

$$F_f = 1 + \frac{KI_e}{kTf} \frac{(1-\alpha_0)^3}{\alpha_0} \frac{(r_b + R_g + r_e)^2(R_g + R_i)^2}{R_g[r_b + R_g + (1+\beta)r_e]^2}, \tag{10.26}$$

where K is a constant which must be determined experimentally. The input resistance R_i may of course be expressed in terms of r_b, r_e, and R_l but for the present purpose it is best to treat it as an independent variable and to determine the optimum value of R_g in terms of it:

From equation (10.26) we obtain the following requirements for minimum flicker-noise figure:

1. α_0 should be as large as possible.

2. I_e should be decreased until the influence of I_e on α_0 becomes important. This requirement is decided mainly by the presence of I_e in equation (10.26) but the increase of r_e as I_e is decreased also contributes to a lowering of the noise figure. For general-purpose transistors the decrease of α_0 with I_e becomes important at $I_e \simeq 0.2$ mA. For the 2N369, for example, $(1-\alpha_0)$ is 30 per cent larger at $I_e = 0.2$ mA than at $I_e = 1.0$ mA, and $I_e \simeq 0.2$ mA seems to be the best operating point. For transistors having a smaller α_0 the best operating point would occur at a lower value of I_e.

3. The value of R_g should be chosen to make F_f a minimum. The relation between R_g and R_i to satisfy this requirement is

$$\frac{R_g\{(r_b+R_g+r_e)[r_b+R_g+(1+\beta)r_e]+2\beta r_e R_g\}}{\{(r_b+R_g+r_e)[r_b+R_g+(1+\beta)r_e]-2\beta r_e R_g\}} = R_i \simeq h_{ie}.$$

(10.27)

Using this expression it is quite easy to find the optimum value of R_g by trial and error. A numerical example will be considered below.

The importance of the above-mentioned criteria for minimum noise when R_g is very small or very large can be seen from equation (10.26). If R_g is very small the last factor in (10.26) causes F_f to be very large but the quantity $F R_g$ which represents the true effect of transistor noise in this case still has a quite reasonable value. Similarly, if R_g is very large, F/R_g has a reasonable magnitude.

4. The effect of collector voltage V_{ce} enters (10.26) through $(1-\alpha_0)$ which decreases slightly with collector voltage and through collector-junction leakage which increases with V_{ce}. Both effects are apparently related to surface conditions and

cannot be expressed numerically with any accuracy. However, the general trend should be for the flicker noise to decrease and then increase as V_{ce} is increased. The effect should be more important for high α than for low α transistors. The decrease of F_f at small collector voltages has been treated in greater detail by Fonger [6].

10.7.3. *Optimum operating conditions for shot noise*

In order to determine the optimum operating conditions from the point of view of shot noise we use Nielsen's formula [8]

$$F_s = 1 + \frac{r_{bb'}}{R_g} + \frac{r_\epsilon}{2R_g} + \frac{(1-\alpha_0)[1+f^2/\{(1-\alpha_0)f_\alpha^2\}](R_g+r_{bb'}+r_\epsilon)^2}{2\alpha_0 r_\epsilon R_g}.$$

(10.28)

In this equation the ohmic base-spreading resistance $r_{bb'}$ and the true emitter resistance r_ϵ are used rather than the low-frequency T-circuit components r_b and r_e. The latter occur in the flicker-noise formula because of our use of the T-circuit to calculate the effect of feedback from the flicker-noise current generator in the collector arm.

Equation (10.28) applies to the CE and CB connections. It is also approximately correct for the CC connection at frequencies below $f_\alpha/2$. For frequencies above f_α an additional factor $[1+(f/f_\alpha)^2]$ in the denominator of the last term of (10.28) causes the CC noise to become constant.

The effect of shot noise on the noise figure of the transistor stage is decided by the following:

1. The magnitude of α_0, which should be as large as possible.
2. The CB cutoff frequency f_α, which should also be as large as possible.
3. The magnitude of I_e, which enters through r_ϵ. If we put

$$A = \frac{1-\alpha_0}{\alpha_0}\left[1+\frac{f^2}{(1-\alpha_0)f_\alpha^2}\right] = \frac{1-\alpha_0}{\alpha_0}+\frac{f^2}{\alpha_0 f_\alpha^2} \quad (10.29)$$

and

$$r_\epsilon = \frac{kT}{qI_e} \simeq \frac{25}{I_e} \text{ at room temperature when } I_e \text{ is in mA}$$

(10.30)

and minimize F_s, $F_s R_g$, or F_s/R_g with respect to I_e, we obtain

$$I_e^2 = \frac{625}{(R_g + r_{bb'})^2} \cdot \frac{1+A}{A}. \tag{10.31}$$

For low frequencies $[f \ll f_\alpha\sqrt{(1-\alpha_0)}]$, $(1+A)/A = 1/(1-\alpha_0)$, and

$$I_e^2 = \frac{625}{(1-\alpha_0)(R_g + r_{bb'})^2}. \tag{10.32}$$

Thus for R_g large, I_e should be small for minimum noise while for small values of R_g, I_e should be larger. For $R_g \ll r_{bb'}$, I_e will be in the range from 0·5 to 2·5 mA. A more accurate analysis by van der Ziel [5] gives the same result except that the optimum value of I_e is probably somewhat larger. For small R_g the condition for minimum shot noise thus differs from that for minimum flicker noise. The effect of the change of α_0 with I_e is also opposite to that occurring for flicker noise.

At high frequencies A is larger than at low frequencies and the optimum value of I_e is somewhat smaller.

4. The value of R_g. For minimum noise this may be determined by differentiation of (10.28) with respect to R_g, which leads to the expression [8]

$$R_g = \sqrt{\left[(r_{bb'} + r_\epsilon)^2 + \left(\frac{2r_{bb'} + r_\epsilon}{A r_\epsilon} \right) \right]}. \tag{10.33}$$

It is seen from equation (10.28) that the above remarks concerning the criteria for minimum noise for different values of R_g apply to shot noise in the same way as to flicker noise.

Before proceeding to the application of these shot-noise formulae we should note that they are not the most accurate ones available and that the calculated value of shot-noise figure obtained from equation (10.28) is usually about 2 db low. However, the expressions derived for values of the operating parameters seem to be accurate enough for practical purposes and they contain constants that are available from manufacturers' specifications or (in the case of $r_{bb'}$ for example) can be quite readily measured. More accurate but more complicated expressions, which take account of the partial correlation between emitter and collector shot-noise generators may be obtained from van der Ziel's paper [5].

It is worth while at this point to consider van der Ziel's expression for the shot-noise figure of a transistor in the CB or CE connection when R_g and I_e have their optimum values. This is

$$F_{s(\min)} = 1 + \sqrt{\left(\frac{1-\alpha_0}{\alpha_0}\right)} + \sqrt{\left(\frac{I_{co}}{\alpha_0^2}\cdot\frac{2qr_{bb'}}{kT}\right)}. \qquad (10.34)$$

This indicates that I_{co} and $r_{bb'}$ should be small and α_0 should be large in a low-noise transistor. van der Ziel quotes an example of a transistor having the following properties: $I_{co} \simeq 1 \ \mu\text{A}$, $\alpha_0 = 0\cdot98$, $r_{bb'} = 100$ ohms. When operated at the optimum emitter current of 80 μA from a generator having optimum resistance the calculated noise figure of this transistor is $1\cdot25$ ($= 1\cdot0$ db).

5. The value of V_{ce}, which affects the base width W and hence $r_{bb'}$. Thus, with the help of equation (6.46) we have, for a p-n-p transistor for which V_{ce} is negative,

$$r_{bb'} \propto \frac{1}{W} \simeq \frac{1}{W_b - C(V_0 + |V_{ce}|)^{\frac{1}{2}}}, \qquad (10.35)$$

where V_{cb} has been replaced by V_{ce}. $r_{bb'}$ and hence F_s increase with collector voltage at a rate which is small at first but becomes large when the magnitude of $C(V_0 + |V_{ce}|)^{\frac{1}{2}}$ approaches that of W_b. The rate of increase will be largest for large-α high-frequency diffusion transistors for which the base region is very thin.

10.7.4. *Determination of optimum operating conditions for a commercial transistor*

As an example of the application of the above formulae we consider the R.C.A. 2N104 which has the noise characteristics shown in Fig. 10.4. The average noise figures shown are measured over a band of 7 c/sec to 12·3 kc/sec. We determine the values of I_e and R_g for minimum noise.

(1 a) *Value of I_e for minimum flicker noise.* The manufacturer's data indicate that $\beta = \alpha_0/(1-\alpha_0)$ decreases with I_c ($\simeq I_e$) from a value of 44 at $I_c = 1\cdot0$ mA to 32 at $I_c = 0\cdot2$ mA—a decrease of 27 per cent. Thus $(1-\alpha)^3$ increases by 150 per cent while I_e

decreases by 80 per cent. From equation (10.26) we therefore expect that for minimum flicker noise the emitter current will be somewhat larger than 0·2 mA.

2N104
TYPICAL NOISE CHARACTERISTICS

COMMON-EMITTER CIRCUIT, BASE INPUT
AMBIENT TEMPERATURE=25°C
MEASURED WITH A NOISE DIODE AND THERMOCOUPLE VOLT-
METER WITH LOAD RESISTANCE=20000 OHMS AND EQUIVALENT
NOISE BANDWIDTH=12.3KC WITH GEOMETRIC MEAN OF 300 CPS

CURVE	GENERATOR RESISTANCE (OHMS)	COLLECTOR-TO-EMITTER VOLTS	COLLECTOR MA
A	518	—	-0.7
B	518	-4	—
C	—	-4	-0.7

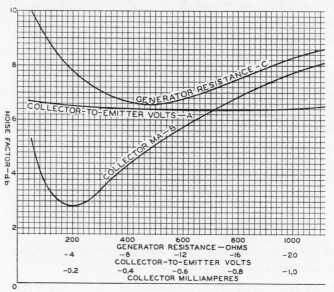

FIG. 10.4. Typical noise characteristics of the 2N104 general-purpose transistor.

(1 b) *Value of I_e for minimum shot noise.* At the low frequencies here considered ($\leqslant$ 12·3 kc/sec) equation (10.32) may be used. We choose $1/(1-\alpha_0) = 32$ on the assumption that I_e will be small and use the value $R_g = 518$ ohms shown in Fig. 10.4. The optimum value of I_e is then found to be 0·17 mA. Thus when both types of noise are taken into account we expect the

optimum value of I_e or I_c to be about 0·2 mA—a value confirmed by Fig. 10.4.

(2 a) *Value of R_g for minimum flicker noise.* We use the following values, estimated for $I_c = 0·7$ mA, for the constants contained in equation (10.27): $r_b = 750$ ohms, $r_e \simeq 30$ ohms, $R_i = 2,400$ ohms, $\beta \simeq 40$ and obtain $R_g \simeq 800$ ohms for the optimum value.

(2 b) *Value of R_g for minimum shot noise.* Using the values $r_{bb'} \simeq 300$ ohms, $r_e \simeq 30$ ohms in equation (10.33) and neglecting the second term of (10.29) we obtain $R_g \simeq 450$ ohms. The optimum value given by Fig. 10.4 is 518 ohms. Since the noise figure plotted in Fig. 10.4 is averaged over a 12·3 kc band for most of which shot noise predominates, this value of 518 ohms is probably a reasonable weighted average of the theoretical flicker and shot-noise values.

(3) *Value of V_{ce} for minimum noise.* The effect of V_{ce} on the noise characteristic of the 2N104 is small because of the relatively low value of α for this transistor. The 2N105 for which $\alpha_0 \simeq 0·982$ has a minimum R.C.A. noise figure of 5·2 dB at $V_{ce} = 18$ V, $I_c = 0·3$ mA with $R_g = 1,000$ ohms. For an optimum noise figure at higher frequencies this voltage would be somewhat smaller because of the predominance of shot noise. For many transistors operation at collector voltages considerably less than 18 volts is desirable because of the importance of surface noise. These factors, coupled with the fact that the minimum in the F vs. V_{ce} curve is quite flat, make it desirable to operate at collector voltages between 5 and 10 volts in most cases.

10.8. Concluding remarks

This survey of noise in transistors has of necessity been brief but it is hoped that it gives sufficient information for a rational approach to the design of low-noise circuits. Further details on most aspects of the transistor noise problem can be obtained from the references given.

We conclude with the following remarks concerning the application of transistors:

1. Low-noise transistor amplifiers fed from low-resistance

sources ($R_g < 50$ ohms) have considerably better noise characteristics than their vacuum-tube counterparts [5] even at frequencies as low as 10 c/sec. Thus transistors are superior to vacuum tubes for d.c. to a.c. converters (chopper amplifiers) fed from thermocouples and for audio amplifiers fed from low-impedance gramophone pickups. For high-resistance sources the noise characteristic of the vacuum tube is superior to that of the transistor.

2. The low-noise properties of a transistor fed from a low-impedance source are maintained up to the CB cutoff frequency.

3. The criteria for low-noise operation of transistor amplifiers depend on the resistance of the source. For operation in the medium-resistance region where the source resistance is of the order of 1,000 ohms the noise figure is the best criterion to use.

4. While many problems concerning noise in transistors remain to be solved, enough information is now available for the design of low-noise transistor stages over the useful frequency range of the device itself. This design procedure would be considerably simplified if more complete information about the noise characteristics of transistors were given by manufacturers. In particular the presentation of two noise figures—one well within the flicker region where shot noise is negligible and one well within the shot-noise region where flicker noise is negligible —would go a long way towards satisfying the needs of most circuit designers.

LOW-FREQUENCY LOW-LEVEL
LINEAR AMPLIFIERS

11.1. Introduction

IN this chapter we apply some of the physical concepts and equivalent circuits developed earlier in the book to the design of amplifiers which fulfil the following criteria:

1. A minimum of distortion is introduced into the amplified signal so that, over the range of frequency for which the circuit is designed (the pass band), the amplifier is a linear element. In such amplifiers the gain is practically constant, independent of frequency, over the pass band and independent of signal amplitude.

2. The upper limit of frequency of the signal to be amplified is sufficiently low that the frequency-independent CE h-parameter equivalent circuit of Fig. 5.12 or the low-frequency T-circuit of Fig. 5.8 may be used. When the circuit design is complete the above assumption of frequency-independent operation should be justified by taking account of first-order frequency effects. As will be seen later, this can be readily done with the help of the equivalent circuit of Fig. 7.10 and the introduction of the first-order approximation to the frequency dependence of β given by equation (7.41).

3. The power output of the amplifier is such that each stage consists of a single low-power transistor (in the sense of § 9.3) operated in the class A mode, i.e. so that the standing (quiescent) d.c. current is greater than the peak value of the a.c. signal current. Such amplifiers will be called low-level amplifiers to distinguish them from the power stages to be considered later.

As these criteria imply, the study of linear amplifiers is most conveniently made in terms of voltage and current gains, input and output impedances, and the variations of amplitude and phase with frequency. We should note here that there is another type of amplifier, which is sometimes used at quite low frequencies although its main application is in the higher-frequency regions. This is the non-linear or pulse amplifier in which the usefulness of the signal depends largely on its magnitude and its position in time relative to other pulses. Such amplifiers are usually specified in terms of rise time, pulse sag or droop, overshoot, and fall time instead of the 'linear' parameters mentioned above. Many aspects of the design of pulse amplifiers are common to the low-frequency and high-frequency versions and they will be considered together in a later chapter.

Three useful papers covering the subject of this chapter are contained in the reference list [1, 2, 3].

11.2. Multistage low-frequency linear amplifiers

The information given in the specification of an amplifier usually includes the frequency range, load resistance and output power (or equivalent information), input-signal magnitude, and internal resistance of the source. A comparison of the required power gain and that available from a single stage usually indicates that two or more stages are necessary. The design then proceeds conveniently from the output stage backwards through driver and low-level stages. Depending on the power required from it, the driver may be treated either as a power stage or as a low-level stage. The design problem thus resolves itself into sections dealing with low-level and high-level amplifiers. The latter will be considered in Chapter XII. The low-level section, which may consist of one or more stages, will be considered in this chapter. In order to demonstrate the effect, on the frequency response, of coupling networks between stages a two-stage amplifier will be designed.

11.3. Coupling methods

One of the first decisions to be made in the design of a multistage amplifier involves the choice of the method of coupling between stages. The common methods, which have been mentioned in earlier chapters are the following:

1. Conjugate-matched transformer coupling.

2. Resistance-matched, or low-frequency transformer coupling.

3. Resistance-capacitance coupling.

4. Direct coupling.

The first of these is normally used only in tuned amplifiers operating at frequencies higher than about 100 kc/sec. It will be considered in Chapter XIV. The second method is used in conventional power stages for coupling the preceding driver stage to the input and for matching the load to the power-stage output resistance. Such applications will be discussed in Chapter XII. Resistance-matched transformer coupling is also used, because of its higher efficiency, in low-power stages in portable equipment where battery consumption is important. However, it has the following important disadvantages:

(a) Transformers of good quality are expensive.

(b) It is usually difficult to obtain wide frequency response with a small phase shift throughout the pass band. As a result the use of appreciable amounts of negative feedback to eliminate distortion and to compensate for variations in transistor characteristics may, from the point of view of circuit stability, be hazardous if not impossible.

(c) Transformers are likely to pick up unwanted signals such as mains hum.

(d) Perfect resistance matching requires a high load resistance which, because of transistor collector capacitance, may be quite unrealistic if the upper limit of frequency is in the kilocycle range. For example, Fig. A11.15 shows that the maximum power gain is achieved, with a 2N369, if the load resistance is 73 kΩ. The collector capacitance ($\simeq h_{fe} C_c \simeq 2,000 \ \mu\mu F$), which is effectively in parallel with the load, has a reactance of 73 kΩ at about 1,100 c/s and the gain of a perfectly matched stage would thus be reduced by 3 db at this frequency.

Resistance matching was used in the early days of transistor development because the only available units were point-contact devices. These are unstable when cascaded in any connection other than CB unless very special precautions are taken (§ 8.10). In multistage amplifiers using point-contact (or junction) transistors in the CB connection, appreciable gains can be obtained only with transformer coupling. However, the CE and CC connections of the junction transistor are stable and capable of giving useful power gain without matching. Simpler coupling arrangements are therefore possible with these connections.

The third method listed above—resistance-capacitance coupling—is the standard form of coupling for low-level low-frequency amplifiers and it will be used in the amplifier design discussed in the sections that follow. The fourth method, direct coupling, may be used advantageously in some cases—especially in the coupling of a driver to a power stage. Examples of it have already been mentioned in Chapter IX. These will be further discussed, and other examples given, in later chapters.

11.4. Factors in the design of a low-level amplifier

In this section we consider the important factors in the design of low-level transistor amplifiers. We shall be concerned with typical intermediate stages in a multistage amplifier and not with unusual impedance matching arrangements at the input and output. We shall therefore confine ourselves to CE stages since these give the largest gain and have the most suitable impedances for the cascading of several stages. As a first step, we estimate the current gain that can be obtained from a two-stage low-level amplifier.

11.4.1. *Current gain*

Consider two CE stages, coupled together as shown in Fig. 11.1. The values of the collector bias resistors R_c and base bias resistors R_1 and R_2 are fairly typical. Transistor $T2$ has a load of 5,000 ohms and a net a.c. load, determined by R_c and R_l in parallel, of 2,500 ohms. Reference to Fig. A11.12 shows that the input resistance is about 1,600 ohms. The a.c. load on the collector of $T1$ is now made up as follows: collector bias resistor, 5,000 ohms; base input resistance of $T2$, 1,600 ohms; base bias resistors of $T2$; 100 kΩ and 50 kΩ in parallel. The net a.c. load resistance for $T1$ is thus 1,170 ohms, and only the current driven into the

($T2$) input resistance of 1,600 ohms represents useful current transfer. The actual signal currents are marked in Fig. 11.1, in which it is assumed that the current amplification per stage is 55. From the figure it is seen that 95·4 per cent of the input current enters the base of $T1$ and that 73·1 per cent of the collector current of $T1$ enters the base of $T2$. 50 per cent of the collector current of $T2$ enters the load, so that the overall current gain

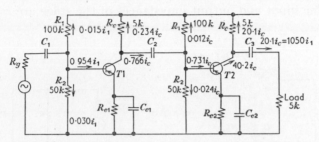

FIG. 11.1. Typical low-level low-frequency amplifier.

is 1,050 times. Thus the unmatched condition gives a current gain that is quite large, though only 35 per cent of the theoretical maximum.

11.4.2. *Frequency response: low-frequency limit*

Gain in a cascaded amplifier decreases as the frequency falls because of the rise in reactance of the coupling capacitors (C_1, C_2, and C_3 in Fig. 11.1) and the emitter by-pass capacitors (C_{e1} and C_{e2}). The coupling capacitor effect may be demonstrated by means of the general coupling network shown in Fig. 11.2. Here R_{out} consists of the collector bias resistor in parallel with the output resistance of the

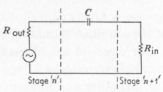

FIG. 11.2. Equivalent circuit of a general coupling network.

nth stage while R_{in} consists of the input resistance of the $(n+1)$th stage shunted by its base bias resistors. It is easily seen that the current gain will have fallen by 3 db (i.e. decreased to $1/\sqrt{2}$ of its maximum value) when the reactance of the coupling capacitor C is equal to the total resistance $R_{in}+R_{out}$. This will occur at a frequency

$$f = \frac{1}{2\pi C(R_{\text{in}} + R_{\text{out}})}. \tag{11.1}$$

The function of the emitter by-pass capacitor is to provide an effective short-circuit across R_e to alternating currents. Any a.c. impedance in the emitter lead gives rise to negative current feedback which has the following effects:

1. The input and output impedances of the stage are raised.

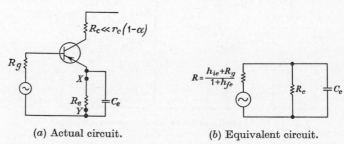

(a) Actual circuit.   (b) Equivalent circuit.

Fig. 11.3. Common emitter stage with by-passed emitter resistor.

2. The current gain of the stage itself is only altered slightly but the overall current gain is reduced because the increase in input impedance reduces the current that can be drawn from the source.

3. The voltage gain is reduced (Appendix X).

The combination of 2 and 3 produces a reduction in the operating power gain G of the stage and in the transducer gain of the amplifier (equation (5.46)).

The effect of the by-pass capacitor on the gain of the stage may be determined with the help of the formulae of Appendix X, but a simpler and more instructive procedure is the following. Imagine that the emitter circuit is opened between the points X and Y in Fig. 11.3 a and, with C_e disconnected, make an impedance measurement between X and Y without disturbing the action of the circuit. This impedance will be the output impedance Z_{oc} of the stage when it is treated as a common collector stage; i.e. Z_t in Appendix X is the a.c. load impedance consisting of R_c in parallel with the external load. In most applications $h_{oc}Z_t \ll 1$ and

$$R = Z_{oc} \simeq \frac{h_{ie}+R_g}{1+h_{fe}}, \qquad (11.2)$$

where R_g is the external series resistance in the base circuit.

The impedance seen from the terminals of the capacitor C_e consists of R in parallel with R_e as shown in the emitter equivalent circuit of Fig. 11.3 b. (The voltage generator, which represents the effect of the signal in the emitter circuit, has zero impedance.) Z_{oc} is typically about 100 ohms or less and is usually much less than R_e. Thus a very large capacitor is required to by-pass the emitter circuit effectively. The voltage gain of the stage (or the current gain from the output of the preceding stage) will have fallen by 3 db when $1/\omega C_e$ is equal to the resistance of R and R_e in parallel.

11.4.3. *Frequency response: high-frequency limit*

As mentioned in § 7.5 there are two main causes of loss of gain at the high-frequency end of the pass band. These are:

1. The CE collector capacitance $C_c/(1-\alpha)$ (Fig. 7.10). Since r_e is very small this capacitance is effectively in parallel with the load and the gain will have fallen by 3 db when its reactance is equal to the a.c. load resistance, i.e. when

$$\frac{1-\alpha}{2\pi f C_c} = R_l, \qquad (11.3)$$

where R_l is the resistance of the collector bias resistor and the load in parallel. The load consists of the input resistance of the following stage in parallel with its bias network.

2. The decrease of current gain as the frequency is increased. For the range of frequency considered in this chapter equation (7.41) indicates this decrease with sufficient accuracy. Thus

$$h_{fe} = \beta = \frac{\beta_0}{1+j(\omega/\omega_\beta)}, \qquad (11.4)$$

where β_0 is the low-frequency value of β and ω_β is the angular frequency at which β has decreased by 3 db. In the design of low-frequency amplifiers it is usually sufficient to ascertain that $f_\beta = \omega_\beta/2\pi$ is beyond the range of interest. If this is not the case either a transistor having a higher value of f_β may be used or the frequency range may be extended with the help of negative feedback (and hence more amplifier stages). We shall not consider the use of feedback for this purpose here as it will be treated in some detail in later chapters.

11.5. Design of a low-frequency low-level amplifier

In order to illustrate the factors discussed in the preceding sections we now consider the design of a simple low-frequency low-level amplifier to meet the following specification:

Frequency range: 60 c/sec to 15 kc/sec (3 db down at these points).

Input: 7·5 mV peak delivered by a generator of negligible internal impedance designed to work into an impedance of 3,000 ohms.

Output: 1 V peak across a load resistance (R_l) of 500 ohms.

Power supply: 12-volt battery.

(This is similar to the specification for a preamplifier fed by a moving-coil gramophone pickup.)

For the reasons outlined in § 11.3 we choose resistance-capacitance coupling. The number of stages may then be determined as follows (all alternating currents and voltages are peak values): The alternating current in the load is 2 mA. Allowing for some loss in bias resistors, this will probably entail a current of 3–4 mA in the output transistor. If a transistor having $h_{fe} \simeq 50$ is chosen the base current drive required is 60–80 μA. Since the generator can supply a current of only 2·5 μA (7·5 mV into 3,000 ohms) a second stage is required. We make this the input stage and allow a circuit efficiency of 50 per cent, i.e. we assume that 50 per cent of its output current is transferred to the second stage. The collector current of this input stage must therefore be in the 120–60 μA range and the stage can be operated at a low quiescent collector current. The available generator current of 2·5 μA should give a collector current of about 125 μA so that two stages will suffice.

We now select the 2N369, whose characteristics are given in Appendix XI, as a suitable transistor for both stages and commence with the design of the output stage. As noted above, we require a current in the load of 2 mA. A current of the same order will be consumed in the collector bias resistor and the d.c. collector current should therefore be fixed at a little more than twice the peak-load current, say 5 mA. A collector bias resistor (R_{c1}, Fig. 11.4) of the same order as the load must now be chosen. It is shown in Appendix XII that maximum efficiency is reached when $R_{c1} = R\sqrt{2}$, which would make $R_{c1} \simeq 700$ ohms. Although we are not primarily concerned with maximum efficiency, and

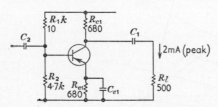

FIG. 11.4. Output stage of a simple audio amplifier.

any value of R_{c1} between R and $2R$ is reasonable, the standard value nearest 700 ohms, i.e. 680 ohms, is a good starting-point. The operating current of 5 mA will cause a drop of 3·4 volts across R_{c1} leaving the collector at −8·6 volts. We now choose an emitter stabilizing voltage equal to one-quarter of the battery voltage as mentioned in Chapter IX—i.e. the emitter is set at −3 volts. The emitter current differs very little from the collector current of 5 mA, so that a value of 600 ohms is required for R_{e1}. A suitable standard value would be 680 ohms. If the base is biased so as to maintain the 5 mA collector current, the emitter will therefore stand at −3·4 volts. The value of V_{ce} is thus 5·2 volts so that the amplifier fits into the 'low-power' category mentioned in Chapter IX.

The load lines may now be drawn on the collector characteristics if these are available. The total d.c. load resistance is $R_{c1} + R_{e1}$ or 1,360 ohms. This corresponds to the line AOB of Fig. 11.5. Since R_{e1} is assumed to be by-passed by a capacitor, the a.c. load consists of R_l and R_{c1} in parallel. The a.c. load line COD which also passes through the quiescent operating point O therefore has a slope of 288 ohms. The instantaneous operating point can be imagined to run along the line *COD*. The collector signal current divides between the collector bias and load resistors in the ratio 1 : 1·35, and in order to provide the specified 2 mA in the load a collector current swing of ±3·47 mA is required. It is apparent that this is readily obtained without either causing the operating point to enter a high-current region where the spacing between curves alters appreciably, or cutting

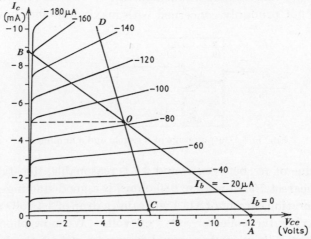

FIG. 11.5. Collector characteristic showing d.c. and a.c. load lines.

off the collector current. Had the available current been insufficient it would have been necessary to choose a new operating point or otherwise to readjust the load line.

The base may now be biased by choosing R_2 (Fig. 11.4) in the range of five to ten times R_e as mentioned in Chapter IX. A suitable standard value is $R_2 = 4\cdot7$ kΩ. Since $I_b \simeq 50$ μA, equation (9.25) then gives $R_1 = 10{,}300$ so that the value $R_1 = 10$ kΩ may be chosen.

We now determine the total input-signal current by adding the current consumed in the bias potentiometer to that entering the transistor itself. R_1 and R_2 appear in parallel to the a.c. signal, thus presenting about 3·2 kΩ across the transistor input resistance. The *CE* input resistance h_{ie} is given, for $I_e = 1$ mA, in Appendix XI. The value of h_{ie} at any other current can then be determined from Fig. A11.9. If the latter curve is not available it may be assumed that h_{ie} varies approximately inversely with emitter current, while β is practically constant over a fairly wide range of operating current (a 10 per cent variation in the value of β for a change in emitter current from 1 mA to 5 mA is typical).

Because the load resistance is very small compared with the collector resistance, the input resistance of the transistor is almost exactly h_{ie} (cf. Appendix X), which is 1,670 ohms at

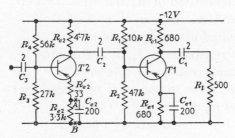

FIG. 11.6. Two-stage audio amplifier showing component values.

$I_e = 1$ mA and about 680 ohms at $I_e = 5$ mA. Assuming a current amplification factor of 50, the required collector current of 3·47 mA calls for a base current drive of 69·4 μA, into the base input resistance of 680 ohms; the input voltage is therefore 47 mV. The base bias network will waste 11·5 μA, so the total input current must be 80·9 μA.

The first stage is designed similarly. The choice of emitter current is now arbitrary. The lower limit for a stage required to develop about 81 μA of signal current would be about 0·2 mA. However, most manufacturers' data are given for an assumed emitter current of 1 mA and it is simpler to use this value. A similar procedure to that adopted in the design of the output stage yields the following (see Fig. 11.6):

Operating current: 1 mA.

Emitter bias voltage: choose 25 per cent of available supply, i.e. 3 volts.

Emitter bias resistor: choose 3·3 kΩ.

Hence emitter voltage = $-3 \cdot 3$ volts.

Hence base voltage = $-3 \cdot 5$ volts.

Base bias resistors: choose R_3. This should be between 5 and 10 times the emitter resistor; 27 kΩ is suitable.

Hence current in $R_3 = 0 \cdot 13$ mA.

Estimated base bias current = $10 \, \mu$A.

Hence current in $R_4 = 0 \cdot 14$ mA.

Voltage drop across $R_4 = 8 \cdot 5$ volts.

Hence choose $R_4 = 56$ kΩ.

Parallel combination of R_3 and $R_4 = 18 \cdot 3$ kΩ.

Required collector current = $80 \cdot 9 \, \mu$A.

Hence required base current = $1 \cdot 62 \, \mu$A.

Base input resistance $\simeq h_{ie} = 1,670$ ohms.

Required input voltage = $2 \cdot 70$ mV.

Signal-current loss in base bias network = $0 \cdot 13 \, \mu$A.

Hence total input current = $1 \cdot 75 \, \mu$A.

Hence net input resistance = $1 \cdot 54$ kΩ.

There remains the selection of the collector bias resistor R_{c2}. The choice is based on considerations that are rather different from those applying to the output stage. The collector voltage swing for this first stage is equal to the input voltage swing for the second stage—which was determined above to be 47 mV peak. It is thus possible to operate the first stage with a low collector to emitter voltage, and hence with a large R_c, without danger of saturation distortion which arises when the operating point crosses the 'knee' of the V_c-I_c curve. This effect clips off the positive peaks of the output voltage of the stage since the collector current cannot exceed the saturation value. At this point, as mentioned in § 7.9, the voltage across the transistor is very small and the collector current is decided by the external resistance. The collector to emitter voltage in the saturated condition is usually in the range of 100 mV to 250 mV but it is temperature-dependent and to allow a safety margin, we should set a lower limit of about 0·5 volt. The voltage taken up across R_{c2} in the high-current saturation condition is therefore

$$12 - 3 \cdot 3 - 0 \cdot 5 = 8 \cdot 2 \text{ volts.}$$

Thus, if the collector current is to be at least 1 mA, R_{c2} must not exceed 8·2 kΩ. The actual value is not critical provided it is less than this and not so low as to divert signal current away from the load, thereby reducing the gain. A good choice would be 4·7 kΩ, which is ten times the load resistance, and yet is low enough to avoid any danger of saturation distortion.

For the circuit thus designed the input resistance is too low, and the gain is higher than specified. The input resistance should be very nearly doubled, thereby doubling the required input voltage but leaving adequate gain. This could be done by merely adding a series resistor. However, a better solution is to leave a portion of the emitter bias resistor un-by-passed, thereby introducing negative-current feedback. It is seen from Appendix X (cf. also § 13.5.1) that the inclusion of a resistor R'_{e2} in the common lead of a four-terminal network modifies the input impedance from the approximate value h_i to Z'_i, where

$$Z'_i \simeq h_i + (1 + h_f) R'_{e2}. \tag{11.5}$$

From this equation we find that a resistance $R_{e2} = 33$ ohms will double the input resistance and increase the maximum required input voltage to 3·5 mV. The specified value of this voltage is 7·5 mV; the voltage gain is therefore more than double the required value. By altering the collector bias resistors or adding an un-by-passed emitter resistor in the second stage it is possible to obtain exactly the specified gain for transistors having the assumed current gain (50). However, in view of the effect on the current gain of temperature and of differences between individual transistors of the same type, we shall postpone consideration of such remedies until the amplifier design is complete.

The resistance components, whose values are shown in Fig. 11.6, have now been determined. Before considering the capacitors we should make certain that distortion of the output will not occur when the amplifier is operated over a reasonable temperature range. If such distortion were to occur it would be necessary to improve the stabilization of the stage concerned and perhaps to change the position of the operating point. The changes in resistor values thus introduced would affect the frequency response of the coupling and by-pass networks.

We consider first the influence of temperature on the output stage. From equation (9.19) (using $r_{bb'} = 300$ ohms) its stabilization factor is found to be $K = 0.11$. The collector to emitter potential is about 5 volts and the transistor dissipation 25 mW, giving a temperature rise of $12.5°$ C. If we allow an ambient temperature rise from 20 to $50°$ C the maximum collector temperature is about $63°$ C and $I_{co} \simeq 72\ \mu A$. Hence, assuming that $h_{FE} = 55$, we have $\Delta I_c \simeq 0.11 \times 56 \times 72 \times 10^{-3} = 0.44$ mA. The variations of I_c produced by ΔV_{be} and Δh_{FE} (equations (9.21) and (9.22)) are found to be about 0.15 mA and 0.22 mA respectively. The operating point therefore moves along the d.c. load line to the point $I_c = 5.81$. When the a.c. load line of 288 ohms resistance is made to pass through this point it is readily seen from Fig. 11.5 that the designed current swing of ± 3.47 mA remains well within the linear region, so that the design of this stage is satisfactory. The input stage may be checked in the same manner and shown to be acceptable.

The values of the coupling and by-pass capacitors—which are decided by the low-frequency response required—may now be determined. Each of the coupling and by-pass networks produces a reduction in gain of 3 db at a frequency of $\omega_1 = 1/CR$, where C is the capacitor concerned and R is given in the coupling case by equation (11.1) or, in the by-pass case, by R_e in parallel with the resistance of equation (11.2). It can be shown [4] that an amplifier containing n independent networks, each having a cutoff frequency ω_1, has a 3 db cutoff frequency ω_c given by

$$\omega_c = \frac{\omega_1}{\sqrt{(2^{1/n}-1)}} \simeq 1.2\omega_1 \sqrt{n}, \qquad (11.6)$$

where the approximate relation is within 10 per cent of the exact one for $n = 2$ and improves as n increases. The present amplifier contains a total of 5 networks of the above type. Thus, if $\omega_1 = 20$ c/sec in each case, equation (11.6) gives

$$\omega_c = 2.7\omega_1 = 54 \text{ c/sec.}$$

Since the specified cutoff frequency is 60 c/sec., this result is satisfactory.

For the reasons given in Chapter XIII, the use of networks having equal cutoff frequencies would be poor design practice when a negative-feedback loop containing three or more such networks exists in the amplifier. However, for the simple amplifier considered here, in which purely local feedback is used, the above procedure is acceptable.

As an example of a coupling capacitor we consider C_2 (Fig. 11.6) which has associated with it the following resistances:

(a) The output resistance of $T2$ in parallel with R_{c2}. Since the transistor output resistance is very large the effective resistance is 4·7 kΩ.

(b) The input resistance of $T1$ in parallel with $R_1 R_2/(R_1+R_2)$ —an effective resistance of 560 ohms.

The value of $(R_{in}+R_{out})$ to be used in equation (11.1) is therefore 5·26 kΩ so that for $f = 20$ c/sec we require $C_2 = 1·52$ μF. The standard value of 2 μF is satisfactory.

As an example of emitter by-pass capacitor determination we consider C_{e2}. The resistance to be by-passed by it is that measured between the points A and B. It is

$$R_{eff} = \frac{(R'_{e2}+R_{o2})R_{e2}}{R'_{e2}+R_{o2}+R_{e2}}, \tag{11.7}$$

where R_{o2}, the CC output resistance of $T2$, is given by equation (11.2). The series resistance in the base lead in this case consists of the source resistance in parallel with $R_3 R_4/(R_3+R_4)$ and is therefore negligible. Hence $R_{o2} \simeq h_{ie}/(1+h_{fe}) \simeq 30$ ohms and $R_{eff} \simeq 63$ ohms. The capacitance having a reactance of 63 ohms at 20 c/sec is 126 μF and any standard value larger than this will be suitable. In Fig. 11.6 an electrolytic capacitor C_{e2} of 200 μF has been chosen.

The other capacitors may be chosen in the same way, completing the formal design process. The values thus obtained are also shown in Fig. 11.6.

The high-frequency response of the amplifier may now be determined as follows: The value of f_α for these transistors is

1·3 mc/sec and $\alpha_0 = 0{\cdot}982$ so that $f_\beta = (1-\alpha_0)f_\alpha = 23{\cdot}4$ kc/sec. The effective output capacitance is $C_c \times h_{fe} \simeq 1{,}900 \ \mu\mu\text{F}$. In the input stage this is shunted by about 500 ohms (the resistance of R_{c2}, R_1, R_2, and h_{ie}, all in parallel) while in the output stage the shunting resistance is about 290 ohms. The frequencies at which each of these circuit constants acting alone causes 3 db loss are 168 kc/sec and 290 kc/sec. The high-frequency response is therefore almost entirely controlled by the cutoff characteristics of the transistors and is down about 6 db at 23·4 kc/sec. At 15 kc/sec the gain is almost exactly 3 db below that at the centre of the pass band.

The completed design thus satisfies the specification for all characteristics except the voltage gain. This quantity, which exceeds the specified value as mentioned above, may be further increased for the following reasons:

(i) The gain will increase appreciably if the temperature of the transistors is raised by a moderate amount, e.g. 30° C, which could easily result from the combination of a rise in ambient temperature and the effect of power dissipated by adjacent equipment. Fig. A11.8 shows that $(1+h_{fb}) = (1-\alpha)$ decreases by 22 per cent over the temperature range 25° C–55° C and β will therefore increase by about 30 per cent. The gain of both stages will increase by the same amount (the small amount of negative feedback in the first stage has negligible effect) so that the overall increase in current gain is 70 per cent. This is partially offset by the increase of input resistance with temperature but the net effect of a rise of 30° C will be to increase the gain by about 50 per cent.

(ii) The value of β chosen in this example is near the minimum (49) for the 2N369 and it will almost certainly be exceeded if the transistors are chosen at random. In an extreme case the gain of the amplifier may increase, from this cause, by a factor of eight.

If all of the factors mentioned are taken into account it is seen that the voltage gain of the amplifier may be anywhere in the range between twice and twenty-four times the specified value. Further, the extent to which the design requirement is exceeded will not be known exactly until the amplifier has been built and tested unless the parameters of the transistors are measured beforehand. Compensation for such large excess gains can be obtained by the use of negative feedback in the final stage and if the feedback resistor is made variable it can also be used as a gain control (cf. § 11.6). However, a predictable amount of voltage gain, which remains constant within x per cent at all temperatures, can only be obtained if the gain without feedback is about $100/x$ times the specified gain. Such an increase requires the addition of a third stage but in view of the additional advantages, such as reduced distortion and improved frequency response, the increased complication is well worth while. This example shows quite clearly the importance of negative feedback in linear transistor amplifiers. The principles involved in the application of negative feedback and some typical circuits are discussed in Chapter XIII.

11.6. Gain control methods

In most low-frequency applications some method of controlling the output power is essential. Such control is usually obtained by one of the following procedures:

(i) Insertion of a variable attenuator in an amplifier whose gain is fixed.

(ii) Control of the gain of the amplifier itself by the use of a variable element in a feedback network.

The attenuator in the first method normally consists of a resistor having a movable tap (potentiometer) which, in order to avoid excessive loss of power, is placed at the beginning of the amplifier or between low-level stages. When feeding a high-resistance load from a relatively low-resistance source, as, for example, when driving the base of a CE amplifier from a CC stage, the potentiometer should be connected as a voltage divider (Fig. 11.7 a). Then, if $R \ll R_{in}$, $v_2/v_1 \simeq n$. The current divider of Fig. 11.7 b is better suited to the case in which a low-resistance load must be driven by a source of higher resistance. Here $i_2/i_1 \simeq m$ provided $R_{in} \ll R$.

Methods of applying the second type of control will be more

apparent when negative feedback is discussed in Chapter XIII. A simple example, referred to above, makes use of an un-by-passed resistor in the emitter lead of a CE stage and makes possible a considerable reduction of gain without appreciably altering the bias condition. The increase of output resistance

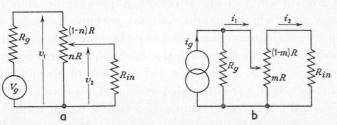

FIG. 11.7. Schematic gain-control circuits. (a) Voltage divider. (b) Current divider.

that accompanies the reduction in gain is usually not important.

An ideal gain control would satisfy the following conditions, which may be used in assessing practical arrangements:

1. Neither the frequency response nor the d.c. bias conditions should be significantly affected at any setting of the control.

2. It should be possible to reduce the gain of the amplifier to zero.

3. The gain should vary in the same way as the potentiometer resistance, e.g. a linear potentiometer should give a linear change of gain.

4. Direct (bias) current should not pass through the control, as this tends to introduce noise whenever the gain is adjusted unless a very high-quality potentiometer is used.

A gain control which satisfies these conditions quite well is shown in Fig. 11.8. The resistance values indicated are typical. The capacitors C_1 and C_2 should each be about twice the normal size. The control is returned to the emitter of the second stage rather than to earth because in the latter case a very low resistance would be reflected into the emitter circuit at low-gain settings. An abnormally large emitter by-pass capacitor would then be required to prevent loss of gain at low frequencies.

In general, feedback controls may be designed to satisfy all of the above conditions with the exception of 2. Also, even though 2 cannot be met exactly, it is often possible to reduce the gain to an adequately low level for practical purposes.

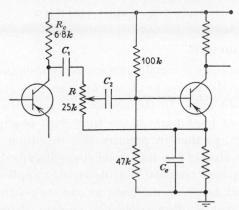

Fig. 11.8. A useful gain-control circuit.

Other methods which are often used, although they do not satisfy all of the above conditions, include the following:

(i) Replacement of a collector bias resistor by a potentiometer. This violates condition 4 and also condition 3 unless the collector bias potentiometer has a total resistance of the same order as the input resistance of the following stage.

(ii) Insertion of a variable resistor in series with the signal, e.g. in a base lead. This violates conditions 2 and 3.

POWER AMPLIFIERS

12.1. Introduction

A TRANSISTOR stage is usually classed as a power amplifier if the output power, distortion level, and load are primarily specified, rather than the gain. In the majority of cases the stage must be operated at least part of the time with nearly maximum power output, so that in practice this definition will usually coincide with that of the high-level stage described in § 9.3.

The term power transistor, while strictly applicable only to a device which has been designed to operate continuously at a high-power level, is often applied to any transistor, regardless of type, which may be employed as a power amplifier stage.

In most power amplifiers it is desirable, from the point of view of frequency response and economy, to use the smallest transistors that will fulfil the design requirements. The important quantity is therefore the maximum signal power that the transistor can safely yield, and it is necessary to consider the factors which limit this power.

12.2. Heat sinks and collector dissipation

As mentioned in § 8.13, the amount of power that a transistor can dissipate depends on its internal construction and on the rate at which heat can be transferred from the transistor case to the surroundings via a heat sink. In this section we consider the details of the heat-transfer process and give numerical data needed in the design of practical transistor-mounting arrangements.

12.2.1. *Factors that retard the removal of heat*

The currents flowing across the emitter and collector junctions of a transistor are approximately equal, while the collector voltage usually exceeds that of the emitter by a considerable amount. Most of the internal heating in the transistor therefore takes place at the collector junction, which is usually in good thermal contact with the case. The case in turn is placed in as good contact as possible with the heat sink. The path followed by the heat generated in the transistor, the 'thermal circuit', thus contains the following elements:

1. The thermal resistance between collector junction and transistor case.
2. The resistance between the case and the heat sink.
3. The resistance in the heat sink and between the heat sink and the surroundings.

These resistances are usually specified in °C/watt. The first is beyond the control of the circuit designer and is given by the transistor manufacturer—although not always in the most convenient form. In many cases the thermal resistance is given in the form of an 'infinite heat sink' rating. A rating of x watts at an ambient temperature of 25° C, for example, implies that the transistor can safely dissipate x watts if the case is held at this temperature. Thus if the maximum allowable junction temperature is $y°$ C, the thermal resistance in °C/watt is $(y-25)/x$; e.g. for a 50-watt transistor having a maximum allowable junction temperature of 85° C the thermal resistance is 1·2° C/watt.

Thermal resistance between the case and the heat sink may arise from imperfect thermal contact or, when the transistor must be isolated electrically from the heat sink, from the presence of a thin sheet of electrical insulation. (Materials that insulate electrically are usually poor heat conductors.) In the absence of such electrical insulation a typical value of thermal resistance is 0·2° C/watt. The insulation usually consists of a mica sheet about 0·002 inch thick or an anodized aluminium washer. When wetted with an involatile (silicone) oil the mica may introduce a resistance of some 0·5° C/watt. Anodized aluminium, which must be handled very carefully to avoid damage to the thin oxide surface, adds between 0·3 and 0·4° C/watt. From this it can be seen that as far as the thermal circuit is concerned it is preferable to fasten the transistor directly to the heat sink and to isolate the latter from the chassis when earthing of the collector is not permitted. However, other considerations such as convenience and the necessity to preserve a small effective collector capacitance may sometimes require that the transistor itself be electrically isolated.

The third item arises for the following reasons:

(*a*) The material of the heat sink has a finite thermal resistance which introduces a difference in temperature between the point at which the transistor is mounted and the outer parts of the sink.

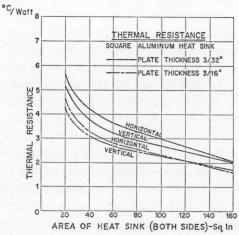

FIG. 12.1. Thermal resistance of square aluminium heat sinks.

(*b*) The sink cannot remove heat unless a temperature difference exists between it and its surroundings. The infinite sink referred to above must therefore have zero thermal resistance and its area must be infinite if it is to dissipate the specified number of watts without permitting the temperature of the transistor case to rise above the ambient level.

In the design of a heat sink it is usually sufficiently accurate to assign a thermal resistance to allow for both the resistance of the sink itself and for the lack of perfect thermal coupling to the environment. Fig. 12.1 shows some typical values of effective thermal resistance plotted against total surface area for aluminium plates in air. From the figure it can be seen, for example, that a 6×6 inch vertical plate $\frac{3}{16}$ inch thick will offer an effective resistance of 2·6 °C/watt. If the '50 watt' transistor considered earlier were fastened directly to this heat sink, the total thermal resistance would be $(1·2+0·2+2·6) = 4·0$ °C/watt and the allowable dissipation for an ambient temperature of 25° C would be 60/4 = 15 watts. Thus even when the heat sink is as large as practicable, the allowable dissipation is considerably less than the infinite heat sink rating. Measured values of the effective thermal resistance of sheets of aluminium and mild steel, under various conditions of mounting and surface finish, have been published by Edwards [1].

In this section we have considered the simple 'ambient' heat sink in which heat is transferred to the surroundings by conduction, convection, and radiation. More complicated systems making use of cooling liquids also exist. A particularly interesting arrangement, which may be applied when cost is not a limiting factor, makes use of thermocouples of a material, such as bismuth telluride, that has a high Peltier coefficient. Passage of a large current cools one junction of each thermocouple. These cold junctions are placed in good thermal contact with the transistor to produce 'spot cooling'. However, in ordinary applications such methods are unlikely to supersede the simple ambient sink and we shall not consider them further.

12.2.2. *The complete collector thermal circuit*

In the preceding section it was tacitly assumed that the flow of power in a thermal circuit under steady-state conditions could be treated in the same way as the flow of current in an electrical circuit. The thermal resistance corresponded to electrical resistance and the temperature to voltage. This concept may be extended to the case of transient heat flow, and the heat capacity then becomes analogous to electrical capacitance [2]. The thermal circuit can therefore be described in terms of an equivalent T or π network of series thermal resistance and shunt thermal capacitance. Associated with each network is a thermal time-constant.

Such an equivalent circuit, representing a power transistor on a heat sink is shown in Fig. 12.2 a. The collector junction is represented by an equivalent T-circuit consisting of elements K_j', C_j'; the power input is P at a temperature θ_j. The mounting base and heat sinks are similarly represented by equivalent T-circuits, and the whole network is terminated by the effectively infinite capacity C_e of the environment.

For most purposes the simplified circuit of Fig. 12.2 b is adequate. Here, the junction thermal capacity C_j, the resistance

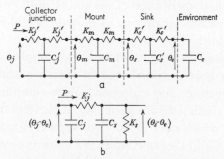

FIG. 12.2. Thermal circuit of the collector junction of a power transistor. (a) Complete. (b) Simplified version of (a).

K_j between the junction and the heat sink, the heat sink capacity C_s, and the effective resistance K_s are considered as lumped elements. If $\bar{P}$ is the average transistor dissipation in the steady state (i.e. any fluctuations in P are of short duration compared with the thermal time constants), then

$$\bar{P} = \frac{\theta_j - \theta_e}{K_j + K_s}. \qquad (12.1)$$

If the system is at rest at room temperature θ_e and is suddenly turned on, the collector temperature will rise exponentially towards the steady-state value, with a time constant τ which is given by

$$\tau \simeq C_s \frac{K_j K_s}{K_j + K_s}. \qquad (12.2)$$

The solution of the thermal network equations for a heat input which is an arbitrary function of time would be out of place in this book but two simple limiting cases may be discussed. These refer to operation in which periods of peak dissipation are either very short or very long compared with the internal time constant $K_j' C_j'$ (Fig. 12.2 a). In the first case the junction temperature is determined by the average power dissipation. An example of such a system is a pulsed amplifier in which the collector is turned off between pulses. Then the average power $\bar{P}$ is DP, where P is the peak power and D is the duty ratio ($0 < D \leqslant 1$). Under these conditions the maximum peak power P_m is given very nearly by

$$P_m = \frac{1}{D} \frac{\theta_{jm} - \theta_e}{K_j + K_s}, \tag{12.3}$$

where θ_{jm} is the maximum permissible junction temperature. The amplifier is described as *average power limited*.

In the second case the periods of peak dissipation are sufficiently long that the junction temperature rises to its maximum allowed value during a single period. The peak and steady-state ratings are then the same and the system is said to be *peak power limited*. In this case

$$P_m = \frac{\theta_{jm} - \theta_e}{K_j + K_s}. \tag{12.4}$$

If the power gain is low, the input-power dissipation and the base bias dissipation may not be negligible. Either or both of these factors may have to be considered when selecting operating conditions.

12.2.3. *Permissible working region*

We have seen how a maximum permissible collector dissipation value may be assigned to a particular transistor under a given set of operating conditions. This limit of dissipation may be drawn on the collector family of curves as shown for a CE stage in Fig. 12.3, where it defines the rectangular hyperbola $I_c V_{ce} = P_m$. The curves in the figure apply to a power transistor which, under certain assumed thermal conditions, has a maximum collector dissipation rating of 10 watts. At any point on the convex side of the hyperbola the dissipation is less than 10 watts, so that any load line which is a tangent to this curve, such as the line ATB, defines one limiting set of operating conditions in which it is impossible to exceed the dissipation rating.

Other limits in the operation of power stages are set by the manufacturer's stipulated maximum permissible collector current and collector-emitter or collector-base voltage. As noted

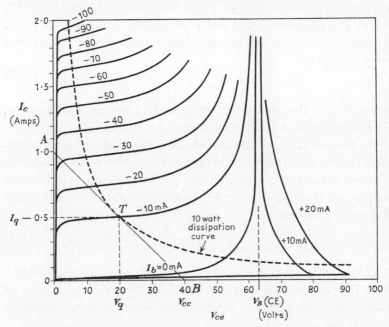

FIG. 12.3. Collector characteristics of a power transistor in the CE connection.

in Chapter VIII, the maximum collector-base voltage $V_B(CB)$ is usually decided by surface breakdown. The maximum collector-emitter voltage $V_B(CE)$, shown in Fig. 12.3 is the voltage at which α becomes unity, and the maximum permissible value of V_{ce} ($V_{ce\max}$), which is limited by the rise in β, is somewhat below this.

It is possible for the operating point to enter the region beyond $V_B(CE)$ if the base current is reversed since i_c can then exceed i_e ($\alpha > 1$). This is a region of negative resistance, similar to that of an avalanche transistor (§ 8.12.3), in which oscillations may build up spontaneously. Methods of protecting power transistors from the bad effects of operation in this region have been described by Lin [3].

The decrease of β at high currents, described in Chapter VIII, is evident from the bunching together of the curves at the top of Fig. 12.3. As this region is approached there is not only a loss of gain but also a progressive increase in distortion.

12.3. Choice of transistor connection

Any of the three transistor connections may be used as a power amplifier, and each has certain merits. The principal features may be summarized as follows:

12.3.1. *The CE stage*

1. This has the highest power gain of the three connections. Allowing for the proper mismatch at input and output terminals (see the next paragraph) a gain of 30 db is typical.

2. It was pointed out in § 8.13.2 that the I_c–V_{be} transfer characteristic of a power transistor is usually more linear than the I_c–I_b characteristic. Minimum distortion is therefore obtained when the stage is driven from a low-resistance source; i.e. it should be deliberately mismatched. The optimum source has a resistance of about one-half the input resistance of the stage. Further mismatching merely reduces the power gain without a commensurate decrease in distortion.

3. Because the gain is high and the linearity fair, negative feedback may be used to exchange gain for linearity. A feedback loop embracing several stages can reduce the total distortion considerably (e.g. by a factor of ten) without introducing the difficult drive conditions that result from too high or too low an input resistance. Because of this flexibility the CE is the most widely used power amplifier.

12.3.2. *The CB stage*

1. The power gain of the CB connection is considerably lower than that of the CE. In general the CB connected amplifier can be operated at a somewhat higher collector voltage than the CE amplifier and may therefore have a larger load impedance. This helps to compensate for the lower current gain of the CB

connection but the CB power gain remains well below that of the CE connection.

2. Because of its lower power gain the CB stage requires a much higher voltage drive, for the same output power, than the CE stage. At first glance it might be thought that the low input impedance of the CB stage would lead to a compensating reduction in input voltage. However, for minimum distortion the input current must be supplied by a high-resistance source so that the requirement of a high-voltage drive remains.

It is perhaps worth while to point out that the difference between the CB and CE input characteristics exists because α changes with collector current to a much smaller extent than β, i.e.

$$\frac{d\alpha}{\alpha} = \frac{1}{1+\beta}\frac{d\beta}{\beta}. \tag{12.5}$$

The V_{eb} vs. I_c characteristic thus resembles the V_{eb}–I_e curve of the emitter junction, and is very non-linear.

3. Because of its higher collector voltage rating the CB amplifier is capable of somewhat greater power output than its CE counterpart.

12.3.3. *The CC or emitter follower stage*

1. The CC connected amplifier, which may be regarded as a CE stage with 100 per cent local negative feedback (i.e. feedback over one stage) has the least distortion and, usually, the smallest power gain of the three connections.

2. Because the voltage gain is less than unity a high-voltage drive is necessary, but the input resistance is nearly constant and the source resistance is not critical.

3. As is pointed out in Chapter XIII, local negative feedback is nearly always less desirable than feedback over several stages. Thus a CE power amplifier which employs a degenerative loop embracing the driver stage as well can generally be made as linear as a properly driven CC stage, while the drive requirements are simpler to meet. As a result the CC connection is used at low frequencies only in rather special applications. One of these involves equipment operated from very low voltages

(e.g. hearing aids) in which the maximum power output is required when the load resistance is small. In this case the CC connection, whose power gain is approximately independent of load resistance when this is small (Fig. A11.15), may have a larger power gain than either of the other connections. A great practical advantage also results from the fact that the d.c. resistance of the load or coupling transformer may serve as the emitter stabilizing resistance, thereby conserving the limited supply voltage.

4. At high frequencies the CC stage may serve as a substitute for an impedance matching transformer and is thus of considerable importance as a wide-band pulse amplifier.

12.4. Class A power-amplifier stages

Amplifier stages are called Class A, B, or C according to whether the transistor conducts for the whole signal cycle, exactly half the cycle, or less than half the cycle, assuming a sine-wave input signal. If the transistor conducts for more than one-half cycle, but less than a full cycle, the stage is said to operate under Class AB conditions.

A single-transistor power amplifier must operate under Class A conditions if the output signal is to follow the complete cycle of the input waveform. Further, if maximum power is to be obtained, the bias must be chosen so as to bring the quiescent operating point to the centre of the largest permissible swing of collector current. We shall discuss three different cases of such a single Class A power-amplifier stage, which vary according to the three possible ways of connecting the load, i.e. the load is direct-coupled, or coupled via a transformer, or through a capacitor.

12.4.1. Class A amplifier with direct-coupled load

If the load is connected directly between the collector and the supply, thus replacing the collector bias resistor, the situation is as illustrated in Fig. 12.3.

The collector voltage can never exceed the supply voltage V_{cc} and the load line must therefore be drawn through the point

$(V_{cc}, 0)$ and may touch, or lie on the convex side of, the dissipation hyperbola (assuming a steady-state or peak-power limited amplifier). When a satisfactory load line such as ATB has been chosen, the quiescent operating point (V_q, I_q) may be selected. Under ideal conditions (i.e. if the saturation voltage and the cutoff current can be neglected) the largest possible swing of collector current and voltage will be obtained when

$$V_q = \tfrac{1}{2}V_{cc}, \qquad I_q = \frac{1}{2}\frac{V_{cc}}{R_l}, \tag{12.6}$$

where R_l is the inverse of the slope of the load line.

With sinusoidal drive we may therefore write, under these optimum conditions:

$$I_c = \frac{1}{2}\frac{V_{cc}}{R_l}(1+K\sin\omega t), \tag{12.7}$$

$$V_c = \tfrac{1}{2}V_{cc}(1-K\sin\omega t), \tag{12.8}$$

where $0 \leqslant K \leqslant 1$ and K represents the fraction of maximum drive.

The average collector power per cycle (obtained by averaging the product $V_c I_c$ over one cycle) is

$$P_c = \frac{1}{4}\frac{V_{cc}^2}{R_l}(1-\tfrac{1}{2}K^2). \tag{12.9}$$

Similarly the power in the load $I_c^2 R_l$, averaged over one cycle, is

$$P_l = \frac{1}{4}\frac{V_{cc}^2}{R_l}(1+\tfrac{1}{2}K^2). \tag{12.10}$$

We therefore note that:

1. The total battery power in the collector circuit, P_c+P_l, is constant, equal to $\dfrac{1}{2}\dfrac{V_{cc}^2}{R_l}$.

2. With no drive the collector dissipation is a maximum, $\dfrac{1}{4}\dfrac{V_{cc}^2}{R_l}$, while at full drive it has fallen to half this value.

3. The a.c. power in the load is $\tfrac{1}{8}K^2\dfrac{V_{cc}^2}{R_l}$, so that the collector efficiency, defined as the a.c. power in the load divided by

the battery power supplied to the collector circuit, is $\frac{1}{4}K^2$. The maximum efficiency (obtained at full drive) is 25 per cent.

12.4.2. *Class A amplifier with transformer-coupled load*

This case is illustrated in Fig. 12.4. Assuming that the winding resistance of the transformer is negligible, the quiescent operating point is (V_{cc}, I_q). Because of the ability of the transformer to store

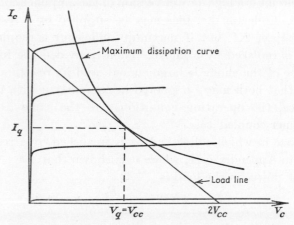

FIG. 12.4. Operating conditions for a Class A amplifier with transformer-coupled load.

energy in the magnetic field ($W = \frac{1}{2}L_p I_p^2$, where W is the stored energy, L_p the primary inductance, and I_p the peak primary magnetizing current) the collector voltage may, ideally, swing between zero and $2V_{cc}$.

Thus conditions are similar to those in § 12.4.1 except that

1. The value of V_{cc} has, in effect, been doubled.
2. There is no d.c. power in the load.

Reasoning similar to that employed in the previous section leads to the following conclusions:

1. The collector dissipation is

$$P_c = \frac{V_{cc}^2}{R_l}(1 - \frac{1}{2}K^2). \qquad (12.11)$$

2. The power in the load is

$$P_0 = \tfrac{1}{2}K^2 \frac{V_{cc}^2}{R_l}. \tag{12.12}$$

3. The total power drawn from the battery by the collector circuit is V_{cc}^2/R_l and the collector efficiency is $K^2/2$. The maximum efficiency is therefore 50 per cent.

12.4.3. *Class A amplifier, load coupled via capacitor*

This circuit is a high-power version of the amplifier considered in § 11.5. Collector d.c. bias may be supplied by a resistor R_c as in Chapter XI, but if maximum efficiency is required this resistor is replaced by a choke. Then, provided the inductive reactance of the choke is large enough and its resistance small enough that both may be ignored in comparison with the load resistance, the operating conditions are the same as in the transformer-coupled case.

The case in which collector bias is furnished by a resistor is treated in Appendix XII, where it is shown that:

1. The power in the load is

$$P_0 = \tfrac{1}{2}K^2 V_{cc}^2 \frac{R_l}{(R_c + 2R_l)^2}. \tag{12.13}$$

2. The collector dissipation is

$$P_c = (1 - \tfrac{1}{2}K^2)V_{cc}^2 \frac{R_l}{R_c} \frac{R_c + R_l}{(R_c + 2R_l)^2}. \tag{12.14}$$

3. The collector efficiency is

$$\eta = \tfrac{1}{2}K^2 \frac{R_c R_l}{(R_c + R_l)(R_c + 2R_l)}, \tag{12.15}$$

which has the maximum value

$$\eta = \frac{K^2}{6 + 4\sqrt{2}}, \tag{12.16}$$

when $$R_c = R_l \sqrt{2}. \tag{12.17}$$

The efficiency is very low in this case since there is a loss of both signal and d.c. power in the resistor R_c.

Equation (12.17) also defines the condition for maximum power output if V_{cc} and I_q are fixed, and R_c and R_l may be chosen at will. On the other hand, if V_{cc} and R_c are fixed and the operating point and load may be chosen, maximum power will be obtained when

$$R_c = 2R_l. \tag{12.18}$$

12.4.4. Class A amplifiers, bias stabilization

The problem of the stabilization of a Class A high-level amplifier has been discussed in Chapter IX. In this section we merely add the following remarks:

1. The amount of power consumed in the bias circuit is not usually an important factor for the following reasons:

(a) The Class A amplifier is relatively inefficient so that other losses are usually considerably greater than those in the bias circuit.

(b) The use of these amplifiers is normally restricted to applications in which power consumption is relatively unimportant because a high-capacity power supply must be provided for other reasons, e.g. in automobile radio receivers.

2. Provided an adequate heat sink is used, present-day power transistors may usually be stabilized with an emitter resistor which drops about 10 per cent of the available supply voltage. Extra thermal stability may be gained by the use of an emitter resistor having a positive temperature coefficient (e.g. copper or nickel) [4].

12.5. Class B operation

The high quiescent power drain, low maximum efficiency, and limited power output of the Class A power amplifier are all features which are particularly undesirable in battery-operated equipment. A single transistor can supply a unidirectional signal with much higher efficiency and almost zero quiescent power if the operating point is located close to either the voltage or the current axis, as indicated by points A and B in Fig. 12.5. Both of these cases illustrate Class B operation. The output resulting from a sine-wave input signal will then consist ideally of half sine pulses.

The two halves of an a.c. wave may be amplified separately by Class B amplifiers if one half is reversed by a transformer or other 'phase inverting' method. Each half of the input wave will then drive its amplifier into the active region. Following amplification the output of one amplifier must undergo phase inversion if a replica of the input signal is to be obtained. A circuit of this type, in which the positive and negative parts of

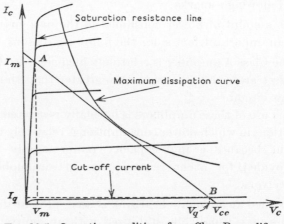

FIG. 12.5. Operating conditions for a Class B amplifier.

the incoming signal are amplified by separate Class B stages, is called a Push-pull Class B Amplifier.

It is clear from this description that Class B amplifiers must be used in push-pull arrangements if distortion-free amplification is to be obtained. The same is true of any amplifier, such as the Class AB, whose output is asymmetrical and consists of pulses that are larger than one half-wave. The combination of the two asymmetrical fractions in a balanced push-pull circuit gives an accurate reproduction of the input wave.

A single Class A amplifier gives a slightly asymmetrical output if the characteristic of the amplifying device is curved. The asymmetry may be reduced by negative feedback as outlined in the next chapter but, if extremely low distortion is required, push-pull operation of the Class A amplifier may also be advantageous. Much of the distortion arising from curvature of a

transistor or vacuum tube characteristic consists of even harmonics of the incoming signal and, as shown in books on radio
engineering [5], these are removed by push-pull operation.

In the design of Class B amplifiers the operating point is
nearly always chosen to have a low collector current. This is
the preferred method of operation because:

1. The loss of power in the bias network is small.
2. The power supply is a voltage source, which is usually
   easier to obtain than a current source.
3. The current gain falls off at high collector currents. Operation at low current therefore gives a more desirable gain
   characteristic, in that the power gain is reduced in the
   presence of strong signals, i.e. there is some compression
   of gain. This is usually preferable to gain expansion with
   large inputs.

12.5.1. *Theoretical efficiency of Class B amplifier*

Both the efficiency and the power input capability of the
Class B stage are higher than those achieved when the same
transistors are operated in Class A. To fix ideas, consider a
push-pull CE stage in which the operating point of each transistor is at the point B in Fig. 12.5. The quiescent current I_q is
small and the quiescent voltage V_q is almost equal to the supply
voltage V_{cc}. Each transistor delivers a half sine pulse of current
on alternate half-cycles; we therefore need to consider only one
transistor during its active half-cycle. If the instantaneous collector current is taken to be

$$I = I_q + KI_0 \sin \omega t \quad (0 < \omega t < \pi),$$
$$= I_q \qquad\qquad (\pi < \omega t < 2\pi),$$

(12.19)

the signal-power output for one transistor over the active half-
cycle is $\frac{1}{2}K^2 I_0^2 R_l$ and this is also the power output averaged
over one cycle for the push-pull pair.

From the figure we obtain the relation

$$R_l = \frac{V_{cc} - V_m}{I_m},$$

(12.20)

where I_m is the peak value of collector current and V_m the minimum value of collector voltage when K is unity (full drive).

Neglecting V_m, $R_l \simeq V_{cc}/I_m$ and at full drive $I_0 \simeq I_m$, so that the power output is approximately

$$P_0 \simeq \tfrac{1}{2}K^2 V_{cc} I_0. \tag{12.21}$$

The supply current rises above the zero drive value I_q by a half sinusoid of peak value KI_0 every half-cycle of drive. The average value of the increase in supply current fed to the active transistor is therefore $(2/\pi)KI_0$ and the average power supplied to the push-pull pair is

$$P_s = 2V_{cc}\left(\frac{K}{\pi}I_0 + I_q\right). \tag{12.22}$$

The power dissipated in the two transistors, P_c, is the difference between P_s and P_0,

$$P_c = 2V_{cc}\left[\left(\frac{K}{\pi} - \tfrac{1}{4}K^2\right)I_0 + I_q\right]. \tag{12.23}$$

When $K = \dfrac{2}{\pi}$, $\dfrac{dP_c}{dK} = 0$, and P_c has a maximum value

$$P_{c\,\text{max}} = 2V_{cc}[(I_0/\pi^2) + I_q]. \tag{12.24}$$

Recalling that at full drive ($K = 1$) the maximum power output $P_{0\,\text{max}}$ is $\tfrac{1}{2}V_{cc}I_0$, we have

$$P_{0\,\text{max}} = 2{\cdot}47P_{c\,\text{max}} - 4{\cdot}94V_{cc}I_q. \tag{12.25}$$

Finally, the efficiency is

$$\eta = \frac{P_0}{P_s} = \frac{\tfrac{1}{2}K^2 V_{cc} I_0}{(2K/\pi)V_{cc}I_0 + 2V_{cc}I_q}. \tag{12.26}$$

If I_q can be neglected, $\eta = \tfrac{1}{4}\pi K$ or $0{\cdot}78K$.

These expressions, (12.25) and (12.26), should be compared with the following equations, obtained from equations (12.11) and (12.12), for the Class A amplifier:

$$P_{0\,\text{max}} = \tfrac{1}{2}P_{c\,\text{max}} \quad \text{and} \quad \eta = \tfrac{1}{2}K^2.$$

The physical reason for the larger power-output capacity of the Class B amplifier is that the transistor is acting more in the manner of a controlled switch than it can in Class A operation. As mentioned in Chapter VII, it is a characteristic of all switching circuits that high powers may be controlled with relatively little dissipation in the switch itself.

In practice these figures are optimistic because I_q can seldom be neglected, the power-supply voltage may not remain constant in the face of large variations in load current, and there is some power consumed in the base circuit. However, an efficiency of 60 per cent can often be achieved, with a peak power output of about twice the maximum collector dissipation [6].

12.5.2. *Distortion and bias in CE Class B amplifiers*
Class AB operation

A true Class B stage operates as a linear amplifier for exactly half the cycle of the applied signal, but in practice, owing to the

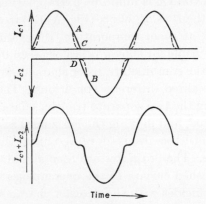

FIG. 12.6. Illustrating cross-over distortion.
(Upper) Currents in the two halves of the
push-pull stage. (Lower) Combined output—low-level signal.

initial curvature of the emitter-base diode characteristic, opera-
tion with zero bias will result in conduction for rather less than a half-cycle (Class C operation). The combined output currents from two such stages in push-pull does not follow the input waveform. The peaks of a sine wave are properly reproduced but a notch occurs near each zero crossing. This effect which is known as cross-over distortion, is illustrated in Fig. 12.6.

In the top two diagrams of the figure the half sine waves

represent the output currents that would flow if each transistor behaved as a linear device for the whole range of its current. However, because of the increase in input resistance when the input signal is small, the output current follows the dotted lines AC, DB, thus leading to an output current of the form shown in the second diagram. Since the points A and B are at fixed distances from the zero current axes, the horizontal distance between A and B decreases as the output current is increased. This distortion therefore has the unique property that it is more pronounced when the signal level is low than when it is high.

Cross-over distortion may be reduced to negligible proportions by applying a small forward bias voltage which is adjusted so as to cause each transistor to conduct for exactly one half-cycle. The correct bias voltage is found by extrapolating the relatively straight part of the I_b vs. V_{be} curve (Fig. A11.5) to cut the V_{be} axis. For germanium, at room temperature, this value lies between 0·1 and 0·2 volt, while for silicon it lies between 0·6 and 1·0 volt. Fig. 12.7 shows the combined transfer characteristics for a push-pull pair under three different conditions. These curves are made by drawing the two separate transfer characteristics, with one curve inverted, and moving the horizontal axes with respect to each other until the abscissae representing the selected bias voltage coincide. The ordinates are then added, and their sum is shown as a dashed curve. In the uncompensated case (a) the dashed curve coincides with the transfer characteristic. In case (b) (perfect compensation), the dashed curve coincides with the extrapolated linear sections of the transfer characteristics, and in the overcompensated case (c) it lies between the two linear sections.

It can be seen from Figs. A11.5 and 12.7 that the value of bias voltage to eliminate cross-over distortion is quite critical. In practice the exact value required cannot be maintained under all conditions of operation because of the effect of temperature on bias requirements. It is then preferable to err on the high side, i.e. to operate under Class AB rather than Class C conditions, as may be illustrated by a determination of harmonic content under the three conditions (Class B, AB, and C). A graphical

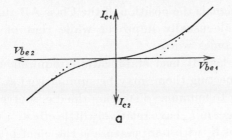

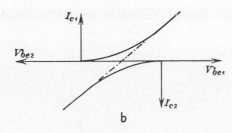

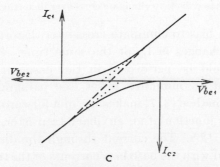

Fig. 12.7. Combined transfer characteristics for a push-pull pair. (a) With no bias. (b) With the correct forward bias for Class B operation. (c) With too large a forward bias (Class AB operation).

analysis of the output of two matched type 2N250 transistors, using their measured transfer (V_{be} vs. I_c) characteristics and a 0·5-volt peak input signal gives the following results:

Class	Bias (volts)	3rd harmonic	Higher odd harmonics
B	−0·2 (optimum)	1%	Negligible
AB	−0·3	6%	2%
C	−0·1	8%	4%

For smaller signals the position of the Class AB amplifier in the distortion scale usually improves while that of the Class C amplifier becomes worse.

The CE Class B bias stabilization requirements, and the methods of meeting them, may be summarized as follows:

1. In order to minimize distortion the d.c. source resistance is low and changes in I_{co} have relatively little effect. Compensation for changes of V_{be} with temperature is the chief problem.

2. The optimum bias arrangement is one which provides a

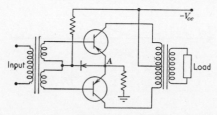

Fig. 12.8. Class B stage employing a forward-biased diode to eliminate cross-over distortion.

small forward bias to eliminate cross-over distortion and compensates for changes in V_{be} at the same time. Further, these functions should be performed in the base rather than the emitter circuit to minimize losses (see paragraph 3 below). The simplest method [3, 7] makes use of a forward-biased diode, or the emitter junction of an auxiliary transistor, connected as shown in Fig. 12.8. The current through the diode should be large compared with the base bias currents of the transistors and relatively constant. The latter condition is attained by feeding it from the main power supply. The resistance–temperature characteristic of the diode should also approximate that of the input resistance of the transistor—a condition met satisfactorily by a junction diode.

This bias arrangement is similar to that outlined in § 9.4.2 for Class A amplifiers. If desired, a padded thermistor may be substituted for the diode but the range of compensation may then be more limited.

A more elaborate procedure consists of separating the two halves of the input transformer secondary and biasing each transistor, by means of its own resistor–diode network, to eliminate cross-over distortion. This arrangement, with the addition of a small, common, emitter resistor as described below, is probably the best of the circuits described in this section [8].

3. Emitter resistance can be used in Class B amplifiers to decrease the effect of changes in V_{be}. The best arrangement is to insert a common emitter resistor between the point A in Fig. 12.8 and earth. However, this usually introduces an intolerable loss

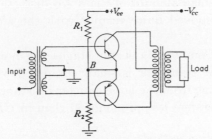

Fig. 12.9. Class B stage employing emitter
bias to eliminate cross-over distortion.

of gain for the following reason: Each input circuit of the Class B amplifier is essentially a half-wave rectifying arrangement and produces a d.c. voltage across the emitter resistor. A by-pass condenser causes this voltage to be maintained at its peak value and this biases the stage well into the Class C region, thus producing a large amount of distortion. The emitter resistor cannot, therefore, be by-passed and unless it has a low value a large amount of signal degeneration results. In practice, a small amount of resistance is sometimes inserted to introduce negative feedback and thereby compensate for differences in transistor characteristics, but the amount of d.c. stabilization thus produced is usually quite small.

4. The bias required for the elimination of cross-over distortion may also be obtained by connecting the emitter to a potentio-meter fed from a positive supply (for p-n-p transistors) as in Fig. 12.9. The component R_2 may be made of material having a positive temperature coefficient (e.g. copper) and used to

compensate for changes in V_{be} as in the Class A case. However, in order that the resistance between point B and earth may be small, a large amount of power must be dissipated in the bias network. This fact, coupled with the need of an extra power supply, usually eliminates this method except in special circumstances.

5. Most arrangements that remove cross-over distortion completely over a reasonable temperature range tend to over-compensate in some part of the range of signal magnitudes, i.e. to introduce a small amount of Class AB distortion. However, this may be removed quite readily with the aid of negative feedback.

In Class B Common Collector stages the non-linear input resistance of the transistor is small compared with the linear component arising from the large emitter resistance. Cross-over distortion is therefore less pronounced than in CE stages.

12.5.3. *Coupling methods*

As mentioned in Chapter XI the driver stage immediately preceding the output stage may be low level or a power stage, depending on the output required from it. (In push-pull amplifiers the driver may also be a phase-inverter capable of supplying both input signals, cf. §§ 13.6.2 and 13.6.3.) Both types of amplifier have been considered and further discussion of driver-stage design is not required. It is, however, necessary to devote some attention to methods of coupling the driver and output stages, and this will be done in the present section.

The type of coupling scheme is decided primarily by the type of output stage used. A Class A output stage, whether it consists of a single transistor or a push-pull pair, may be coupled to its driver by resistance-capacitance, transformer, or direct coupling, without particular difficulty. On the other hand a Class B output stage (which may be driven by either a Class A or a Class B push-pull stage) is restricted to transformer coupling or to some other scheme in which signal currents rectified by the emitter-base diode cannot continually modify the operating point, as they would for instance in a simple resistance-capacitance (RC) coupled Class B amplifier. If RC coupling is used, a discharge path must therefore be provided for the coupling capacitor during the half-cycle when the emitter-base diode is turned off. A pair of junction diodes such as A and B in Fig. 12.10 will perform this function. Their characteristics are not critical as long as their forward resistances can be made lower than the E-B junction resistance of the transistor. These forward resistances can be controlled by varying the resistance R_1. An amplifier capable of 6 watts undistorted output can, in fact, be

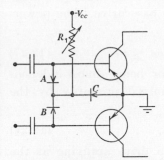

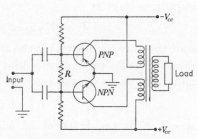

FIG. 12.10. Class B stage with capacitor-diode coupling.

FIG. 12.11. Class B complementary symmetry push-pull circuit.

operated satisfactorily using high-conductance point-contact diodes for A and B. C should be a junction diode as mentioned in connection with Fig. 12.8.

Probably the most useful application of capacitor-diode coupling of this type is to the direct-coupled driver (see § 12.6 below). Almost any point-contact diode can then be used to prevent the relatively small input transistor from charging the coupling capacitor.

The necessary discharge path for the coupling capacitor is provided automatically in the Class B Complementary Symmetry circuit in which two well-balanced transistors, one n-p-n and the other p-n-p, are connected as shown in Fig. 12.11. Single-ended drive at the common input circuit will then give push-pull operation at the two collectors [9]. Because one transistor input diode is always forward-biased there is no reason why RC coupling may not be used. Stabilization of this circuit may be obtained by replacing R by two forward-biased diodes in series or a padded thermistor.

12.5.4. *Class B stage with synchronously rectified power supply*

An important field of application of Class B amplifiers is the control of power to servo-motors. In this case the signal frequency is fixed at the frequency of the basic power supply, and the efficiency may be increased considerably by feeding the collectors with full-wave rectified, unsmoothed, current [10, 11].

Consider an ideal Class B stage whose power-supply voltage is a half sine pulse in phase with the base drive. The power-supply voltage is

$$V = V_0 \sin \omega t \quad (0 \leqslant \omega t \leqslant \pi) \tag{12.27}$$

and the current drawn by the transistor, being almost independent of collector voltage and determined primarily by the sinusoidal base drive, is

$$I = K I_0 \sin \omega t, \tag{12.28}$$

where K is the fraction of maximum drive applying at the instant considered, e.g. for K small the servo-motor will be approaching its balance point.

As in § 12.5.1, the mean power in the load R is

$$P_0 = \tfrac{1}{2} K^2 I_0^2 R_l = \tfrac{1}{2} K^2 V_0 I_0, \tag{12.29}$$

while the mean supply power, averaged over one cycle for the push-pull pair, is

$$P_0 = \tfrac{1}{2} K V_0 I_0. \tag{12.30}$$

Hence the mean collector dissipation is

$$P_c = \tfrac{1}{2} V_0 I_0 K(1-K). \tag{12.31}$$

The maximum value of P_c is $\tfrac{1}{8} V_0 I_0$, when $K = \tfrac{1}{2}$, and corresponds to a collector efficiency of 50 per cent. As $K \to 1$ the collector dissipation tends to zero and the efficiency approaches 100 per cent as the device approximates a loss-free switch more closely. In Fig. 12.12 the line V_0 illustrates the half sine pulse of output voltage. For a normal amplifier with smooth d.c. supply voltage V_{cc} the voltage across the transistor at time t_1 is V_{tc}, while a half sine-wave supply voltage V_{ca} gives the voltage V_{ta}. It is clear that, in the second case the transistor dissipation is much reduced because the signal voltage 'tracks' the power-supply voltage.

12.6. Direct-coupled drive methods

The preceding sections have been concerned with transformer- and capacity-coupled drive methods. In many cases methods in which the drives and output stages are direct-coupled have advantages. In this section we consider such methods briefly.

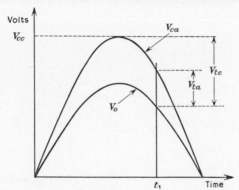

FIG. 12.12. Collector and output voltages for
d.c. and half sine-wave power supplies.

Unless otherwise stated, our remarks apply to all push-pull classes.

The input impedance of a CE power stage capable of supplying 5 watts will vary typically from 80 ohms at very low drive to perhaps 15 ohms at full drive; a driver output resistance of 10 ohms is therefore suitable. If a CE driver, whose output resistance is of the order of 1,000 ohms, is used a step-down transformer of some 10 : 1 turns ratio is required. If a transformer is considered undesirable or uneconomical, the low-output resistance of a CC stage may be employed. In its simplest form the driver emitter is then connected directly to the power-stage base. In Class B stages forward bias for both stages is applied to the driver base, and a discharge diode is connected from each input capacitor to earth as in Fig. 12.13.

Connecting the two collectors together yields the Darlington

Compound mentioned in § 9.4, which may be regarded as a single transistor of very high performance. Its principal advantages in the CE connection result from the increased input resistance and the improved power-handling capacity, when compared with a single transistor. The improved capacity is obtained when the two devices forming the compound have similar power ratings, since the input transistor then carries an appreciable fraction of the load current when the output is large (cf. § 9.4.1). If this increased power handling capacity is not required, and the driver

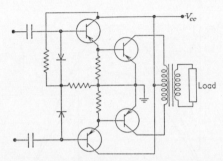

FIG. 12.13. Direct-coupled Class B push-pull amplifier.

is a low-power device, it makes little difference whether the transistors are in fact connected as a compound or as a direct-coupled CC–CE amplifier, especially since in practice some current may have to be bled away from the first unit to mask the worst effects of the variable input resistance and leakage current of the second unit [12].

The compounding scheme may be extended to three or even more transistors, and is of great value in current regulating amplifiers (see Chapter XIII). An analysis of its frequency characteristics has been given by Fillipov [13].

12.7. The load resistance in push-pull amplifiers

In Class A push-pull operation, equal and opposite signal currents (i.e. an increase and a decrease in the quiescent current) flow simultaneously in R_e and the battery. Thus, as far as the signal is concerned, the circuit may be opened at points AA' in Fig. 12.14 without producing any difference in operation; the transistors are equivalent to two generators, connected in series through the internal emitter resistances, feeding a transformed load $n^2 R_l$ which should thus be twice the optimum collector load for either transistor alone. Hence, in Class A, the rule is that the collector-collector load is twice the collector load of one transistor. In Class B, on the other hand, only one transistor is operating per half-cycle, so that the load each collector sees during its period of conduction is $(\tfrac{1}{2}n)^2 R_l + R_e$. Therefore,

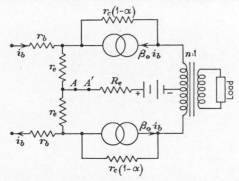

Fig. 12.14. Low-frequency T-circuit representation of a push-pull stage.

neglecting R_e, the collector-collector load should be *four times* the collector load for one transistor.

12.8. Other push-pull circuits

The conventional or symmetrical push-pull circuit discussed above is one of a family of circuits which may be derived from the four-transistor bridge of Fig. 12.15. In this circuit, if all the transistors pass equal quiescent currents in the absence of applied d.c. signals, there is no net d.c. in the load. Application of the double push-pull drive, indicated by the arrows, will upset the balance of the bridge, forcing current into the load.

All the transistors shown are of the same conductivity type. However, either the upper or lower pair may be changed—if the base drive is altered at the same time—without affecting the operation. Fig. 12.16 shows one such complementary symmetry bridge.

We could use only one half of either of these bridges. Thus, if in the circuit of Fig. 12.15 we replace transistors $T1$ and $T2$ by resistors, chokes, or batteries, $T3$ and $T4$ make up a conventional CE push-pull pair. Again, cutting the bridge down the vertical centre line, replacing $T2$ and $T4$ by batteries, leaves

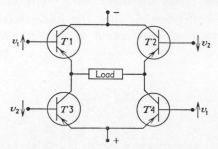

Fig. 12.15. Push-pull bridge circuit.

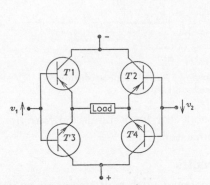

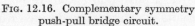

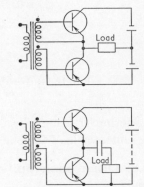

Fig. 12.16. Complementary symmetry push-pull bridge circuit.

Fig. 12.17. Series push-pull circuit.

$T1$ and $T3$ in the so-called 'series push-pull' configuration [14, 15, 16]. Here the d.c. feed is to the two transistors in series, while each is effectively in parallel with the load. This circuit, of which two versions are shown in Fig. 12.17, is of particular value because the matched load impedance is one-quarter that of the conventional push-pull arrangement, and further, the two halves of the signal may be recombined in the load without using a transformer. The next logical step in this direction would be to use complementary symmetry to eliminate the need

for either an input transformer or a phase inverter, as shown for
a capacitance-coupled load in Fig. 12.18. A little thought shows
that, if one side of the battery is to be grounded as far as signal
is concerned—i.e. if batteries may not float at signal frequency
—and if isolating transformers may not be used to alter the d.c.
levels of the signals, then only the *CC* stage may be used in
complementary symmetry series push-pull circuits. The only
exception to this rule is provided by the case in which the drivers

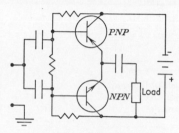

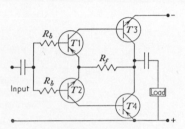

Fig. 12.18. Complementary
symmetry series push-pull
circuit.

Fig. 12.19. Complementary symmetry
series push-pull amplifier employing
negative feedback.

are directly connected to the output stage, as in Fig. 12.19
[9, 17, 18].

Negative feedback, both for d.c. and signals may be provided
in Fig. 12.19 by the resistor R_f, which may be reduced to zero in
the limit to give 100 per cent negative feedback. In this case the
whole stage (amplifiers plus drivers) operates as an impedance
transformer, having a voltage gain of about unity. Either a.c.
coupling with a single battery as shown in the figure or d.c.
coupling with a battery centre tap, is admissible. However, if
d.c. in the load is not permitted, the latter calls for more accurately balanced complementary transistors. The driver bases
should be fed through resistors R_b of the order of 2,000–5,000
ohms, to enable them to 'float' and thereby to assist in the d.c.
balancing process which occurs by virtue of the negative feedback connection. If the values of the resistors R_b are reduced
the circuit will require more carefully matched transistors. For
example, assume that $T3$ conducts a little more than $T4$. Their
common point then assumes a more negative potential than in

the case of perfect balance. By virtue of the feedback connection, this will tend to turn off $T3$ (via $T1$) and the circuit will
come to rest with a small error in balance. The balancing process
will be assisted if the bases of $T1$ and $T2$ are able to acquire

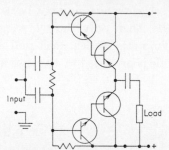

Fig. 12.20. Series push-pull circuit
employing complementary compound transistors.

different potentials because of the presence of external base
resistors.

Another useful circuit, capable of similar performance, consists of a complementary pair of compounds (Fig. 12.20). This
circuit is very tolerant of lack of balance of the transistors. The
scheme shown in the figure for applying forward bias to reduce
cross-over distortion is of course equally applicable to the circuit
of Fig. 12.19.

SIMPLE APPLICATIONS OF
NEGATIVE FEEDBACK

13.1. Introduction

IN this chapter we will discuss one of the most important techniques in transistor amplifier design, namely the use of negative feedback. When a fraction of the output of an amplifier is returned to the input terminals so as to oppose the input signal the amplifier is said to use negative feedback. Other names are inverse or degenerative feedback, and degeneration: we will use the single word 'feedback' when it is plain from the context that the word 'negative' is to be understood. Negative feedback can be used to compensate for variations in the properties of transistors and in the supply voltage, and to produce almost any desired input and output resistance. Examples of the feedback of direct currents and voltages have already been given in Chapter IX in the description of methods of stabilizing the operating point, and some indication of the desirability of negative feedback of signal currents was given in connection with the design of a low-level amplifier in Chapter XI.

We will first describe some of the simpler methods of applying negative feedback and examine briefly the principal results of such application. Some useful circuits in which feedback is used to enhance a particular property, such as a very high input resistance, will then be given. Next we will discuss the design of degenerative voltage and current regulators, and finally indicate how feedback may be used in the synthesis of special frequency response curves.

13.2. Types of negative feedback

The way in which negative feedback affects the properties of an amplifier depends markedly on the methods by which the feedback signal is obtained from the output and applied to the input. There are the following two ways of deriving a feedback signal from the output:

1. A feedback voltage v_f proportional to the output voltage v_o may be used. We shall call this parallel-derived feedback. One method of obtaining v_f, which makes use of a high-resistance potential divider across the output, is shown in Fig. 13.1. Pro-

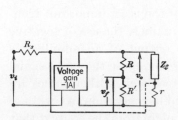

FIG. 13.1. Schematic diagram showing methods of deriving negative feedback.

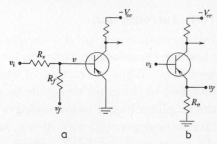

FIG. 13.2. Methods of returning the feedback signal to the input of the amplifier. (a) Parallel-fed. (b) Series-fed.

vided that $(R+R') \gg Z_l$ the divider will not affect the output voltage.

2. The feedback voltage may be taken from a small resistance in series with the load and thus becomes proportional to the load current. A connection of this type is shown by the dashed line of Fig. 13.1. We shall call this series-derived feedback.

The feedback signal may also be returned to the input in two ways as follows:

3. It may be added in parallel with the input voltage v_i. We shall call this parallel-fed feedback. A typical arrangement which uses a resistive network to perform this function is shown in Fig. 13.2 a. If the voltage at the base is v we have

$$\frac{v_i - v}{R_s} + \frac{v_f - v}{R_f} = \frac{v}{R_i},\tag{13.1}$$

where R_i, the input resistance of the amplifier, consists of the input resistance of the transistor ($\simeq h_{ie}$) in parallel with that of its bias network. Thus:

$$v = \frac{(v_i/R_s) + (v_f/R_f)}{(1/R_s) + (1/R_f) + (1/R_i)}\tag{13.2}$$

and is proportional to the sum of v_i and v_f after each has been weighted by the value of its summing resistor R_s or R_f respectively. The feedback will be negative if v_i and v_f are opposite in sign, implying that there must be an odd number of phase reversals in the amplifier.

4. The feedback signal may be inserted in series with the input voltage. In this case we shall call it series-fed feedback. A typical arrangement of this type is shown in Fig. 13.2 b, in which v_i and v_f are effectively in series and the net input voltage is nearly the voltage difference between them. If the voltage gains were the same for signals applied at base and emitter (i.e. the CE and CB voltage gains were equal) it would be the true difference. Because of the subtraction inherent in the way the voltages are applied the signs of v_i and v_f must be the same, so that an even number of phase reversals is required.

There are four possible ways of combining 1 or 2 with 3 or 4 to complete the feedback connection. These could be called parallel-parallel, parallel-series, series-parallel, and series-series connections, where the first word refers to the way in which the feedback voltage is derived and the second refers to the way in which it is applied to the input terminals of the amplifier. These names are not in common use: the more usual practice is to define the feedback, solely by the way it is derived, as 'voltage' (parallel) or 'current' (series) feedback. As will be seen later in the discussion of input and output impedances these terms are incomplete and a procedure that defines all four possibilities is preferable. Applications of the four combinations will be given later in this chapter.

13.3. Elementary properties of negative feedback

The essential properties of negative feedback are summarized, in most cases without proof, below. The subject is so extensive that only the barest outline can be given here; the interested reader is referred to specialized books on feedback amplifier and control systems [1, 2].

If a fraction B of the output voltage v_o is fed back and added to the input voltage v_i, and if the open-loop voltage gain (i.e. the gain with no feedback) is A the net input voltage is v where

$$v = v_i + Bv_o.$$

Then since

$$v_o = Av$$

we have

$$v_o = \frac{A}{1-AB}v_i. \qquad (13.3)$$

The voltage gain is therefore changed from A to $A/(1-AB)$ by the feedback. The latter value is often called the closed-loop voltage gain.

The two quantities A and B may be interpreted as the values of the forward and backward voltage gains within the closed feedback loop. We have assumed so far that the forward gain A is negative, or in other words that the amplifier inverts the input signal. This is the case if the amplifier consists of an odd number of RC coupled CE stages. B must then be positive, as in the circuit of Fig. 13.2 a in which the input and feedback signals are added in a resistive network. If the amplifier does not invert the signal the sign of either A or B may be changed by adding a polarity-inverting transformer in the forward or the backward part of the loop. More simply, B can be made negative by effectively subtracting the feedback signal from the input as in Fig. 13.2 b.

In general both A and B are complex quantities, whereas we have treated them as either positive or negative real numbers. This amounts to assuming that the phase shift associated with the forward and backward gain is always either 0° or 180°. This is nearly true so long as the operating frequency lies well within the normal pass band of the amplifier. We will consider the effects of additional phase shifts in § 13.4.

It can be seen from equation (13.3) that negative feedback reduces the voltage gain of an amplifier by the factor $(1-AB)$. It has become common practice, although it is incorrect, to describe twenty times the common logarithm of this factor as the number of 'decibels of feedback'. (Since the decibel is a unit of power gain some convention must be used when voltage or current gain is expressed in decibels. It is standard practice to assume that the power ratio is equal to the square of the voltage or current ratio.) Thus the phrase '20 db of feedback' implies that the closed-loop voltage gain is one-tenth of the gain obtained when the feedback loop is opened.

Denoting the magnitude of the closed loop voltage gain by A', from equation (13.3)

$$A' = \frac{A}{1-AB},\qquad(13.4)$$

hence

$$\frac{dA'}{A'} = \frac{dA}{A} \cdot \frac{1}{1-AB},\qquad(13.5)$$

so that fluctuations in the gain of an amplifier having negative feedback are reduced in the same ratio as the gain. Since the feedback voltage may be derived from an accurate device, such as a resistance divider, an important use for negative feedback is to stabilize the gain of the amplifiers. Almost any desired stability may be obtained by using sufficient open-loop gain. Thus, in the field of analogue computers it is not uncommon to find $A = 10^5$, $A' = 10$, in which case $\dfrac{dA'}{A'} = 10^{-4}\dfrac{dA}{A}$.

One of the most important effects of negative feedback is thus to increase the stability of the gain by the same factor that the gain is reduced. A second effect is the modification of both input and output impedances. Parallel-derived feedback tends to maintain a constant-voltage output, thus lowering the output resistance of the amplifier by (approximately) the gain reduction factor $(1-AB)$. Series-derived feedback, on the other hand, causes a more nearly constant-current output, the equivalent of raising the output resistance.

In a similar way, the input resistance is reduced by parallel-fed feedback and increased if it is series-fed. Thus, referring to the circuit of Fig. 13.2 a, the current in R_s is $(v_i-v)/R_s$. If the open-loop gain is high, v is a very small voltage and the input resistance hardly differs from R_s, implying that the effective resistance between base and earth is very small [3].

The input resistance of the series-fed circuit of Fig. 13.2 b is

$$R_i' = \frac{v_i}{i} = \frac{v_i}{v_i-v_f}R_i,$$

where R_i is the input resistance without feedback. From equation (13.3) we see that $v_i/v = v_i/(v_i-v_f) = (1-AB)$ so that

$$R_i' = (1-AB)R_i. \tag{13.6}$$

This type of feedback thus offers a convenient means of raising the normally low input impedance of a transistor amplifier, and is often employed solely for this purpose.

A third effect of the proper application of negative feedback is that distortion generated anywhere inside the closed loop is reduced by the factor $(1-AB)$. This is readily seen by considering any such distortion voltage as being produced by a fictitious generator added within the closed loop of a distortionless amplifier. The same applies to spurious voltages from external sources provided these are not introduced outside the feedback loop, in which case they will not be affected. However, in some cases the reduction in gain and the change of input and output impedance may actually introduce more distortion (e.g. by overloading at the input) outside the loop than the feedback can cancel inside it; it is thus necessary to use care in the design of feedback amplifiers.

The fourth major effect which we shall consider briefly is the modification of the frequency response of an amplifier. In general, the pass-band will be increased in width, as may be seen from the following qualitative argument.

Consider a multistage RC coupled amplifier. The lower frequency limit of the pass band is determined by the time constants of the coupling and by-pass networks, the upper limit by the stray capacitance to earth from every collector and base, as well as by the frequency limitations of the transistors. We shall restrict the discussion to this upper limit, although a similar argument, with only modifications in detail, can be applied to the low-frequency limit.

Fig. 13.3 shows a collector-base coupling circuit (a) together with an approximate equivalent circuit (b) which applies for frequencies in the upper half of the pass band (in which the reactance of the coupling capacitor is negligible). If the base resistance $r_{bb'}$ of $T2$ is neglected—an acceptable procedure in the present discussion of feedback principles—we may add the output capacitance of $T1$, the input capacitance of $T2$ and their accompanying stray capacitances to produce an equivalent capacitance C. (From the hybrid-π equivalent circuit of Fig. 7.11 we can readily determine that the output capacitance of $T1$ and the input capacitance of $T2$ are approximately $(1+\beta)C_{b'c}$ and $C_{b'e}$ respectively.) Similarly all parallel resistances, including bias resistors and the element $1/g_{b'e}$ of $T2$, appear as R.

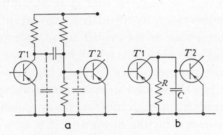

FIG. 13.3. Coupling circuit between transistor stages. (a) Circuit arrangement. (b) Approximate equivalent circuit.

The current i flowing in R is related to the collector current i_c of $T1$ by the expression

$$i = \frac{i_c}{1+j(f/f_c)},\qquad(13.7)$$

where $f_c = 1/2\pi CR$. The internal signal voltage $v_{b'e}$ of $T2$ is iR and its frequency dependence is also given by equation (13.7). When the operating frequency is equal to f_c the amplitude of $v_{b'e}$ will be $i_c R/\sqrt{2}$ and its phase will lag i_c by 45°. A network of this type is described as a phase-lag circuit or often merely as a 'simple lag'.

The expression for the open-loop voltage gain contains at least as many terms of the form (13.7) as there are stages. For the present let us assume that one of these has a value of f_c which is lower by an order of magnitude than that of any of the others, so that the high-frequency response can be said to be dominated by a single lag network. For frequencies in the vicinity of f_c the voltage gain A is then given by

$$A = \frac{A_0}{1+j(f/f_c)},\qquad(13.8)$$

where A_0 is the mid-band voltage gain. Substitution of (13.8) in the expression (13.4) for the closed-loop gain gives

$$A' = A'_0\frac{1}{1+j(f/f'_c)},\qquad(13.9)$$

where $\quad A'_0 = A_0/(1-A_0B)\quad$ and $\quad f'_c = f_c(1-A_0B)$. $\quad(13.10)$

We see that $A_0f_c = A'_0f'_c$ so that it is possible to exchange excess gain for increased bandwidth in any amplifier in which the frequency response is controlled by one simple circuit. If there are several such networks which have cutoff frequencies f_c of the same order it is necessary to pay a higher penalty in gain reduction to secure the same increase in bandwidth (cf. §§ 13.5.3 and 15.3.3). Similarly at high frequencies approaching $1/2\pi Cr_{bb'}$ the single lag concept breaks down and it is no longer possible to have a direct exchange of gain for bandwidth.

13.4. The stability problem

All circuits which introduce a progressive attenuation with change of frequency give rise to a phase shift which is a function of frequency. This phase shift is a necessary consequence of the attenuation, and cannot be eliminated; it can only be reduced to a minimum value for a given attenuation. When this is the case the network responsible is said to be a minimum phase-shift network [4]. The maximum attenuation, which is approached asymptotically at high frequencies, is 6 db per octave (i.e. the voltage or current is halved when the frequency is doubled) in a network of this type. Both the simple CR high pass (lead) circuit, in which the capacitance is in series with the 'live' signal connection, and the RC low pass (lag) circuit, in which the capacitance is between the live connection and earth, are minimum phase-shift networks. In a capacitance-coupled amplifier the coupling networks usually control the low-frequency response and each such network introduces a phase lead which approaches 90° at very low frequencies. At very high frequencies a phase lag approaching 90° results from the characteristic described by equation (13.7).

At intermediate frequencies the phase shift associated with each stage may be resolved into two components, one of which is 90° out of phase and one that is either in phase or 180° out of phase with the incoming signal. In a multistage feedback amplifier the overall loop gain AB may be treated in the same manner as the gain of a single stage. The feedback component that is 90° out of phase with the input signal has negligible effect on the stability properties of the stage (unless it is so large that the stage becomes overloaded) and we shall not discuss it further. In the region in which frequency-dependent effects are negligible the other component is 180° out of phase with the input. However, if there are several lags in the system, this component may be in phase with the incoming signal at high frequencies, thus making the feedback positive. If it is also larger the circuit will be unstable and oscillations will result. In the design of oscillators this condition is produced intentionally (cf. Chapter XVII) but in the present case it must be avoided.

This condition that the in-phase component of the feedback must not exceed the input signal is expressed very elegantly by Nyquist's Criterion [1, 2, 5]. However, for practical purposes, when minimum-phase networks are involved, it is sufficient to use a simpler condition for stability which states that the magnitude of the feedback signal should drop below that of the input signal before it reaches the condition of phase coincidence with the input (i.e. positive feedback). In terms of equation (13.3) the magnitude of AB must then become less than unity before AB becomes positive.

An obvious method of meeting this condition is to decrease the magnitude of $A_0 B$ while maintaining the closed-loop gain $A_0/(1 - A_0 B)$ constant at the specified value. If this procedure is carried far enough the magnitude of AB can always be made to drop below unity before the phase angle of the feedback has altered sufficiently to bring it into phase with the input. However, when the feedback has been reduced to this extent, most of the benefits obtainable from it may have been lost.

The problem of avoiding oscillation, while maintaining an appreciable amount of negative feedback over the pass band of the amplifier, may be solved in some cases by reducing the overall loop gain AB *outside the pass band* in such a manner that AB becomes less than unity before it has reached the condition of phase coincidence with the input. It can be shown that the simplest way of attaining this end is to attenuate AB by means of minimum phase-shift networks at a rate of 12 db per octave or less [1, 2, 6]. If the cutoff frequencies of the networks are of the same order no more than two may be used. A particularly simple way of achieving stability is the 'dominant lag' method in which a network is introduced whose cutoff frequency is an order of magnitude lower than those of other networks in the system. If the dominant lag is added artificially the method has the disadvantage that the open-loop bandwidth is necessarily reduced and, although the closed-loop bandwidth may be considerably larger than the new open-loop value, it may not differ very much from the open-loop bandwidth of the original amplifier.

In the remainder of this section we shall apply these ideas to determine the maximum amount of feedback that may be applied to the following simple transistor amplifiers:

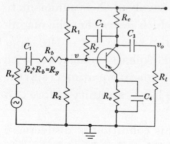

FIG. 13.4. Single-stage a.c. 'parallel-parallel' feedback amplifier.

1. A single-stage amplifier such as that of Fig. 13.4. The low-frequency response in this case is limited by the reactances C_1 and C_3, which are outside the feedback loop (and thus not important from the point of stability) and C_4 which is inside the loop. The high-frequency response is limited by the effective collector capacitance $(1+\beta)C_c$ of the transistor, to which is added any stray capacitance in the collector circuit, and by the intrinsic gain reduction, which may be expressed in terms of the elements $C_{b'e}$, $g_{b'e}$ of the hybrid-π circuit or by the frequency dependence of β. There are thus two minimum phase-shift net-

works controlling the frequency within the feedback loop at the
high end and one at the low end. The attenuation rates cannot
therefore exceed 12 db per octave. The amplifier is uncondi-
tionally stable and we may apply 100 per cent feedback ($B = 1$)
if we wish.

2. A two-stage amplifier whose coupling network is indicated
in Fig. 13.3 a. As mentioned in connection with equation (13.7)
the output elements of $T1$ may be combined with the input
elements of $T2$ to produce a single phase-lag network. Two other
such networks exist at the input of $T1$ and the output of $T2$ so
that there are three sources of phase shift at the high-frequency
end. If the resistance $r_{bb'}$ of $T2$ could not be ignored it would be
necessary to take four lag networks into account. Similarly there
are three or four phase-lead networks which affect the frequency
response at the low-frequency end.

In our analysis of the two-transistor amplifier we shall consider the condition for stability at the high-frequency end when
there are three lag networks. The method of extending the
analysis when there are four lags will be obvious. A similar
analysis may also be applied to the lead networks in the study
of low-frequency stability.

The complex open-loop gain of an amplifier having three lag
networks has the form

$$A = A_0 \cdot \frac{1}{1+j\theta_1} \cdot \frac{1}{1+j\theta_2} \cdot \frac{1}{1+j\theta_3}, \tag{13.11}$$

where $\theta_1 = f/f_{c1}$, etc. and A_0 is the voltage gain at a low frequency at which attenuation and phase shift are negligible. If
B is real, as we shall assume in the present discussion,† AB also
has the form of (13.11). Upon multiplying out the denominator
we obtain

$$AB = \frac{A_0 B}{(1-\theta_1\theta_2-\theta_2\theta_3-\theta_3\theta_1)+j(\theta_1+\theta_2+\theta_3-\theta_1\theta_2\theta_3)}. \tag{13.12}$$

---

† In some cases B may contain a factor which tends to cancel one of the
terms in the denominator of (13.11). This forms the basis of one of the many
stabilizing techniques that we cannot consider further here because of lack of
space. Excellent discussions of them are contained in references [1] and [2].

The simple stability criterion mentioned above requires that the feedback signal be less than the input signal when the two are in phase. In order for the phase coincidence to occur AB must be real, i.e. the imaginary term of (13.12) must be zero. The limiting condition when input and feedback signals are equal is $AB = 1$. Hence

$$\theta_1 + \theta_2 + \theta_3 - \theta_1 \theta_2 \theta_3 = 0.$$

If we put $\theta_1 = \theta$, $\theta_2 = m\theta$, $\theta_3 = n\theta$ this equation becomes

$$\theta^2 = (m+n+1)/mn. \tag{13.13}$$

Substitution of (13.13) into (13.12) gives

$$AB = \frac{A_0 B}{1 - \theta^2(m+n+mn)}$$

and substitution of the limiting condition $AB = 1$ gives $(A_0 B)_{\text{max}}$, the maximum permissible (negative) value of $A_0 B$ for stability, in terms of the three constants. Thus

$$(A_0 B)_{\text{max}} = -\left(\frac{1}{m} + \frac{1}{n}\right)(1+mn) - \left(2 + \frac{m}{n} + \frac{n}{m}\right). \tag{13.14}$$

We now consider two special cases in which:

(i) The three time constants are equal so that $m = n = 1$. Then $(A_0 B)_{\text{max}} = -8$. This small amount of feedback is the maximum that can be allowed if instability is to be avoided. The resulting improvement of amplifier properties is very small.

(ii) Two time constants are equal and the third is very much larger. Here $m = 1$, making two time constants equal and $n \gg m$, giving

$$(A_0 B)_{\text{max}} = -\left(2n + \frac{2}{n} + 4\right). \tag{13.15}$$

Thus if $n = 10m$, $(A_0 B)_{\text{max}} \simeq -24$, a considerable improvement over case (i)

This is the dominant lag method and equation (13.15) is usually interpreted as a statement of the minimum spacing between time constants or cutoff frequencies. For example, a gain reduction $(1 - A_0 B)$ of one hundred (40 db) would require that the large time constant be at least 48 times larger (the cutoff frequency 48 times smaller) than the other two. This is about 5·8 octaves and implies an average rate of attenuation of 6·9 db per octave.

Similar considerations apply to a three-stage amplifier [7]. Here, however, the total phase shifts from parasitic elements (distributed capacitances) must be very carefully considered if a significant amount of feedback is to be used. Not only the 'paper design' but also the actual wiring and the position of components must be shown with care.

13.5. Practical feedback amplifiers

13.5.1. *Emitter resistor not by-passed*

A *CE* stage with an emitter resistor which is not by-passed to the common terminal is the simplest feedback amplifier we shall study. The gain and the relevant impedances have been considered in Chapter XI. The feedback signal developed across the emitter resistance is in series with the input signal and raises the input resistance. Since the feedback voltage is series-derived, the output resistance is also raised. An approximate but instructive analysis of this circuit (Fig. 13.5) may be made as follows:

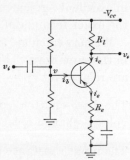

Fig. 13.5. Single-stage amplifier with un-by-passed emitter resistor.

The effective base voltage v is

$$v = v_i - i_e R_e,$$

where i_e is the increment of emitter current produced by a positive base-signal current i_b. Hence, assuming that

$$R_l \ll r_c(1-\alpha),$$

$$v = v_i - R_e \frac{i_c}{\alpha}$$

and

$$v = v_i - R_e \frac{-v_o}{\alpha R_l}. \qquad (13.16)$$

If the voltage gain when R_e is properly by-passed is A, then

$$v_o = Av$$

and the voltage gain when R_e is not by-passed is $v_o/v_i = A'$, where

$$A' = \frac{A}{1-AR_e/\alpha R_l}, \qquad (13.17)$$

which is in the standard form $A/(1-AB)$ if the feedback factor is taken to be $R_e/\alpha R_l$ or approximately R_e/R_l. Thus consider a CE stage using a 2N369 transistor with a standing emitter current of 1 mA and a load resistor of 5,000 ohms. The voltage gain calculated from the exact formulae given in Appendix X, and using the numerical data of Appendix XI, is -158. A resistor of 100 ohms in series with the emitter lead will give a feedback factor $B = 0.0204$, so that $(1-AB)$ is 4.21. The voltage gain determined by this method becomes -37.5, a result which is in excellent agreement with the value of -37.4 calculated from the exact formula of Appendix X.

We may calculate the effect of feedback on the input resistance in the same way. The base current i_b and the emitter current i_e are related by

$$i_e = (1+\beta)i_b. \qquad (13.18)$$

The base-emitter voltage change v resulting from an input voltage change v_i is

$$v = v_i - i_e R_e. \qquad (13.19)$$

The input resistance of the transistor is $R_i = v/i_b$ and the input resistance as modified by feedback is $R_i' = v_i/i_b$. Hence, upon dividing equation (13.19) by i_b, we have

$$R_i' = R_i + R_e(1+\beta), \qquad (13.20)$$

and it can be seen that the base input resistance has been increased by $(1+\beta)R_e$. Applying this rule to the CE stage with an emitter resistor of 100 ohms previously considered, we predict that the input resistance will be raised from 1,587 ohms by 56×100 ohms to give a total of 7,187 ohms while the exact formula gives a value of 6,680 ohms.

An extreme case of emitter feedback is the Common Collector stage. Here the feedback factor B is unity, but the output is taken from the emitter; this is therefore an example of parallel-derived voltage feedback, leading to a low output resistance. As seen from the input terminals the input and output voltages are in series, so that the input resistance is high.

13.5.2. *The operational amplifier*

The operational amplifier is of fundamental importance in generating precise waveforms and hence in the design of analogue computers. The name stems from the ability of the amplifier to carry out several mathematical operations with high accuracy. Parallel-derived feedback is used, and is returned in parallel with the input voltage. The amplifier, and variants of it, have been used so extensively that this particular type of feedback is often called 'operational feedback'.

We have already encountered one amplifier which uses this feedback loop, namely the combination-stabilized amplifier discussed in Chapter IX. As mentioned there the circuit may be used to stabilize both bias and gain. The circuit of Fig. 13.4 may be used as an a.c. coupled single stage CE amplifier of this type. From equation (13.2) the net base-signal voltage v, when the open-circuit voltage of the source is v_i and the feedback voltage v_f is replaced by the output voltage v_o, is given by the expression

$$v = U\left(\frac{v_i}{R_g} + \frac{v_o}{R_f}\right), \qquad (13.21)$$

where $R_g = R_s + R_b$ is now the effective source resistance and $U = 1/[(1/R_g) + (1/R_f) + (1/R_i)]$. Applying the relation $v_o = Av$ to equation (13.21) we obtain

$$v = \frac{Uv_i}{R_g} \cdot \frac{1}{1 - (AU/R_f)}, \qquad (13.22)$$

so that the voltage gain A' is given by

$$A' = \frac{v_o}{v_i} = \frac{A}{1 - (AU/R_f)} \cdot \frac{U}{R_g},$$

or

$$A' = -\frac{R_f}{R_g} \cdot \frac{1}{1 - (R_f/AU)}. \qquad (13.23)$$

If $A \gg 1$ and if R_f, R_g, and R_i are all of a similar order the second quantity in the denominator of (13.23) is small and we may write

$$A' \simeq -\frac{R_f}{R_g}\left(1 + \frac{1}{A} \cdot \frac{R_f}{U}\right), \qquad (13.24)$$

which can be made to approach $-R_f/R_g$ as closely as we please by making the open-loop gain A sufficiently large. The value of the circuit is now apparent; the gain is fixed at very nearly the ratio of two resistances and can thus be made very stable. When extreme accuracy and constancy of gain are required, a multistage amplifier, with a single feedback connection from output to input, may be used.

A comparison of the calculated and measured voltage gain

TABLE 13.1

R_f (kilohms)	$\dfrac{R_f}{R_g}$	A_v (calculated)†	A_v (measured)
0·975	0·089	0·087	0·09
3·21	0·292	0·284	0·29
6·35	0·57	0·56	0·57
10·00	0·91	0·87	0·90
20·90	1·90	1·74	1·80
32·3	2·93	2·60	2·70
52·0	4·73	3·94	4·00
68·0	6·19	4·91	5·10
97·5	8·86	6·50	6·70

† Calculated from equation (13.24).

A_v of the amplifier of Fig. 13.4 with the ratio R_f/R_g, for various values of R_f, is given in Table 13.1. A type 2N369 transistor, fed from a 12-volt supply, was used and the values of the circuit components were as follows:

$$R_1 = 100 \text{ k}\Omega \quad R_c = R_b = 10 \text{ k}\Omega \quad C_1 = C_2 = C_3 = 1 \ \mu\text{F}$$
$$R_2 = \ 56 \text{ k}\Omega \quad R_b = 10\text{·}4 \text{ k}\Omega \quad \text{whence } R_g = 11 \text{ k}\Omega$$
$$R_e = \ \ 8\text{·}2 \text{ k}\Omega \quad R_s = 600 \text{ ohms} \quad C_4 = 100 \ \mu\text{F}$$

All measurements were made at 1,000 c/sec. The open-loop properties were:

voltage gain $A_v = -73$,   input resistance $R_i = 5\text{·}9 \text{ k}\Omega$.

It is apparent from the table that the single-stage amplifier does not have sufficient (open-loop) gain for accuracy in computing unless the closed-loop gain is very low. The open-loop gain may be raised almost without limit by using more than one stage, and several multistage operational amplifiers have been described [9, 10, 11]. Their design is very specialized and will not be discussed further.

If one of the resistors R_f or R_g in the amplifier of Fig. 13.4 is replaced by a suitable network a mathematical operation may be performed on the input voltage. Consider an operational amplifier in which the open-loop voltage gain is so high that, using equation (13.24), we may write:

$$v_o = -\frac{R_f}{R_g} v_i. \qquad (13.25)$$

If we replace R_f by a capacitor C which has an impedance $1/(j\omega C)$ at an angular frequency ω, then

$$v_o = -\frac{1}{j\omega C R_g} v_i. \qquad (13.26)$$

A necessary condition for a circuit to form the time integral of a sinusoidal input voltage is that it should have a frequency response of this type—as may be seen by taking the integral with respect to time of the function $v = Ve^{j\omega t}$. The circuit will therefore act as an integrator when the input voltage can be expressed as a linear combination of sinusoids. It can be shown [2] that the device is a true integrator under much more general conditions; thus the output will be a uniformly changing voltage (a linear ramp) if the input is a step function. This form of operational amplifier is known as the 'Miller integrator' and has been used extensively as a time-base generator. It is described in Chapter XVII.

In the same way, if R_g is replaced by a capacitor whose reactance at the frequencies under consideration is comparable to the value of R_f, the circuit becomes a differentiator. Tables of more complex operations, and the corresponding networks, have been given by Williams, Ritson, and Kilburn [8], and by Heggs [9].

The operational amplifier is also valuable as a linear adder. Because the input and output resistances are very low, the base voltage may be made accurately proportional to the sum of a number of separate input voltages each 'weighted' by its own summing resistor. Thus, in Fig. 13.6,

$$v = \left(\frac{v_1}{R_1} + \frac{v_2}{R_2} + \frac{v_3}{R_3} + \frac{v_f}{R_f}\right)R, \qquad (13.27)$$

where
$$\frac{1}{R} = \frac{1}{R_1} + \frac{1}{R_2} + \frac{1}{R_3} + \frac{1}{R_f} + \frac{1}{R_i}.$$

(The output resistance is assumed to be negligible compared with R_f.) If the voltage gain is high and all the above resistances are of the same order we may put $v \simeq 0$ in equation (13.27) and obtain
$$v_o \simeq v_f \simeq -\left(\frac{v_1}{R_1} + \frac{v_2}{R_2} + \frac{v_3}{R_3}\right)R_f. \tag{13.28}$$

Except for the change in sign, the output voltage is thus the sum of the (weighted) input voltages.

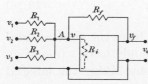

FIG. 13.6. Schematic diagram of summing amplifier.

It is worth noting that the operational amplifier can only function properly if the effective resistance at the amplifier terminal (point A in Fig. 13.6) is very low—a condition produced by the parallel-fed feedback. The low effective resistance is not a serious disadvantage since the input resistance of the complete amplifier is decided by the series resistance (R_1, etc., in Fig. 13.6 or R_b in Fig. 13.4) and may be well above that of a normal CE stage.

As a final example of the use of operational type feedback we shall consider briefly the Goldberg chopper stabilized wideband d.c. amplifier [12]. The chief problem in the design of amplifiers to pass d.c. is to reduce slow changes in the operating conditions of the transistors to a minimum. These changes, which are called drifts, are indistinguishable from very-low-frequency signals. They are discussed in some detail in § 16.2. The usual way of overcoming this difficulty is to translate the very-low-frequency signals to a narrow band of frequencies centred at a fixed 'carrier' frequency with a special type of modulator called a 'chopper'. This modulation and the subsequent recovery of the amplified signal are discussed in § 16.3 and need not concern us here. The problem which remains is that the upper frequency limit of the pass band is restricted to a value much lower than the frequency of the carrier current. In the Goldberg amplifier the upper frequency limit is extended by combining the (d.c.)

output of a narrow-band chopper-amplifier with that of a wide-band d.c. amplifier, using overall negative feedback to secure a smooth response for the whole system in the region of the frequency spectrum in which the responses of the individual amplifiers overlap. The general arrangement is shown in Fig. 13.7. The very-low-frequency signal currents (including those of zero frequency) which flow through the low-pass filter are amplified $-|A_1|$ times by the drift-free chopper amplifier, whose output is

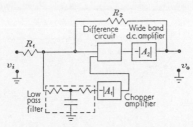

FIG. 13.7. Goldberg's chopper-stabilized amplifier.

fed to one terminal of the difference circuit. The incoming signals whose frequency is too high to permit them to pass through the filter are fed to the other input terminal, and one signal is subtracted from the other to give an output voltage consisting of the sum of the low-frequency signals which have been amplified $(1+|A_1|)$ times, and the incoming signals of higher frequency. This voltage is applied to the wide-band amplifier which has a gain of $-|A_2|$. The total gain in the low-frequency channel is $-(1+|A_1|) \cdot |A_2|$, while in the other it is $-|A_2|$. However, $|A_2|$ is made so large that when the external feedback loop is closed (by connecting R_2 into the circuit), the gain in each channel approaches the value $-(R_2/R_1)$. In this way the excellent d.c. stability of the narrow-band chopper system is obtained in the wide-band amplifier; low-frequency signals reaching the latter have been made large enough to be unaffected by drifts in this part of the circuit.

13.5.3. *Amplifiers employing feedback over two stages*

The feedback amplifiers described so far in this chapter are restricted in performance by the limited gain which can be

obtained from a single stage. Much greater flexibility is possible
if two stages are placed inside the loop [13].

In this section we shall describe two practical two-stage amplifiers. The first, Fig. 13.8, is useful if the overall feedback factor
is not too large. The loop is closed between the second collector
and the first emitter; the feedback signal is thus parallel-derived
and series-fed so that the input resistance is raised and the output
resistance is lowered. The small un-by-passed emitter resistor

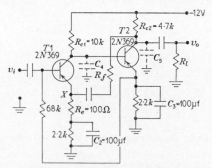

FIG. 13.8. Amplifier with 'parallel-series'
feedback over two stages.

also produces an increase in input resistance that adds to the
effect of R_f. The open-loop gain is high compared with that of a
single stage, and hence the results are more predictable. Some
measurements made with this circuit are listed in Table 13.2.
The expected performance may be calculated roughly by computing the open-loop voltage gain and the feedback factor B
which is approximately $R_e/(R_e+R_f)$.

If a large feedback factor is required the output of this
amplifier must be reduced. For example, in the last case in
Table 13.2 the feedback potential divider has a total resistance
of about 900 ohms and thus severely limits the output current
available to the load. The circuit of Fig. 13.9 may then be
preferred. Here the feedback is to the input base from the
output emitter, resulting in a low input and a high output
resistance. (In practice the separate a.c. and d.c. feedback
paths would often be combined.) Because of the low input
resistance the voltage gain A'_v must be defined in this case as

TABLE 13.2

R_f (k ohms)	A'_v	Input resistance R_i (k ohms)	Output resistance R_o (ohms)	f_c (kc/sec)	$A'_v f_c$ (Mc/sec)
∞	1,400	7	2,500	13·3	18·6
360	1,000	9	1,800	18	18·0
36	316	22	560	57	18·0
10	100	33	180	170	17·0
3	31·6	50	60	520	16·4
0·86	10	55	20	850	8·5

Notes: $R_l = 10 \text{ k}\Omega$ A'_v = measured voltage gain.
R_o = Output resistance measured when the amplifier was driven by a source of 600 ohms resistance at 1,000 c/sec.
f_c = Upper frequency at which A'_v was reduced by 3 db below its value at 1,000 c/sec.

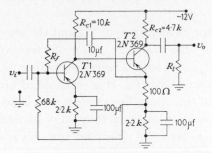

FIG. 13.9. Amplifier with 'series-parallel' feedback over two stages.

the ratio between the output voltage v_o and the open circuit voltage v of a source of finite internal resistance—here chosen to be 600 ohms. (For the circuit of Fig. 13.8 in which $R_i \gg 600$ ohms this refinement is unnecessary and the voltages may be determined at the amplifier terminals.) Some measurements made on the amplifier of Fig. 13.9 when $R_l \gg 4·7 \text{ k}\Omega$ (which is not a necessary requirement) are shown in Table 13.3.

TABLE 13.3

R_f (ohms)	A'_v	Input resistance (ohms)	Output resistance (ohms)	f_c (kc/sec)	$A'_v f_c$ (Mc/sec)
∞	2,200	1,850	4,000	12	26·4
11,500	1,000	120	4,500	35	35
3,000	316	33	4,600	88	27·8
540	100	10	4,700	150	15
180	31·6	3	4,700	180	5·7

As may be seen by comparing the entries in the last column of the two tables 13.2 and 13.3 the circuit of Fig. 13.9 is the less effective of the two as regards the improvement of the high-frequency response when the amount of feedback is large. To explain this we must examine the causes of significant amounts of phase shift in the upper half of the pass band. There are three such sources within the feedback loop in the circuit of Fig. 13.8, and all introduce lags. They are:

1. The CE current gain of $T2$ whose cutoff frequency is f_β. The collector capacitance of $T1$ and the stray capacitance C_4 can be incorporated into the emitter diffusion capacitance of $T2$ with small error as in § 13.3. The result is a reduction in the effective value of f_β.

2. The collector capacitance of $T2$ and the stray capacitance C_5 in conjunction with R_l and R_{c2}. The effective collector capacitance of $T2$ is $C_c(1+\beta)$ which becomes smaller as the operating frequency is raised above f_β. If a substantial amount of feedback is employed the upper limit of the pass band may be much higher than f_β and the cutoff frequency associated with the collector time constant will also tend towards some value very much higher than f_β.

3. The CB current gain of $T1$. The feedback signal is applied to the emitter terminal and, if the base resistance is not too large, $T1$ behaves towards signal currents inside the closed loop as a CB stage, with an associated cutoff frequency which is of the order of f_α rather than f_β.

In applications involving nearly all general-purpose transistors and many high-frequency units the cutoff frequencies associated with items 2 and 3 will be similar, both being much higher than that due to 1, which becomes the dominant lag. Therefore, for several octaves above f_β the frequency response within the loop differs little from that of a single CE stage. The slope of the amplitude vs. frequency curve approaches 6 db per octave in this region and for every reduction of 6 db in voltage gain due to increased negative feedback the cutoff frequency will be raised about one octave—i.e. there is a direct exchange of gain and bandwidth.

In the circuit of Fig. 13.9 the principal sources of phase shift at high frequencies are:

1. The CE current gain of $T1$.
2. The CC current gain of $T2$, modified by the inclusion of the collector capacitance $C_c(1+\beta)$ of $T1$ and the stray capacitances to earth.

The cutoff frequencies associated with 1 and 2 are similar and the slope of the gain vs. frequency curve ultimately approaches 12 db per octave, making it impossible to exchange gain for bandwidth directly. It is worth noting that a feedback circuit with two equal lagging time constants is the low-pass analogue of the equal Q double-tuned circuit. This is described in § 14.4, where it is shown that there is a special condition, known as transitional coupling, under which the frequency response curve is at its flattest and the product of gain and bandwidth is at a maximum. In the same way the condition $A'_{vo} B = -1$, where A'_{vo} is the open-loop gain corresponding to a reduction of A'_v by a factor 2 as shown in the second line of Table 13.3, results in the maximum product of the quantities A'_v and f_c. However, the value of this product can be seen to fall steadily as the feedback factor B is increased, whereas in the case of the dominant lag amplifier of Fig. 13.8 and Table 13.2, the same quantity remains nearly constant until B becomes very large.

A study of Tables 13.2 and 13.3 reveals the greater flexibility and precision of design of amplifiers which use feedback over two stages as compared to the single-stage circuits discussed earlier. This is an aspect of the general principle that one loop enclosing a high-gain circuit is better in practically every respect than several minor loops. Exceptions arise when a large amount of feedback is applied over several stages. An additional filter network which may be a dominant lag network as discussed in § 13.3, may then be required to preserve stability. This filter may reduce the bandwidth to the point where cascaded minor-loop amplifiers could perform as well.

13.5.4. *Feedback in high-level amplifiers*

In the application of feedback to high-level amplifiers complications are usually introduced by phase shifts in the load and in coupling devices. The loads of such amplifiers usually consist of servomotors, loudspeakers, etc., which have large reactive components. In addition, matching transformers are often employed. The use of negative feedback is accordingly restricted to a two- or possibly three-stage loop, no attempt being made to exceed a gain reduction factor of about ten. A low-impedance output is usually required, so that parallel-derived feedback is very common. An exception is the high-level amplifier used to drive magnetic deflection coils for a cathode-ray tube; these coils require an accurate current source (i.e. a source of high impedance), which is obtained by the use of current feedback.

13.6. Special applications of negative feedback

In this section we consider some selected examples in which negative feedback is applied for special purposes. The techniques demonstrated should be especially useful to readers who intend to use transistors experimentally.

13.6.1. *Amplifiers with high input resistance*

Several examples of the use of series-fed negative feedback to increase input resistance (equation (13.6)) have already been mentioned. They include the CE stage with a series emitter resistor which is not by-passed, the CC or emitter-follower stage, and the amplifier of Fig. 13.8. The ability to raise the input resistance in this way is most useful, but it cannot be fully exploited if a normal base bias network is employed. Thus, the low-frequency input resistance of a CC stage may be one or two megohms, but a bias network which represents a parallel path of less than one-tenth of this is usually required. The shunting effect of the network may be avoided by placing a low-impedance feedback path between the base bias source and the emitter as illustrated in Fig. 13.10. Base bias is obtained from a potential divider in the usual way, and an additional

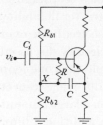

Fig. 13.10. 'Boot-strapped' bias network.

resistor R, which may be quite small (e.g. 10 kΩ) is used to isolate the base-signal source from the bias feed point X. The feedback network is completed by a low-impedance path through the capacitor C. If we neglect the reactances of C and the coupling capacitor C_i the signal voltage across R is $(v_i - Av_i)$, where A is the voltage gain between the base and the emitter. The signal current drawn from the source is

$$i = \frac{v_i(1-A)}{R}. \tag{13.29}$$

Hence the contribution of R to the input resistance is v_i/i or $R/(1-A)$, which becomes large without limit as the value of A tends toward unity. In a CC stage A may differ from unity by 0·5 per cent, so that the bias network is isolated from the base at signal frequencies by an apparent resistance of some two hundred times R. At very low frequencies, when the reactance of C is not negligible, and at high frequencies, when the relative phase shift between the isolation provided by R is reduced. However, it is possible with a well-stabilized CC circuit to maintain an a.c. input resistance of about 1 megohm over the audio frequency range.

The process of multiplying the apparent value of a resistance by applying nearly equal signal voltages to each end is known as 'bootstrapping'. It can be applied to the internal resistance parameters of the transistor as well as to circuit components. For example, it can be seen from the low-frequency CC T-circuit (Fig. 5.9) that the upper limit of input resistance (when the load resistance approaches infinity and all of the current generator output passes through $r_c(1-\alpha)$) is $r_c + r_b$. The bootstrap principle has been applied, with the help of a second transistor, by Stampfl and Hanel [14] to increase the apparent value of r_c, and thus the input resistance. We shall not discuss this special type of circuit here; the interested reader is referred to the survey articles in references [15, 16, 17].

13.6.2. *Conventional phase inverter*

The balanced signals required to operate a push-pull amplifier may be obtained with the help of negative feedback in several ways. In the most common method the load resistor is divided between the emitter and the collector as in Fig. 13.11; the output voltages are then in phase opposition, i.e. they are inverted with respect to each other. The large amount of current feedback resulting from the emitter resistor reduces the voltage gain to very nearly unity at both output terminals if the emitter and collector loads are equal. However, this simple circuit may need modification for the following reason: when viewed from the

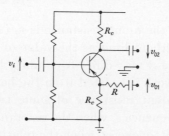

FIG. 13.11. Conventional phase
inverter.

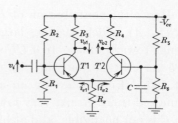

FIG. 13.12. The 'long-tail pair'
circuit.

collector output terminal the feedback voltage is series-derived, resulting in a very high output resistance. When viewed from the emitter output terminal it is parallel-derived, and produces a very low output resistance. In practice it turns out that the output resistance seen from the collector is very nearly the value of the collector bias resistor R_c. At the same time R_c is usually so much smaller than the internal resistance $r_c(1-\alpha)$ that the characteristics seen from the emitter terminal hardly differ from those of a pure CC stage. The addition of a series resistor R equal in value to R_c will almost equalize the impedances seen when looking back from the two output terminals and make it possible to feed equal currents to the following bases.

13.6.3. *The long-tail pair*

A circuit diagram of this extremely important stage is shown in Fig. 13.12. Its action can be described in several ways. When used as a phase inverter the base of transistor $T2$ has a signal earth connection through a large capacitor C. Signal current entering $T1$, the input transistor, returns to earth via R_e and the resulting change in potential across R_e alters the emitter current of the second, or mating, transistor; i.e. an increase in current in $T1$ is supplied largely by a decrease in current in $T2$. If R_e is large and the collector resistors R_3 and R_4 are equal, very nearly balanced push-pull voltages from sources of equal impedance are available at the two collectors. Apart from this application as a phase inverter the circuit is extremely important because of its use as a difference amplifier [18], in which case inputs are fed to both bases. If R_e is large (it may be made as large as we please by returning the fixed end to a positive bias supply instead of to earth) signals appearing simultaneously and in the same sense at each base have little effect on the collector currents, i.e. the gain is small. If we imagine the two bases to be connected together the stage operates as a CE amplifier with a large un-by-passed emitter resistor. However, the amplification of the difference of two signals, or of a signal appearing at only one base (the so-called differential gain) is large because R_e is effectively by-passed by the low resistance seen when looking into the emitter of the other transistor. The ratio of the two gains described above is called the common-mode rejection ratio and is a figure of merit for a difference amplifier. Such amplifiers are used extensively in biological work where it is necessary to provide high sensitivity to voltage differences between a pair of exploratory electrodes. The absolute voltage of each is simultaneously changed because the whole apparatus is immersed in an interfering field such as that of the surrounding electricity supply wiring. A careful analysis of the circuit is quite tedious and the results bear out the general reasoning given above. In particular, it may be shown that [18]:

(a) The input resistance is twice that of a normal CE stage plus the source resistance in the base of the mating transistor. For the reason mentioned under (c) below the source resistance is usually small unless the stage is used as a difference amplifier.

(b) The common-mode rejection ratio is increased if the value of R_e is made large. With typical general-purpose transistors a ratio of 1,000 can be obtained if R_e is about 35 kΩ. Assuming an emitter current of 1 mA per transistor, this necessitates the provision of a bias supply of 70 volts. A useful alternative is the addition of a transistor which is arranged to have a nearly constant emitter current as shown in Fig. 13.13. A dynamic resistance of 50 kΩ to 100 kΩ is obtained in this way, without the

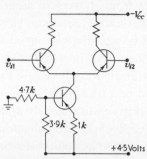

necessity for a high-voltage bias source. The ability to reject common-mode signals depends to a pronounced extent on the phase relation between the *CE* current gains of the transistors forming the long-tail pair and deteriorates rapidly above about 10 kc/sec.

(*c*) In a phase-inverter application, the outputs are most nearly balanced when the base of the mating transistor is earthed to signal frequencies by means of the capacitor *C*.

Fig. 13.13. Long-tail pair with auxiliary transistor to reduce bias voltage.

(*d*) Because of the common mode rejection property, power-supply fluctuations applied to the bases of the transistors tend to cancel each other and the long-tail pair is useful as a direct coupled amplifier [19]. In such an application the transistor $T2$ may be regarded as a substitute for an emitter by-pass capacitor which will provide an effective by-pass impedance at very low frequencies. Several stages may be cascaded to form a balanced direct-coupled amplifier. The base of the mating transistor in the first stage is a convenient high-impedance point at which to insert an overall negative feedback signal.

It is worth noting that, if the effect of R_3 is ignored, Fig. 13.12 may also be considered to be the circuit diagram of a *CB* amplifier directly coupled to a *CC* driver stage.

13.7. Degenerative voltage and current regulators

In this section we shall describe very briefly the application of negative feedback to improve the performance of regulated power supplies. The simplest circuit of this type [20] uses a series regulator between the (variable) source and the load as shown in Fig. 13.14. The base of the regulating transistor is connected to the battery and is maintained at a voltage that is almost constant with respect to earth. The small voltage drop across the forward-biased emitter-base diode holds the emitter voltage very close to that of the base, the remaining voltage $V_i - V_o$ being consumed across the reverse-biased collector-base junction. Because of the high resistance at this junction, variations in input voltage have relatively little effect on the output. In other words the device is a d.c. connected emitter follower, and advantage is taken of the low output impedance to maintain

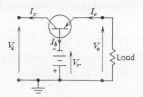

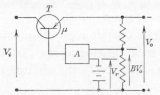

FIG. 13.14. Simple series regulator.

FIG. 13.15. Voltage regulator with d.c. feedback loop.

the output voltage almost constant in the face of varying load currents. The d.c. current gain is $(1+h_{FE})$ which is not very large, so that the current drawn from the reference source may be undesirably high. This current may be reduced, almost without limit, by replacing the single transistor by a Darlington compound of two or more stages (Chapter IX).

A fundamental improvement may be made by inserting a d.c. feedback loop as in Fig. 13.15 [21–25]. The voltage V_r of a stable reference source is subtracted from a fraction B of the output voltage V_o. The fraction B is obtained from a stable voltage divider, and the subtraction may be carried out in a difference amplifier of the type discussed in § 13.6.3 or by some other means. We shall assume that a difference amplifier is used and that it has a differential voltage gain A. Then the input to the difference amplifier is

$$v = V_r - BV_o \qquad (13.30)$$

and if the voltage gain of the series transistor T is μ, the voltage available to control the regulator (the 'forcing' voltage) is μAv. As long as μA is very large, v is very small. Thus in a high-gain system it is very nearly true that

$$V_r = BV_o. \qquad (13.31)$$

Now let V_o change by δV_o as a result of a change δV_i in input voltage V_i.

The correction voltage is $\mu A B \, \delta V_o$; hence

$$\delta V_i + \mu A B \, \delta V_o = \delta V_0,$$

or
$$\frac{\delta V_o}{\delta V_i} = \frac{1}{1 - \mu A B}. \tag{13.32}$$

This describes the input regulation, or the ability to reject changes of input voltages; it may be improved by increasing the product $\mu A B$.

The output regulation is defined in terms of an equivalent internal resistance R_o. Assuming that the output current I_o is changed by δI_o, the change in output voltage is δV_o, where

$$\delta V_o = -R_o \, \delta I_o.$$

The increase in current drawn from the input source causes a change δV_i in input voltage which is given by

$$\delta V_i = -R_i \, \delta I_o,$$

where R_i is the resistance of the source. Hence

$$\delta V_o = -\frac{R_i \, \delta I_o}{1 - \mu A B} = -R_o \, \delta I_o$$

and
$$R_o = \frac{R_i}{1 - \mu A B}. \tag{13.33}$$

Strictly speaking neither equation (13.32) nor (13.33) is correct, since we have not specified the conditions under which the small changes of current and voltage were made. (These changes should be partial rather than ordinary differentials.) An outline of the way in which a rigorous analysis may be made is given in Appendix XIII.

It is important to note that any change at the input of the amplifier is not affected by the feedback. Thus, if the reference voltage changes by δV_r, we see from equation (13.31) that the change in output voltage will be $\delta V_r / B$. In practical regulators B is normally between $\frac{1}{2}$ and $\frac{1}{10}$ so that we can take the maximum possible stability of the output voltage to be poorer than that of the reference source by a factor lying between two and ten.

In practice it will be worse than this because of the internal drift of the difference amplifier. For very precise work a chopper-type amplifier is required, but this can never cancel any drift in the reference source.

The most useful reference source in transistor work is a regulating diode. If the reference voltage is in the vicinity of 7 to 8 volts the temperature coefficient of voltage can be made as low as 0·001 per cent/°C at 25° C. (This low value is achieved by placing two diodes back to back; the negative temperature coefficient of the forward-biased unit can be arranged to compensate for the positive coefficient of the reverse diode. This positive coefficient has the correct magnitude when breakdown occurs at about 8 volts.)

The principles outlined above may also be used in a current regulator. The feedback voltage is then taken from a small series resistor instead of from a high-resistance divider.

13.8. Frequency selective feedback

In a filter amplifier, i.e. an amplifier with pre-determined frequency-selective characteristics, it is possible to place the filter network in the forward (A part) or the reverse (B part) of the feedback loop. Thus, in Fig. 13.16 a the filter is in the forward part. If the complex frequency response of the filter can be expressed as some function $g(\omega)$, the response of the amplifier is of the form

a

b

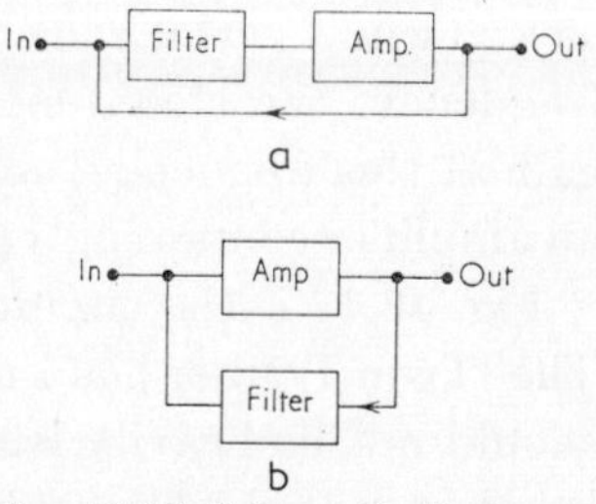

FIG. 13.16. Schematic diagrams of frequency-selective feedback circuits. (a) Filter in forward part of loop. (b) Filter in return part of loop.

$$\frac{v_o}{v_i} = \frac{A(\omega)\,g(\omega)}{1 - BA(\omega)\,g(\omega)}. \quad (13.34)$$

where $A(\omega)$ is the complex open-loop gain and B is assumed to be a real number.

As long as the second term in the denominator is large compared with unity, the gain tends to $-1/B$. This is still true if B is itself a function of frequency, provided the whole system is linear. Thus, a substantial amount of negative feedback will force the overall closed-loop frequency response to equal the inverse of the response of the B part of the loop. If B is constant the gain will be constant over a wide range of frequencies and the feedback will 'flatten' the open-loop frequency response.

If the filter is placed in the B part, as in Fig. 13.16 b the response is described by

$$\frac{v_o}{v_i} = \frac{A(\omega)}{1 - BA(\omega)\,g(\omega)}. \tag{13.35}$$

For large feedback factors, this tends to $-1/B\,g(\omega)$. Thus, if B is real and constant, the closed-loop frequency response is

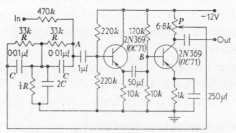

FIG. 13.17. 'Twin-T' bandpass amplifier.

the inverse of the filter response. If the filter is a network such as a 'Twin T', which has a null or zero in transmission at some frequency, the closed-loop response will have a maximum of gain at this frequency, and will closely resemble the response of an amplifier containing a parallel resonant collector load [26, 27].

Fig. 13.17 is the circuit diagram of an amplifier of this type. The 'Twin T' filter has a null at 400 c/sec. Because this network should not be heavily loaded it is connected to an emitter follower stage, which may be biased by the method of Fig. 13.10 if a larger input impedance is desired. The signal is fed in at the high-impedance point A rather than the point B which looks into the low-output resistance of the emitter follower. At frequencies close to the resonant point the response is that of a parallel resonant circuit whose Q factor (which indicates the ratio of the resonant frequency to the mean bandwidth, as discussed in Chapter XIV) may be as high as 20.

In the simple circuit of Fig. 13.17 the ratio of the gain at the resonant frequency to that at frequencies far removed from resonance is decided by the gain of a single stage. This ratio could be improved either by the addition of (external) filters to cut down response outside the pass-band or by an increase in the number of amplifier stages.

As a more commonplace example we shall describe an equalizer for a gramophone pick-up which is to play records made to the

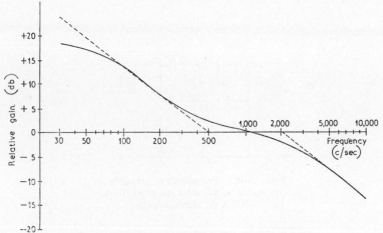

FIG. 13.18.   R.I.A.A. playback characteristic.

R.I.A.A.† standard characteristic. To play such a record properly with a pick-up whose output voltage is proportional to stylus velocity (e.g. a magnetic pick-up, or a heavily loaded piezo-electric device) requires the insertion of an equalizing filter having the frequency response depicted in Fig. 13.18. This shows a bass 'boost' with 500 c/sec as a corner frequency, asymptotic to 6 db per octave but reduced in the vicinity of 50–100 c/sec, and a treble cut or 'roll-off', again asymptotic to 6 db per octave, with 2,020 c/sec as corner frequency.

The bass boost is achieved by placing a bass cut filter, e.g. a capacitor and resistor in series, in the return part of a voltage (parallel-parallel) feedback loop as shown in Fig. 13.19. At the corner frequency the resistance and reactance are equal. For 500 c/sec suitable component values are thus $0\cdot02\,\mu$F, and 15 kΩ.

† Record Industries Association of America.

The 2,020 c/sec corner frequency roll-off is achieved by placing a capacitor in parallel with the 15 kΩ resistor. This capacitor should have about one-quarter the capacitance of that responsible for the bass boost—4,700 $\mu\mu$F is suitable. In this way the feedback factor is made to increase as the frequency rises, causing a reduction in gain which eventually reaches 6 db per octave. A resistor of 1,500 ohms, placed in series with the smaller

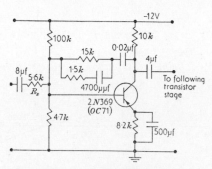

Fig. 13.19. Pre-amplifier capable of equalizing a velocity pick-up to the R.I.A.A. characteristic.

capacitor reduces the feedback factor at very high frequencies, thus compensating for loss of gain in other parts of the system.

Some 'rounding off' is required at the extreme bass end. If the open-loop gain of the amplifier is high this can be achieved by reducing the size of the coupling capacitor outside the feedback loop. If only a single stage is used, the rounding-off is automatically secured because of the low open-loop gain. At frequencies below about 100 c/sec $|AB|$ is no longer large compared with unity and the amount of bass boost approaches its saturation point. If it were necessary to carry the bass boost to lower frequencies while retaining high mid-band gain, a higher open-loop gain would be required. This could be obtained by using an amplifier of the type shown in Fig. 13.8 and replacing R_f by an equalizing network of the above type.

Another method of extending the bass boost to lower frequencies consists of increasing the resistance (R_s in Fig. 13.2 a) in series with the signal source. This decreases the shunting effect of the pick-up and increases the feedback. The ratio of low-frequency to mid-band response is thus increased at the expense of mid-band gain. For the component values used in Fig. 13.19 the bass rounding-off of Fig. 13.18 is obtained with $R_s = 5 \cdot 6$ kΩ. The mid-band gain is then about 10 db and the voltage gain is about 3.

The resistance component of the output impedance of this circuit varies approximately inversely with frequency. The input resistance of the following stage should therefore be fairly large (e.g. 10 kΩ) since too low a value would increase the high-frequency response and offset the bass boost. The circuit of Fig. 13.8, whose input resistance is raised by feedback, would be suitable.

TUNED HIGH-FREQUENCY AMPLIFIERS

14.1. Introduction

IN this chapter we will describe the more important features of the most widely used type of high-frequency transistor amplifier —the tuned band-pass amplifier. For this purpose the term 'high frequency' applies to any band of frequencies above the audible range, extending upwards to the limit at which it is possible to achieve useful power gain.

As mentioned in § 7.8 two types of high-frequency amplifiers are in general use, tuned amplifiers and untuned wide-band or video amplifiers. The former type is usually matched while the latter is almost invariably a cascade of unmatched stages.

The tuned amplifier group may be further subdivided into narrow-band and wide-band amplifiers. For our present purpose narrow-band amplifiers are considered to satisfy the following conditions:

(i) The transistor parameters are constant throughout the pass-band.

(ii) Simple approximations to the properties of circuit components such as transformers may be made.

This chapter is concerned largely with the properties of this type of amplifier but wide-band tuned amplifiers, in which neither of the above conditions is fulfilled, are considered briefly. The chapter ends with a description of a procedure for the measurement of input and output resistance and an outline of methods of gain control in high-frequency amplifiers.

It should be emphasized that, although this chapter discusses the formulae for tuned circuits in some detail and presents a design example, it is intended to supplement rather than replace design information from other sources. There is a wealth of data on the design of coupling circuits for vacuum-tube amplifiers (cf. for example reference [1]) which can be used for transistor tuned amplifiers provided the differences in the characteristics of the active devices are kept in mind. One of the chief purposes of this chapter is to enable the reader to apply such information to transistors.

14.2. General features of tuned-amplifier operation

The properties of tuned amplifiers may be described by means of a general curve of matched power gain vs. frequency such as

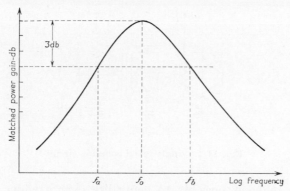

FIG. 14.1. General form of the curve of matched power gain vs. frequency for a tuned amplifier.

that shown schematically in Fig. 14.1. The power gain at the centre frequency f_0 is defined as the stage gain. The two frequencies f_a, f_b at which the power gain has dropped to one-half of the centre frequency gain (i.e. is down by 3 db) define the 3 db bandwidth or pass-band (f_b-f_a).

The characteristic of Fig. 14.1 is obtained by the use of resonant circuits which are included in the transistor input and output networks. By the addition of suitable tap points or coupled windings the inductive elements in these resonant circuits may also serve as impedance matching transformers. At the same time a feedback path may be added to neutralize the internal feedback within the transistor.

Any of the three connections could in principle be used in a tuned amplifier. However, for the reasons discussed in § 7.7.1 the CE and CB connections are the only ones found in practice.

At frequencies well below f_α the CE connection yields more power gain than the CB, and the impedance ratio of the matching transformers is lower. However, the CE gain falls rapidly at frequencies above f_β and in the neighbourhood of f_α there is little to choose between the two connections. The CB connection has the advantages that the internal feedback is lower and the transistor properties (e.g. the h-parameters) show less variation with frequency than those of the CE connection. These charac-

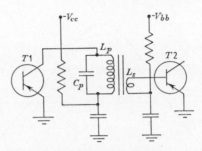

Fig. 14.2. Single-tuned coupling circuit.

teristics make it possible to neutralize over a wider band of frequencies than with the CE connection. The larger impedance ratio required to match a pair of CB stages may in some cases make the transformer difficult to design, since it is not easy to maintain tight coupling (i.e. to have a large fraction of the magnetic flux link both windings) when the two windings differ considerably in numbers of turns.

The characteristics of tuned amplifiers depend to a large extent on the output and input properties of the transistors. For convenience in calculation it is usually best to express these properties in admittance form. The input and output circuits then each consist of a resistance (or conductance) and a capacitance in parallel. In what follows parallel resistances of this type will be identified by capital letters (R's) while small r's will be used for series components.

The resistance R which is in parallel with the primary of the coupling transformer, e.g. that of Fig. 14.2, consists of the following:

1. The input resistance of the driven transistor $T2$ reflected into the primary of the coupling transformer.

2. The parallel output resistance of the driving transistor $T1$.

3. A component R_p whose dissipation is equal to sum of the losses occurring in the coil resistances, in the core of the transformer and in the tuning capacitor. The parallel resistance represents these effects accurately provided $R_p \gg \omega_0 L_p$. If the loss in r_p, the series resistance of the primary coil, is large compared with the other losses we have

$$R_p = \frac{\omega_0^2 L_p^2}{r_p}. \tag{14.1}$$

The total capacitance in the coupling circuit is composed of:

1. The distributed and stray capacitance of the coil and wiring.
2. The input capacitance of the driven transistor.
3. The output capacitance of the driving transistor.
4. The additional tuning capacitance.

Since the effect of the secondary inductance is small the inductance component of the resonant circuit may be assumed equal to L_p, the primary inductance.

14.3. Single-tuned circuits

Assuming constant transistor parameters (§ 14.1), the input and output impedance of the transistor may each be represented by a simple network of passive components R, C, or L which are constant and independent of frequency over the working bandwidth of the amplifier. The amplifier design therefore resolves itself into the following processes:

(a) Evaluation of the equivalent input and output networks of the transistor.

(b) Provision of suitable coupling arrangements to provide a high power transfer from the output of one stage to the input of the next with the desired filter characteristic.

The simplest form of coupling arrangement is one in which the shape of the power gain vs. frequency characteristic is decided by the properties of the primary circuit of the coupling transformer near resonance and the secondary winding is designed to resonate with the input capacitance of the following stage at a frequency well removed from the pass-band of the primary resonant circuit. Such an arrangement, which is called a single-tuned circuit, is shown in Fig. 14.2. Here the collector of $T1$ is connected to a parallel resonant circuit consisting of L_p and C_p, and the secondary winding L_s is tightly coupled to L_p. The frequency response of the transformer is then almost identical to that of a single parallel-resonant circuit.

In principle it is possible to bring the secondary inductance L_s into resonance at the desired centre frequency and to move the resonant frequency of the primary outside the region of interest, but in practice it is usually more convenient to tune the high-impedance primary side of the transformer.

14.3.1. *Filter characteristics of the single-tuned circuit*

The single-tuned circuit has the following properties [1] which determine its filter characteristic:

(i) Peak response is obtained at a frequency very close to the resonant frequency of the collector circuit.

(ii) The impedance of the resonant circuit (Fig. 14.2) at an angular frequency ω, is

$$Z_1 = \frac{d}{d + j(\omega/\omega_0 - \omega_0/\omega)}, \tag{14.2}$$

where $\omega_0 = 2\pi f_0$ is the angular frequency of parallel resonance and d is the dissipation factor which is the inverse of the circuit magnification Q. Thus

$$d = \frac{1}{Q} = \frac{1}{\omega_0 CR} = \frac{\omega_0 L}{R}, \tag{14.3}$$

where R consists of the parallel components mentioned in § 14.2.

(iii) As may be readily seen from equation (14.2) the voltage gain and the (matched) power gain for a single stage each fall by 3 db at angular frequencies given by

$$\left| \frac{\omega}{\omega_0} - \frac{\omega_0}{\omega} \right| = d. \tag{14.4}$$

Thus, if the frequencies given by (14.4) are ω_1 and ω_2, we have

$$\omega_1 - \frac{\omega_0^2}{\omega_1} = \frac{\omega_0^2}{\omega_2} - \omega_2 = \frac{1}{CR}. \tag{14.5}$$

Manipulation of this equation gives

$$\omega_1 \omega_2 = \omega_0^2, \tag{14.6}$$

$$\omega_1 - \omega_2 = \frac{1}{CR}. \tag{14.7}$$

Equation (14.6), which applies for any two frequencies giving the same power gains (not only the 3 db points), shows that the relation between the frequencies is geometric. The curve of Fig. 14.1 is therefore symmetrical if the frequency is plotted logarithmically. From equation (14.7) the 3 db bandwidth is seen to be

$$B = \frac{\omega_1 - \omega_2}{2\pi} = \frac{1}{2\pi CR}. \tag{14.8}$$

Using equations (14.3) and (14.8) we see that

$$Q = \omega_0 CR = \frac{f_0}{B}. \tag{14.9}$$

(iv) For n cascaded identical single-tuned circuits, with no interaction, the power gain is proportional to Z^n and the 3 db bandwidth is

$$B_n = \frac{1}{2\pi CR} \sqrt{(2^{1/n} - 1)}. \tag{14.10}$$

As shown in Table 14.1 the bandwidth ratio $(2^{1/n} - 1)^{\frac{1}{2}}$ decreases quite rapidly as n increases.

TABLE 14.1

Multiple-stage to Single-stage Bandwidth Ratio

Number of stages (n)	1	2	3	4	5	6
$(2^{1/n} - 1)^{\frac{1}{2}}$	1·0	0·64	0·51	0·44	0·39	0·35

(v) If some power ratio P, other than 3 db, is used to define the bandwidth per stage, the overall bandwidth of a cascade of

n stages becomes

$$B_{P,n} = \frac{1}{2\pi CR} \sqrt{(P^{1/n}-1)}, \qquad (14.11)$$

e.g. for a 6 dB bandwidth, $P = 4$.

14.3.2. *Matching characteristics of the single-tuned circuit*

In this section we consider the matching of the input and output of the single-tuned circuit to provide maximum power transfer. Because of the presence of the resonant circuit such matching is more complicated than in low-frequency amplifiers but it is still straightforward provided certain conditions hold. These can be described most readily with the help of Fig. 14.3, which is the equivalent circuit of the coupling network of Fig. 14.2. Here M is the mutual inductance between the transformer windings. The required conditions are:

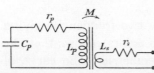

Fig. 14.3. Equivalent circuit of Fig. 14.2.

1. The resonant frequency of the secondary circuit should be much greater than that of the primary.

2. The coupling coefficient K, which indicates the extent to which the magnetic flux of one winding links the other, should be between 0·8 and 1·0. K is defined by the equation

$$M^2 = K^2 L_p L_s. \qquad (14.12)$$

In modern transformers using ferrite cores K can be kept within the above range for frequencies up to about 100 Mc/sec. A common design makes use of a ferrite 'pot', surrounding the (concentric) coils, and a ferrite core within them, which can be moved in or out to provide some adjustment of the self-inductance. This arrangement gives a coupling coefficient of about 0·9 (tight coupling) and also provides good magnetic shielding.

When these conditions are fulfilled the following assumptions can be made:

(i) If the self-inductance depends primarily on the number of turns (because of similar winding geometry or the use of a core of high permeability) the equivalent parallel resistance of R_p, as seen from the secondary terminals, is

$$R_{\text{eq}} \simeq K^2\left(\frac{N_s}{N_p}\right)^2 R_p, \qquad (14.13)$$

where N_p and N_s are the numbers of turns of the primary and secondary windings.

(ii) The condition for maximum power transfer to the load is the same as that applying in the ideal case of zero coil, core, and capacitor losses, viz. that the transformed load impedance must equal the output impedance of the generator. (Thus we ignore the presence of R_p when matching impedances although we use it in the determination of Q.) This condition holds provided the bandwidth—and hence according to equation (14.9), the Q—of the practical circuit is the same as that of the ideal circuit. As might be expected, however, the power transferred to the load is less when the coupling circuit has losses. The actual transferred power, P, is given by

$$P = i^2\left(\frac{Q_0-Q_w}{Q_0}\right)^2 \frac{R_0^2 R_i}{(R_0+R_i)^2}, \qquad (14.14)$$

where
$$Q_0 = R_p/\omega_0 L_p \qquad (14.15)$$

is the Q of the open-circuited transformer measured from the primary side. Q_w is the magnification factor, also measured from the primary side, when the transformer is connected in the circuit. It is called the loaded or working magnification factor. Hence

$$Q_w = \frac{R'R_p}{R'+R_p}\frac{1}{\omega_0 L_p}, \qquad (14.16)$$

where
$$R' = \frac{R_o R_i}{R_o+R_i}. \qquad (14.17)$$

Here R_o is the parallel output resistance of the generator and R_i is the parallel load resistance transformed to the primary side. The equivalent circuit (with C_p and L_p omitted since they present infinite impedance at frequency ω_0) is shown in Fig. 14.4.

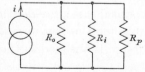

FIG. 14.4. Primary equivalent circuit of single-tuned circuit at the resonant frequency.

A remark about the measurement of Q should be made at this point. In principle Q_0 and Q_w could be obtained by measurement of the 3 db bandwidth with the help of equation (14.9). However, this procedure is usually quite inaccurate and a special instrument called a Q-meter, which is described in most books on radio-frequency measurements, should be used.

From equations (14.15) and (14.16) we obtain the relation

$$\omega_0 L_p = R' \frac{Q_0 - Q_w}{Q_0 Q_w}. \tag{14.18}$$

The effect of circuit losses on the power gain is usually expressed in terms of the insertion loss λ, which is the ratio in db of the power transferred by a loss-free coupling circuit to that transferred by the real coupling arrangement. In a loss-free circuit $Q_0 \to \infty$ and equation (14.14) becomes

$$P_0 = i^2 \frac{R_0^2 R_i}{(R_0 + R_i)^2}. \tag{14.19}$$

Hence
$$\lambda = 10 \log \frac{P_0}{P} = 20 \log\left(\frac{Q_0}{Q_0 - Q_w}\right). \tag{14.20}$$

Some values of insertion loss for various values of the Q ratio q $(= Q_0/Q_w)$ are given in Table 14.2.

TABLE 14.2

Insertion Loss of Coils of Various Q Ratios

Insertion loss (db)	15	10	6	5	4	3	2	1
$q = Q_0/Q_w$	1·2	1·5	2·0	2·2	2·7	3·4	5	9

The information given in these two sections 14.3.1 and 14.3.2 is sufficient for the design of a coupling circuit in the tightly coupled case provided equipment, such as a 'Q-meter', is available for the measurement of transformer properties. Such a design is outlined in the next section.

14.3.3. *Example of coupling-circuit design*

The design of a broadcast-band *IF* amplifier, to meet the following specification, is required:

Centre frequency: 455 kc/s.

Overall 3 db bandwidth: 10 kc/s.

Number of coupling transformers: 3, each single-tuned.

Output resistance and capacitance of transistor: 70 kΩ, 25 $\mu\mu$F in parallel.

Input resistance and capacitance of transistor: 1·1 kΩ, 810 $\mu\mu$F in parallel.

Assuming that the three transformers are equally loaded, the problem is to develop a coupling scheme and compute the insertion loss of each transformer. If three identical stages are used, Table 14.1 shows that, in order to give the required overall bandwidth of 10 kc/s, the bandwidth of each must be 10/0·51 or 19·6 kc/s. Thus the working magnification factor must be

$$Q_w = \frac{455}{19\cdot6} = 23\cdot2.$$

Preliminary coil-design data may be obtained from manufacturers' information on ferrite cores [2]. In the present case a suitable core, upon which was wound a coil of 50 turns of 'Litz' stranded wire, was found to give a self-inductance of 0·76 mH with an unloaded magnification factor (Q_0) of 120. Hence the equivalent parallel loss resistance is

$$R_p = \omega_0 L Q_0 = 257 \text{ k}\Omega,$$

while the net equivalent parallel resistance in the circuit must be

$$R = \omega_0 L Q_w = 49\cdot7 \text{ k}\Omega.$$

This is made up from the output resistance, the transformed input resistance, and the loss resistance, all in parallel. The first two of these must therefore contribute 61·6 kΩ; under matched conditions they will be equal and hence each must be 123 kΩ. The generator resistance of 70 kΩ must therefore be transformed to reflect 123 kΩ across the whole coil. This may be done by connecting the collector to a tap on the primary winding at a fraction $(70/123)^{\frac{1}{2}}$ or 0·754 of the whole winding (38 turns). The secondary load of 1·1 kΩ must be transformed to 123 kΩ across the whole primary; the turns ratio is therefore 10·6:1 and 4·72 turns are required on the secondary. (In practice 5 turns will have to be used.)

These transformer data are shown in Fig. 14.5. The dots indicate the phase relation between primary and secondary voltages—an important factor when neutralization is considered below. It remains to estimate the reflected reactances and compute the required tuning capacitance C_t.

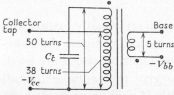

FIG. 14.5. Single-tuned interstage transformer.

The transistor output capacitance of 25 $\mu\mu$F, connected between the collector tap and the end of the primary winding connected to the power supply (the 'signal earth') reflects approximately 25(38/50)² or 14·4 $\mu\mu$F across the whole primary. The input capacitance of the following stage, 810 $\mu\mu$F, is similarly transformed to approximately 8·1 $\mu\mu$F. The total capacitance reflected is therefore 22·5 $\mu\mu$F. The tuning capacitance required to bring a 0·75 mH coil into resonance at 455 kc/s is 163 $\mu\mu$F, so that C_t should be 140·5 $\mu\mu$F. An allowance of about 5 $\mu\mu$F may be made for stray wiring capacitance, etc., so that in practice C_t would be made 135 $\mu\mu$F and the inductance would be 'trimmed' by adjustment of the iron core to bring the circuit into resonance.

The insertion loss of each transformer is found, from equation (14.18) to be 20 log 1·24, or 1·9 db.

In this example the portion of the winding between collector and battery (38 turns) could form the whole primary coil. The secondary winding would then be unchanged, but the capacitance required to bring the smaller primary winding to resonance would be larger. The practice of 'tapping down' on a large winding is commonly adopted because in many cases the inductance required between the collector and the signal earth is quite small and it may prove difficult to obtain a high value of Q_0 when using a small inductance with a large capacitance. As an example, consider a popular type of transistor, much used for 455 kc/s amplification in radio receivers, whose R_0 is about

5 kΩ. To obtain a (loaded) Q_w of 35, which is typical in this sort of application, an inductance between the collector and signal earth of only 25 μH is needed. The tuning capacitor, if placed across this inductance, would have to be 4,888 $\mu\mu$F. Such a low ratio of L to C would result in a low Q_0 unless rather expensive components were used. By connecting a smaller capacitor across a larger inductance, tapped at 25 μH, a relatively inexpensive high-Q transformer may be built.

14.3.4. *Other single-tuned coupling schemes*
Our attention has so far been confined to a coupling scheme which is equivalent to a single parallel resonant circuit, followed

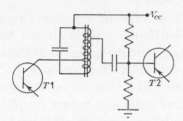 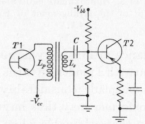

FIG. 14.6. Single-tuned circuit employing an auto-transformer.

FIG. 14.7. Coupling transformer with series resonant secondary.

by an ideal isolating transformer. An obvious modification consists of replacing the isolating transformer by an auto-transformer, thus obtaining the tapped tuned transformer of Fig. 14.6. This is quite satisfactory provided the base bias resistors are large compared with the base-input impedance at signal frequency so that negligible signal current is diverted from the base by these resistors.

Fig. 14.7 shows a more fundamental change; instead of bringing the high-impedance (collector) side into parallel resonance, the low-impedance (base) side is brought into series resonance. The primary winding L_p is untuned and serves only as a coupling winding. An approximate equivalent circuit for this arrangement, in which all resistances have been transferred to the secondary side, is shown in Fig. 14.8. Here the output capacitance of $T1$ is neglected and r_i and C' are series components of the input impedance of $T2$, i.e. components of the complex h_i for this transistor. Note that it is now necessary to consider the series rather than the parallel components, initially at least, in order to determine the value of the external tuning capacitor C. Once this has been done we can convert to parallel components as shown below and make use of formulae mentioned earlier in

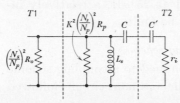

this chapter. An alternative and somewhat more direct method would be to use series components throughout—in which case series analogues of equations (14.15), (14.16), and (14.18) would be required.

FIG. 14.8. Approximate equivalent circuit of the arrangement of Fig. 14.7.

This type of coupling circuit is particularly useful if the impedance ratio is very large. It can combine a high impedance ratio with a moderate turns ratio since the voltage across $(r_i + C')$ can be made considerably smaller than that across L_s. The transformer may thus have a lower ratio and tighter coupling than that attainable when a parallel resonant circuit is used.

The two capacitances in Fig. 14.8 may be combined to give

$$C'' = \frac{CC'}{C+C'}. \tag{14.21}$$

If we ignore core and capacitor losses we may put, as in equation (14.1),

$$R_i = \frac{\omega_0^2 L_s^2}{r_i}, \tag{14.22}$$

where R_i is a resistance in parallel with C'' and L_s. Then from equations (14.17) and (14.18), assuming that the transformed value of R_0 is equal to R_i, we obtain

$$\omega_0 L_s = \tfrac{1}{2} R_i \frac{Q_0 - Q_w}{Q_0 Q_w} \tag{14.23}$$

or, with the help of (14.22),

$$\omega_0 L_s = 2 r_i \frac{Q_0 Q_w}{Q_0 - Q_w}. \tag{14.24}$$

As in the parallel resonant case described earlier, a tapped auto-transformer may be used as a coupling device if desired.

14.4. Double-tuned circuits

The rapid reduction of bandwidth as synchronous (i.e. tuned to the same frequency) single-tuned stages are cascaded has already been noted. This would be partly overcome if the top of the amplitude response curve were made flatter and the 'skirts' made steeper. Additional steepness of the skirts would also provide better discrimination between desired and undesired signals whose frequencies differ by a small amount. Both these requirements can be met if the coupling transformers are double-tuned, i.e. the primary and secondary circuits are tuned separately to resonance at the same frequency and coupled together.

A general discussion of the properties of double-tuned circuits is outside the scope of this book; they are treated extensively in references [1] and [3] while the entirely analogous theory of coupled oscillators will be found in references [4] and [5]. We shall confine ourselves to a qualitative description of the effect of transformer properties on the frequency response of the circuit and shall present formulae to make possible a preliminary design.

If the two circuits are identical, the behaviour is most readily described in terms of the very strong dependence on the product KQ. When $KQ \ll 1$ the shape of the amplitude response curve is very similar to that of two identical isolated single-tuned circuits in cascade. As KQ is increased towards unity the gain at the band centre rises and the top of the curve becomes flatter, reaching maximum flatness when $KQ = 1$. A further increase in the value of KQ produces a decrease in band centre gain and the appearance of two distinct peaks in the response curve, one above and one below the resonant frequency of the separate windings. The behaviour is quite similar if the primary and secondary circuits are not identical as long as their resonant frequencies, when isolated from each other, are the same.

The circuits are said to be transitionally coupled when the amplitude response is at its flattest, and critically coupled when the power transferred to the load at band centre is highest. If

Q_p and Q_s are the working magnification factors of the primary and secondary circuits respectively, it may be shown that the coefficient of coupling in the transitional case is

$$K_t = \sqrt{\frac{1}{2}\left(\frac{1}{Q_p^2}+\frac{1}{Q_s^2}\right)}, \qquad (14.25)$$

and in the case of critical coupling

$$K_c = \sqrt{\frac{1}{Q_p Q_s}}. \qquad (14.26)$$

In the special case when $Q_p = Q_s = Q$,

$$K_c = K_t = \frac{1}{Q}. \qquad (14.27)$$

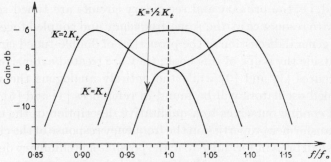

FIG. 14.9. General behaviour of equal Q double-tuned circuit.

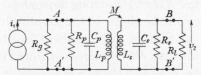

FIG. 14.10. Inductively coupled double-tuned circuit.

The general behaviour of the equal Q double-tuned circuit is summed up by the curves of Fig. 14.9 which gives the amplitude response obtained with various degrees of coupling expressed as fractions of transitional coupling. It is clear that while under-coupling ($K < \frac{1}{2}K_t$) yields a curve which is very similar to that of two isolated single-tuned circuits, the behaviour in the vicinity of transitional coupling is a strong function of K and leads to a double hump when $K > K_t$.

In Fig. 14.10 the equivalent loss resistances of the windings are represented by R_p and R_s while R_g and R_l represent the parallel output and input resistances of the two transistors which are to be coupled.

The available power from the first transistor is

$$P_1 = \tfrac{1}{4}|i_1|^2 R_g. \tag{14.28}$$

The useful power transferred to T_2 is

$$P_2 = \frac{|v_2|^2}{R_l}. \tag{14.29}$$

Hence
$$\frac{P_2}{P_1} = \frac{4}{R_g R_l} \frac{|v_2|^2}{|i_1|^2} = 4 \frac{|Z_{21}|^2}{R_g R_l}, \tag{14.30}$$

where Z_{21} is the forward transfer impedance of the four-terminal circuit $AA'BB'$.

It is shown in reference [1] that the absolute value of Z_{21} is given by
$$Z_{21} = \frac{s\sqrt{(R_1 R_2)}}{\sqrt{\{(1+s^2)^2 - (2s^2 - b)F^2 + F^4\}}}, \tag{14.31}$$

where R_1, R_2 are the total parallel resistance values across the windings, and
$$s = K\sqrt{(Q_p Q_s)}, \tag{14.32}$$

$$b = \left(\frac{Q_p}{Q_s} + \frac{Q_s}{Q_p}\right), \tag{14.33}$$

$$F = \left(\frac{\omega}{\omega_0} - \frac{\omega_0}{\omega}\right)\sqrt{(Q_p Q_s)}. \tag{14.34}$$

In this equation, Q_p and Q_s are the working Q factors of the primary and secondary circuits, and ω_0 is the frequency of parallel resonance to which both primary and secondary circuits are tuned.

It can be shown that the ratio P_2/P_1 is a maximum, for a given bandwidth, coil loss, and coupling coefficient when the working Q factors are equal [6]. This is the matched condition.

14.4.1. Bandwidth of double-tuned, transitionally coupled circuits

The most generally useful type of coupling in double-tuned circuits is transitional coupling. Since it is also the most readily treated analytically, and gives a power transfer that is not too far from the optimum, we shall deal chiefly with this case. Some data applying to the general case (any coupling coefficient) will be given later.

If we set $Q_p = Q_s = Q$ in equation (14.31) we obtain

$$Z_{21} = \frac{KQ\sqrt{(R_1 R_2)}}{\sqrt{\{(1+K^2Q^2)^2 - 2(K^2Q^2-1)F^2 + F^4\}}}. \qquad (14.35)$$

For transitional coupling $KQ = 1$ and

$$|Z_{21}| = \frac{\sqrt{(R_1 R_2)}}{\sqrt{(4+F^4)}}. \qquad (14.36)$$

Expression (14.36) should be compared with the absolute value $|Z_1|$ of the impedance of a single parallel-tuned circuit which may be obtained from equation (14.2). Thus

$$|Z_1| = \frac{d^2}{\sqrt{\{d^2 + (\omega/\omega_0 - \omega_0/\omega)^2\}}}. \qquad (14.37)$$

Because of the dependence upon F^4 instead of F^2, the curve which is obtained by plotting $|Z_{21}|$ against frequency is flatter at the top and has steeper edges than the curve obtained from equation (14.37). This means that the bandwidth of a cascade of double-tuned circuits, each isolated from the others by a unilateral network, may be made to decrease more slowly than in the single-tuned case if all circuits are tuned to the same frequency. This is not true if the successive single-tuned circuits are resonant at different frequencies ('stagger tuned'). By grouping such stages in cascades of pairs the same $(4+F^4)^{-\frac{1}{2}}$ law can be made to hold. Indeed, we can synthesize a tuning curve in which the power of F is $2n$, where n is the number of independent tuned circuits [1].

To find the bandwidth of a single stage at an arbitrary power ratio P, we note that the power gain G_m of a matched stage is proportional to $|Z_{21}|^2$, i.e.

$$G_m \propto \frac{1}{4+F^4}. \qquad (14.38)$$

At band centre $F = 0$. The values of F at which the power gain is reduced by a factor 'p' are therefore given by setting

$$4+F^4 = 4p.$$

With the help of equation (14.34) and the relation $\omega_1 \omega_2 = \omega_0^2$, which holds for any circuit satisfying an equation of the form of (14.34), the two real roots may be written as ω_1 and ω_2 where

$$\omega_1 - \omega_2 = \omega_0 \frac{\sqrt{2}}{Q} (p-1)^{\frac{1}{4}}. \tag{14.39}$$

Hence the bandwidth B_p at a power ratio p is

$$B_p = \frac{\omega_1 - \omega_2}{2\pi} = f_0 \frac{\sqrt{2}}{Q} (p-1)^{\frac{1}{4}}. \tag{14.40}$$

In the special case of the 3 db bandwidth, B, $p = 2$ and

$$B = f_0 \frac{\sqrt{2}}{Q}. \tag{14.41}$$

The overall bandwidth of m identical transitionally coupled transformers arranged in cascade, with no interaction, can be found from equations (14.38) to (14.40) if $p^{1/m}$ is substituted for p. Thus the overall bandwidth at a power ratio p is

$$B_{p,m} = f_0 \left(\frac{\sqrt{2}}{Q}\right)(p^{1/m}-1)^{\frac{1}{4}}, \tag{14.42}$$

which is the bandwidth of a single stage between the same $1/p$ power points, multiplied by $(p^{1/m}-1)^{\frac{1}{4}}$, the bandwidth ratio. Some shrinkage factors for the case $p = 2$ (3 db bandwidth) are given for various values of m in Table 14.3.

TABLE 14.3

Multiple-stage to Single-stage Bandwidth Ratio for Double-tuned Circuits

Number of stages (m)	1	2	3	4	5	6
$(2^{1/m}-1)^{\frac{1}{4}}$	1·00	0·80	0·71	0·66	0·62	0·59

A comparison of this table with Table 14.1 shows that the reduction of bandwidth is appreciably smaller than in the single-tuned case.

14.4.2. *Outline of design procedure for double-tuned circuits*

In this section we shall summarize the design procedure for double-tuned circuits but shall not consider numerical values, which may be determined by methods analogous to those used in § 14.3.3. We shall assume that the bandwidth, generator, and load resistances are specified, and that the unloaded Q factor is known.

Let R_p, R_s be the equivalent parallel loss resistances of the primary and secondary windings. Let R_0, R_i be the generator and load resistances respectively. We assume that the unloaded Q factors of the windings are equal and identified by the symbol Q_0.

Considering the primary:

$$R_p = \omega_0 L_p Q_0, \qquad \frac{R_p R_0}{R_p + R_0} = \omega_0 L_p Q_w,$$

where Q_w is the primary loaded Q factor. Hence

$$R_0 = \left(1 + \frac{R_0}{R_p}\right)\omega_0 L_p Q_w = \left(1 + \frac{R_0}{\omega_0 L_p Q_0}\right)\omega_0 L_p Q_w$$

and
$$L_p = \frac{R_0(1 - Q_w/Q_0)}{\omega_0 Q_w}. \tag{14.43}$$

We have already observed that maximum power will be transferred into the secondary load when the working Q factors of primary and secondary circuits are the same. Assuming that this condition applies we have

$$L_s = \frac{R_i(1 - Q_w/Q_0)}{\omega_0 Q_w}. \tag{14.44}$$

Equations (14.43) and (14.44), together with the requirement that $L_p C_p = L_s C_s = 1/\omega_0^2$, contain almost all the necessary design information. Usually, however, it is the bandwidth which is specified rather than Q_w and we therefore seek to express the bandwidth in terms of Q_w. In the special case of transitional coupling we have the simple relation $B Q_w/f_0 = \sqrt{2}$ from equation (14.41). In the more general case [6] when $K = nK_t$ $(0 < n < 1)$ a similar relation may be obtained from equation (14.35). In this way Fig. 14.11 has been prepared, relating the fractional bandwidth B/f_0 and the working magnification factor Q_w to the fractional coupling K/K_t, the only restriction being that the primary and secondary Q factors must be the same.

In practice the two windings are usually wound to the same

inductance value and their spacing adjusted until they have
the required coefficient of coupling. Either one or both could
then be tapped (as in § 14.4.3). Such a coupling scheme is
illustrated in Fig. 14.12. Alternatively, the base of the second
stage could be connected to a 'capacitor tap' as shown in
Fig. 14.13. In this case the tapping ratio is the ratio of the

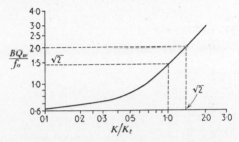

FIG. 14.11. Fractional bandwidth and working
magnification factor as functions of fractional
coupling.

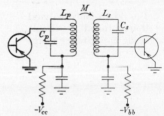

FIG. 14.12. Double-tuned circuit
using tapped windings.

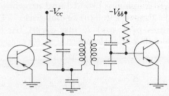

FIG. 14.13. Double-tuned circuit
with secondary capacitor tap.

capacitive reactances, and the two capacitors in series must
present the required tuning capacitance.

In high-frequency broad-band amplifiers (e.g. 20 Mc/sec
bandwidth at 60 Mc/sec centre frequency) the required coupling
coefficient may be quite large (> 0.5). The design of the inductive components may then be simplified and their cost made
lower by the use of the coupling networks shown in Fig. 14.14
which are electrically equivalent to those of Figs. 14.12 and
14.13. The circuits of Fig. 14.14 must, of course, be isolated
by blocking capacitors from the d.c. bias voltage of the transistors. In circuit b the bias circuits may be simpler since the
connection between X and Y may be a d.c. open circuit. The

circuit *a* has the advantage that the coupling coefficient is easily adjusted.

In narrow-band double-tuned amplifiers a capacitor C_m, connected as shown in Fig. 14.15, may be used to give the desired coupling. In this case $K = C_m/\sqrt{(C_p C_s)}$.

Many other coupling schemes, devised originally for vacuum-

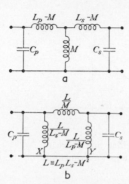

a

b

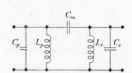

FIG. 14.14. Coupling networks used in high-frequency broad-band amplifiers. (*a*) *T*-network. (*b*) π-network. The values of L and K are given by the following equations:

$$L = L_p L_s - M^2,$$

$$K = \frac{M}{(L_s - M)(L_p - M)}.$$

FIG. 14.15. Narrow-band double-tuned circuit using capacitance coupling.

tube amplifiers [7], may be applied to transistors if modifications, to take account of the relatively low input and output impedances, are made.

14.5. Practical methods of neutralizing *CB* and *CE* amplifiers

The coupling transformers described in the preceding sections serve to match impedances and to shape the pass-band, but the behaviour of the amplifier is predictable only if the stages are individually neutralized. If signal energy can pass backwards through the amplifier the effects mentioned in § 7.7 will be present—the most important consequences being an undesirable peaking of the frequency-response curve, which in an extreme case may lead to oscillation, and a lack of isolation between the tuned circuits of the individual stages. This unwanted coupling means that the tuned circuits of an n-stage amplifier form an n-fold tuned transformer, so that the tuning of any one stage affects that of all the others.

Two typical unilateral CB stages are shown in Fig. 14.16. The first of these is bridge-neutralized and the neutralization condition is $r_{bb'}/R_n = C_n/C_c$, where the bridge elements corre-

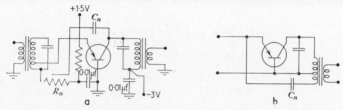

FIG. 14.16. CB unilateral stages. (a) Bridge neutralized. (b) Impedance neutralized.

spond to those of Fig. 7.14. The resistance R' in that figure is so large that it is normally omitted. In this circuit the input is 'floating' so that an isolating input transformer must be used. The second circuit of Fig. 14.16 is impedance-neutralized and a common ground may be used provided that the two sections of the input transformer are tightly coupled. The magnitude of C_n depends on the transformer ratio as discussed in § 7.7.1. The resistance R_n, which is in parallel with C_n in the complete impedance neutralization circuit, is so large for the CB connection that it may be omitted.

In the outline of neutralization methods given in Chapter VII it was pointed out that admittance neutralization of the CE stage may be carried out quite readily using the hybrid-π parameters. This type of neutralization is sometimes used in wideband tuned amplifiers. However, when the required bandwidth is not too great it is usually more convenient to use series resistance and capacitance (impedance neutralization) and it is then best to transform the hybrid-π circuit, at the frequency of interest, to a π or T circuit. To obtain a π equivalent circuit, for example, a comparison of the y parameters of the hybrid-π

and the π circuits is made. The resulting π circuit elements are not, in general, independent of frequency and are only applicable to narrow-band amplifiers in which the elements may be considered as constants over the pass band.

In this way the hybrid-π circuit of Fig. 14.17 is transformed to the π of Fig. 14.18. The actual computation, though simple in principle, is tedious and will be omitted. An excellent discussion of it has been given by Jansson [8] whose results are outlined, for convenience, below. All elements of Fig. 14.18

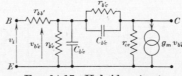

FIG. 14.17. Hybrid-π circuit.

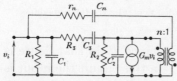

FIG. 14.18. π circuit, equivalent to hybrid-π at a single frequency. Neutralizing elements are also shown.

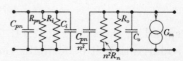

FIG. 14.19. Equivalent circuit of unilateral CE stage with neutralization loss included.

except C_3 are frequency dependent. The elements responsible for undesired feedback are C_3 and R_3, which are given in terms of the hybrid-π parameters by

$$R_3 = r_{bb'}\left[1+\frac{C_{b'e}}{C_{b'c}}\right]+\frac{1+r_{bb'}/r_{b'e}}{r_{b'c}\,\omega^2 C_{b'c}^2}, \tag{14.45}$$

$$C_3 = \frac{C_{b'c}}{1+(r_{bb'}/r_{b'e})-(r_{bb'}\,C_{b'e}/r_{b'c}\,C_{b'c})}. \tag{14.46}$$

We now add a phase-inverting transformer and two neutralizing elements r_n, C_n as shown in Fig. 14.18, to make the current in the external feedback path equal in amplitude and opposite in phase to that flowing through C_3 and R_3. If the transformer ratio is $n:1$ the values of the neutralizing elements are $C_n = nC_3$ and $r_n = R_3/n$. The equivalent circuit of the resulting unilateral stage is shown in Fig. 14.19. The values of the circuit elements are given by the following formulae:

$$R_i = r_{bb'} + r_{b'e} \frac{r_{b'e} + r_{bb'}}{r_{b'e} + r_{bb'} + \omega^2 (C_{b'e} + C_{b'c})^2 r_{b'e}^2 r_{bb'}}, \qquad (14.47)$$

$$C_i = \frac{C_{b'e} + C_{b'c}}{\{1 + (r_{bb'}/r_{b'e})\}^2 + \omega^2 (C_{b'e} + C_{b'c})^2 r_{bb'}^2}, \qquad (14.48)$$

$$G_0 = \frac{1}{R_0} = g_{ce} + g_{b'c} + g_m \frac{g_{b'c}(g_{bb'} + g_{b'e}) + \omega^2 C_{b'e} C_{b'c}}{(g_{bb'} + g_{b'e})^2 + \omega^2 C_{b'e}^2}, \qquad (14.49)$$

$$C_0 = C_{b'c} \left[1 + \frac{g_m(g_{bb'} + g_{b'e})}{(g_{bb'} + g_{b'e})^2 + \omega^2 C_{b'e}^2} \right], \qquad (14.50)$$

$$G_m = \frac{g_m}{[(1 + r_{bb'}/r_{b'e})^2 + \{r_{bb'}\,\omega(C_{b'e} + C_{b'c})\}^2]^{\frac{1}{2}}}. \qquad (14.51)$$

The effect of r_n and C_n on the input and output impedances is obtained by transforming the series circuit formed by them into an equivalent shunt CR which will appear across the input terminals. The same shunt CR, multiplied by n^2, the impedance ratio of the transformer, will appear across the output terminals.

Thus, if R_n, X_n are the equivalent parallel components of the series circuit r_n, C_n, we have

$$R_n = \frac{r_n^2 + 1/\omega^2 C_n^2}{r_n}, \qquad (14.52)$$

$$X_n = \frac{r_n^2 + 1/\omega^2 C_n^2}{1/\omega C_n} \quad \text{or} \quad C_{pn} = \frac{1}{\omega X_n} = \frac{C_n}{1 + \omega^2 r_n^2 C_n^2}. \qquad (14.53)$$

These elements are also shown in Fig. 14.19. A numerical example in which the above formulae are used has been given by Jansson [8].

14.5.1. *Imperfect neutralization: the stability factor*

If the neutralization is incomplete, i.e. the stage is under-neutralized, a residual feedback impedance, which will be almost purely capacitive, will remain. In Fig. 14.20 it is shown as a small capacitance C. The feedback through C can lead to oscillation if the product of the forward and

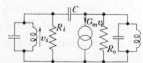

Fig. 14.20. Incompletely neutralized *CE* stage.

reverse feedback gains exceeds unity, and the overall phase shift around the loop is 360°. Assuming resonant circuits of similar Q factors at input and output terminals, it turns out [8] that a matched stage will oscillate at one of the two frequencies at which the gain is reduced by 3 db if

$$C \geqslant 4\left(\frac{Q_0}{Q_0-Q_w}\right)^2 \frac{2}{\omega G_m R_i R_o}, \tag{14.54}$$

where the numerical factor 4 is the closed-loop loss due to matching, the bracketed term is the coil loss, and the further factor 2 arises from the loss of $\sqrt{2}$ at the input and output terminals due to operation at the 3 db point.

It is convenient to define a stability factor S, which is the ratio of the feedback capacitance which will just allow oscillation to the actual residual capacitance. It is generally found that adequate stability combined with negligible interaction between successive tuned circuits can be obtained if $S \geqslant 4$. This criterion should not be taken too literally however, as operating conditions may vary considerably. For example, the gain of a stage is often controlled by varying the emitter current (see § 14.8). For very small values of I_e the input and output resistances become very large and produce a decrease of stability factor which may exceed the improvement in stability arising from reduction in gain.

14.5.2. *Adjustment of neutralized amplifiers*

Transistor-manufacturing techniques have now been improved to such a point that it is possible to calculate the values of the components required to make an amplifier stage unilateral with some assurance that the performance will be satisfactory. However, trial and error methods are often required in the final adjustment. It is a simple matter to adjust the neutralizing components if access can be had to a signal generator capable of giving an amplitude modulated output of the order of one volt. The signal generator output is fed to the *output* terminals of the amplifier and a diode probe is used to explore the base circuits of each stage in turn. The neutralizing elements are adjusted for minimum detected signal. It will usually be found that the capacitor value is much more critical than that of the resistor; the latter may often be fixed at a value that is approximately correct or may even be left out in low-gain amplifiers.

14.6. Wide-band tuned amplifiers

In this section we consider briefly the factors affecting the design of wide-band tuned amplifiers which for the present purpose are defined as tuned amplifiers whose fractional bandwidth, i.e. $(f_b - f_a)/f_0$ in Fig. 14.1, is of the order of one-tenth or larger. The methods by which bandwidth may be increased include the following:

1. In matched amplifiers:
   (a) Admittance neutralization (§ 7.7.3) may be used.
   (b) Double-tuned transformers may be used to increase the stage bandwidth.
   (c) Staggered tuning or negative feedback may be used to increase the bandwidth of a multistage amplifier without necessarily requiring a commensurate increase in stage bandwidth.

The application of procedures (b) and (c) to vacuum tube amplifiers has been discussed fully by Valley and Walman [1]. The design procedure given by them is applicable to transistor amplifiers as long as the reduction of current gain at the highest frequencies is negligible. If this is not the case, and a predictable frequency response is required, it is possible in principle to insert equalizing networks between stages to compensate for variations in current gain. This is not very practicable, however, because such networks inevitably cause loss of gain and must be adjusted to suit individual transistors. Operating a transistor in a wide-band stage at frequencies close to f_α produces an asymmetric response curve because the transistor gain falls off at the higher-frequency end of the pass band as fast as the response of the tuned circuit can rise or fall. This is one reason why a CB stage is sometimes preferred for wide-band applications; at frequencies near f_α the rate of change of α with frequency is less than that of β. In effect the CB stage may be looked upon as a CE amplifier in which the bandwidth has been increased at the expense of the gain by means of local negative feedback (see Chapter XV).

2. The resistances connected in parallel with the input and output circuits of the transistors may be made considerably smaller than the values required for matching. The purpose of this may be seen as follows:

Equations (14.8) and (14.41), supplemented by (14.3), show that any attempt to increase the bandwidth of a matched tuned amplifier (for which R is constant) will ultimately be limited by the residual capacitances listed in § 14.2. For maximum power transfer these capacitances should be matched and their ratio thus decides the turns ratio of the coupling transformer. In order to increase the bandwidth further it is necessary to add parallel 'damping' resistance to the primary and secondary windings, i.e. to mismatch the transistor. Sometimes it is sufficient to add this damping resistance to one winding only.

Under proper conditions this mismatching has the following advantages:

(i) It is possible to exchange power or voltage gain for bandwidth over a limited range. This cannot be carried very far because neither the total resistance nor the capacitance will remain constant over the pass band of a very wide band amplifier. In general a tuned transistor amplifier does not possess a simple figure of merit analogous to the constant gain-bandwidth product of a tuned vacuum-tube amplifier. However, the ability to effect this exchange, even over a limited range of bandwidths, is of considerable value.

(ii) Neutralization is no longer required. While the forward gain is reduced by the mismatch loss the loop gain to an undesired feedback signal is reduced by the square of the same quantity. This may be sufficient to lower the tuning interaction between the separate resonant circuits to an acceptable level. The technique offers a simple alternative to wideband neutralization at the price of some gain reduction.

(iii) Gain may be varied over a wide range with negligible change in tuning or bandwidth. This is difficult to accomplish in matched amplifiers (see § 14.8 below).

An illustration of the use of mismatching to extend the bandwidth and eliminate neutralization is given by Peniston and

Hall [9] who describe an amplifier with a gain of 100 dB, a centre frequency of 60 Mc/sec and a half-power bandwidth of 20 Mc/sec. Eight tetrode transistors are used. A mismatch ratio of 5 is found to be sufficient to ensure an acceptably small amount of interaction between the tuned circuits and thus to make the predicted and measured response curves agree closely. The gain can be varied over a range of 60 dB with negligible change in the tuning or the bandwidth by controlling the bias voltage applied to the second base of three of the tetrodes. This would have been quite impracticable had these stages been neutralized and matched.

The loss of gain due to mismatching at the output of a stage may be readily determined. If we put $R_l = mR_0$, where m is defined as the mismatch ratio, the portion of the collector signal power entering the load is $i_c^2 R_0 m/(1+m)^2$. The maximum value is the available power $i_c^2 R_0/4$, obtained when $m = 1$. The mismatch loss P, which is defined as the ratio of the power flowing in a matched load to the power in a load mR_0, is

$$P = \frac{4m}{(1+m)^2}. \tag{14.55}$$

In an n-stage amplifier this quantity expressed in db represents the loss per stage for all but the first stage. The mismatch loss (in db) at the output of the first stage must therefore be added to n terms of the form (14.55) to give the total mismatch loss.

14.7. Measurement of input and output resistance

The situation may arise in which little is known of the high-frequency parameters of a transistor, and elaborate measuring equipment is not available. It is possible to measure the input and output impedances in such a case with the aid of a signal generator and a grid-dip meter. The latter, which is a most useful and inexpensive instrument, consists of a low-power vacuum-tube (or transistor) oscillator whose resonant circuit inductance is external to the instrument and is normally a plug-in coil. This coil may be loosely coupled by mutual inductance to the coil of another resonant circuit if the two coils are placed near each other. The grid current (or rectified base current in the transistor version) is registered on a microammeter. If the instrument is coupled to an otherwise unenergized tuned circuit and its oscillator frequency brought to the resonant frequency of that circuit, the meter will show a sharp dip in grid current whose magnitude is a function of the Q factor of the tuned circuit. This dip, which is due to the absorption of energy by the tuned circuit, makes it possible to determine the parallel load presented by the input or output terminals of a transistor, as follows: the transistor is

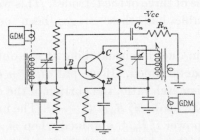

Fig. 14.21. Circuit for the measurement of
transistor input and output impedance.

set up as in Fig. 14.21 between two tuned circuits, and the bias is adjusted to bring the emitter current to a reasonable value (e.g. 1 mA). The input and output inductances are adjusted to bring both circuits to resonance at the chosen frequency and the neutralizing network is balanced by the method indicated above. The grid-dip meter tank coil is now brought within a few inches of the output coil and adjusted so that a reasonable dip is obtained. No signal is applied to the transistor during this process. From this point on neither the meter nor the amplifier may be moved. The transistor is removed from its socket and the output coil is 'trimmed' to bring it into resonance again. (This will be a small adjustment if the fixed capacitance included in the circuit is large compared with the output capacitance of the transistor.) A fixed resistor, inserted between the collector and emitter terminals, may now be chosen to give the same dip as that obtained when the transistor was connected. This fixed resistor must be equal in value to the parallel output resistance of the transistor.

Exactly the same method may be applied in the determination of the parallel resistance of the input circuit.

The parallel capacitance components of the input and output impedances may be calculated from the change in resonant frequency brought about in each tuned circuit by the removal of the transistor. The fixed capacitances across the windings should, of course, now be as small as possible and it is desirable to retune the input and output circuits to satisfy this condition. The grid-dip meter is again used to indicate the occurrence of resonance; the dip frequencies are determined by coupling energy from a signal generator into the dip meter by means of a small coil. The signal generator frequency at which the dip meter current reaches a maximum is then the frequency required.

These measurements can of course be made more accurately and quickly with an admittance bridge, but the bridge is expensive and usually requires a considerable amount of auxiliary equipment.

14.8. The control of gain in high-frequency amplifiers

To complete our brief discussion of tuned amplifiers we consider methods of controlling the gain automatically to enable the transistor to handle a wide range of incoming signal amplitudes. This automatic gain control (AGC), which finds its main application in radio receivers, results from the application of a d.c. bias voltage obtained by rectification and filtering of the output voltage of the amplifier. The d.c. voltage may be used to control a transistor parameter (internal control) or the amount of negative feedback in the circuit (external control). The method may also be applied to the automatic control of low-level video amplifiers (Chapter XV) and to manual gain control systems if an external d.c. source is used.

The internal control methods are the following:

1. Variation of emitter d.c. current I_e—usually by control of the base current. Appreciable control of current gain may be obtained in this way if the emitter current is sufficiently small. This is demonstrated by Fig. 14.22 which shows the change with emitter current of the operating power gain of a 2N247 drift

transistor when operated in an (unneutralized) single-tuned amplifier at 0·5 Mc/sec. It should, however, be noted that this amplifier was matched for an emitter current of 1·0 mA and both the input and output resistances increased and the accompanying capacitances decreased as the emitter current was decreased. Consequently part of the reduction in operating power gain arose from impedance changes.

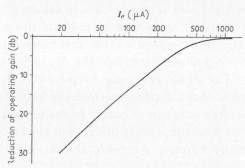

FIG. 14.22. Variation of operating power gain with emitter current for a 2N247 drift transistor amplifier.

2. Variation of collector voltage V_{ce}. This method makes use of the change of current gain with collector voltage in the saturation region ($V_{ce} \leqslant 0·5$ volt). It is therefore restricted to low-level stages. Increases of input and output impedance occur with reduction of the control parameter (V_{ce}) in this case also.

The chief disadvantages of the internal methods of controlling gain are the detuning and impairment of neutralization that occur because of the change of input, output, and feedback admittances (cf. equations (14.45) to (14.50)). Detuning also occurs in the external-gain control method described below. Consequently stages incorporating gain control are usually mismatched intentionally so that these effects will be lessened. In extremely critical cases it is possible to make use of a complementary change of resistance in a reverse-biased silicon junction diode in the base-emitter circuit to balance changes in input resistance due to bias variation [10]. This arrangement makes it possible to have a stage more nearly matched without an objectionable change in bandwidth as the AGC bias is altered,

A circuit suitable for either type of internal control [11] is shown in Fig. 14.23. If the transistor is operated well away from the saturation region but at a low value of emitter current, a decrease in I_b produces a reduction in gain. If it is operated near saturation an increase of base current produces a reduction in V_{ce} and hence lowers the gain.

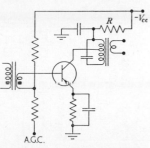

Another practical method of controlling the current gain makes use of the second base of a high-frequency tetrode. It has the advantage that the capacitance required for neutralization varies less than that of a triode.

Fig. 14.23. Circuit for the application of internal methods of controlling gain.

External methods of gain control usually employ auxiliary diodes or transistors as voltage-sensitive resistors, either to vary the amount of negative feedback applied to an amplifier or to act as a voltage-controlled potential divider [12, 13]. One such method, in which a diode is used as a controlled resistor over a limited range of reverse-biased operation, is shown in Fig. 14.24. The small-signal resistance of the diode is sufficiently low in the forward-biased condition that the emitter resistor is adequately by-passed by a capacitor. When the diode is reverse-biased its resistance impedes the by-pass action and produces negative current feedback. In this way the gain may be reduced by about 30 db per stage with no change in emitter current and no loss of signal handling capacity. More complex feedback circuits may be readily devised.

This external diode AGC system requires a larger change of bias voltage than the internal systems. A method of evading this difficulty is to use an external element to improve the performance of an internal control system. One system of this type employs a reverse-biased diode in parallel with the tuned winding of a collector transformer [14]. A change of emitter current resulting from AGC bias causes the diode to conduct, thereby increasing the damping of the tuned circuit. This increases both the mismatch loss and the bandwidth. The latter effect, which causes the bandwidth to be greater for strong signals than for weak ones, may be desirable in receivers. Fig. 14.25 shows a typical arrangement. The diode, which is normally

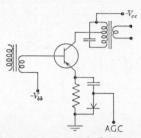

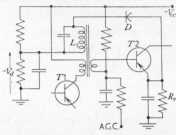

FIG. 14.24. Control of current feedback by means of a diode.

FIG. 14.25. Control of damping resistance by means of a diode.

reverse-biased, has negligible effect until the emitter current of $T2$, reduced by the control bias due to a strong signal, causes the voltage drop across R_e to fall to a value nearly equal to V_d. The diode then becomes forward-biased and begins to shunt the resonant winding L_1. There are several possible arrangements of this type. In one of these the collector is connected to a tap on the resonant winding instead of a separate winding as in the present case. To minimize distortion this method should be applied to a low-level stage.

VIDEO AMPLIFIERS

15.1. Introduction

THE term video amplifier originated in television practice, but is now applied to most amplifiers in which the low-frequency limit may be of the order of tens or hundreds of cycles per second, while the upper limit may extend to hundreds or thousands of kilocycles per second. Thus, although the absolute bandwidth may not be very large, a video amplifier must cover many octaves—i.e. the ratio of maximum to minimum frequency must be large.

Even if it were possible to design suitable matching transformers for frequency ranges of this type their cost would be prohibitive and an unmatched cascade is mandatory. All intermediate stages must therefore use the CE connection. The CB and CC connections are only used as terminal stages; the CC may start and end a chain in order to give a high input resistance and a low output resistance, while the CB may be used as a final stage if very high voltage output is required.

In this chapter we first consider the frequency limits of video amplifiers and describe methods by which the high-frequency response may be extended. Simple equivalent circuits that may be used for practical design work are then described and applied in a discussion of small-signal transient response.

Articles dealing with the design of video amplifiers in considerably greater detail than is possible here are mentioned in the list of references for this chapter [1, 2, 3].

15.2. Frequency limits of video amplifiers

The low-frequency limit of a video amplifier is determined by the same considerations as those discussed, for low-frequency amplifiers, in Chapter XI. The high-frequency limit is set principally by the transistor, both by the reduction in the value of α at high operating frequency and by the increased diversion of current from the external collector circuit to the internal collector capacitance. We now consider how these factors influence the response of the three possible transistor connections.

15.2.1. *The CB stage*

In the discussion of CB video amplifiers we shall make use of the simple high-frequency equivalent T circuit of Fig. 15.1

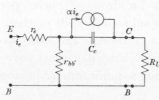

FIG. 15.1. Simple CB high-frequency equivalent circuit.

which is obtained from Fig. 7.7 by omitting the emitter capacitance. This capacitance is in parallel with the small resistance r_ϵ and its effect is normally unimportant at frequencies below f_α. The feedback generator and the internal collector resistance r_c may also be omitted because the load resistance must be small to minimize the effect of collector capacitance on the high-frequency gain. This simple circuit is accurate enough for most CB steady state applications and it gives a picture of transistor operation that is not obscured by second-order effects.

Fig. 15.1 indicates that the high-frequency response of the CB video amplifier may be limited by either or both of the following time constants:

(i) The α time constant $T_\alpha = 1/2\pi f_\alpha$.

(ii) The collector time constant which, assuming $r_{bb'} \ll R_l$, is given by $T_c = C_c R_l$.

In our discussion of the α time constant it is sufficient to consider the modulus of α which is very well represented, for frequencies below $2f_\alpha$, by the following equation:

$$\alpha = \frac{\alpha_0}{1+j(f/f_\alpha)}. \tag{15.1}$$

As indicated in Chapter VII, this expression is similar in form to the response of a circuit consisting of a single capacitance and a resistance.

Each of the above time constants, acting alone, would impose an ultimate rate of attenuation with increase of frequency amounting to 6 db per octave. If the two associated cutoff frequencies f_α and $1/2\pi C_c R_l$ are very different the current gain falls by 3 db from the low-frequency value α_0 at the smaller cutoff frequency. Since CB stages are generally used when a high-voltage output is required, the bandwidth is usually limited, as implied above, by T_c rather than T_α.

15.2.2. *The CE and CC stages*

When rearranged for the CE connection the simple circuit of Fig. 15.1 becomes that of Fig. 15.2. In this case the load resistor is usually the input resistance of the following stage and the collector resistance $r_c(1-\alpha)$ can be neglected. Note, however, that the effective collector capacitance becomes $C_c(1+\beta)$ in agreement with the low-frequency T-circuit of Fig. 7.10.

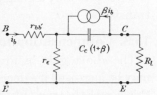

FIG. 15.2. Simple CE high-frequency equivalent circuit.

Since the load resistance is small the input resistance is given by

$$R_i \simeq h_{ie} = r_{bb'} + (1+\beta)r_\epsilon, \qquad (15.2)$$

which is typically between 300 and 1,000 ohms.

The low-frequency current gain is β_0 and the low-frequency voltage gain is

$$A_v = \frac{\beta_0 R_l}{r_{bb'} + (1+\beta_0)r_\epsilon}. \qquad (15.3)$$

As in the case of the CB stage the high-frequency response is controlled by either the current-gain time constant $(T_\beta = 1/2\pi f_\beta)$ or the collector time constant $(T_c \simeq C_c(1+\beta_0)R_l)$.

We note that the product of low-frequency current gain and current-gain cutoff frequency for the CE stage (the current-gain-bandwidth product) is the same as for the CB stage, i.e.

$$\beta_0 f_\beta = \alpha_0 f_\alpha. \qquad (15.4)$$

Similarly for the product of current gain and collector cutoff frequency

$$\frac{\beta_0}{2\pi C_c(1+\beta_0)R_l} = \frac{\alpha_0}{2\pi C_c R_l}. \qquad (15.5)$$

These current-gain-bandwidth products are often used as 'figures of merit' in choosing transistors for (unmatched) video amplifiers. The most suitable transistor will have the largest gain-bandwidth product.

The CC video stage is used almost entirely for matching impedances at the beginning and end of an amplifier chain. In this case the collector capacitance is effectively across the input and the high-frequency cutoff is usually decided by the current gain. Determination of a gain-bandwidth product is complicated by the large amount of feedback inherent in the connection but (15.4) is probably a good general criterion for choosing a suitable transistor.

15.3. Compensation for loss of gain at high frequencies

The above gain-bandwidth products imply that bandwidth may be increased if a decrease of gain can be tolerated. However, this is strictly true only in that part of the frequency spectrum which is dominated by a single time constant. At higher frequencies, where a second time constant comes into play, the gain-bandwidth product will decrease.

The correct approach to this problem of exchanging gain for bandwidth leads to complications that cannot be considered in this book. We can, however, consider some of the common techniques in an elementary manner provided we confine ourselves to signal amplitudes that are constant over the pass band and ignore amplitude and phase characteristics that are special functions of frequency. These methods give results that are only first-order approximations at best, but they form a useful basis for practical work.

15.3.1. *Current-gain compensation*

One of the simplest methods of compensating for the decrease of current gain with frequency consists of using an inductive impedance in parallel with the load. At low frequencies signal current is drawn off through the impedance and the effective gain of the circuit is decreased. As the frequency increases the output-signal current also increases and the current gain of the circuit approaches that of the transistor itself. The upper cutoff frequency is thus extended to the point at which the transistor current gain has dropped to the low-frequency circuit gain.

For CE circuits it is convenient to put an inductance in series with the collector bias resistor. This is illustrated by L in

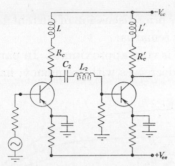

FIG. 15.3. Circuit to illustrate gain compensation and peaking methods.

Fig. 15.3 which may, for example, be chosen so that its react-ance at the CE cutoff frequency is equal to R_c, i.e.

$$L = \frac{R_c}{2\pi f_\beta}. \tag{15.6}$$

At low frequencies, where $\omega L \ll R_c$, the gain is

$$A_{i0} = \frac{\beta_0}{1 + R_i/R_c}, \tag{15.7}$$

where R_i is the low-frequency input resistance of the following stage. (The loss of current in the base bias resistors of the following stage is assumed to be negligible.)

The current gain, as a function of frequency, is given by

$$A_i = \frac{\beta_0}{1 + j\omega/\omega_\beta} \times \frac{R_c + j\omega L}{(R_c + R_i) + j\omega L}. \tag{15.8}$$

Substituting the value of L given in (15.6) and simplifying, this may be written:

$$A_i = \frac{A_{i0}}{1 + jf/f_c},$$

where
$$f_c = f_\beta(1 + R_i/R_c). \tag{15.9}$$

Hence
$$A_{i0}f_c = \beta_0 f_\beta. \tag{15.10}$$

Response curves computed from equations (15.6) and (15.8) are shown in Fig. 15.4. In the uncompensated case it is assumed that $R_c \gg R_i$. In the other cases the power gain is expressed in decibels relative to the low-frequency power gain of the uncompensated amplifier.

We conclude this brief discussion of current gain compensation with the following remarks:

(i) The analysis is very approximate. In particular the variation of R_i, which decreases with frequency, has not been taken

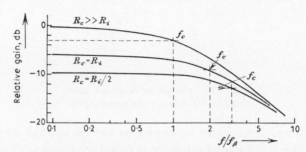

FIG. 15.4. Response curves for a CE gain-compensated amplifier.

into account. This variation will partially offset the loss of current gain of the preceding stage.

(ii) The compensating inductance may be inserted in some other parallel network such as the base bias potentiometer of the stage in question, or the following stage. It is usually preferable, however, to use the lower-resistance collector bias circuit.

(iii) The method is not usually applied to CB stages. The effect of collector capacitance is much more important in this case.

(iv) In CC stages the inductive impedance is usually placed in parallel with the load. The resulting increase of effective load impedance with frequency compensates for the decrease of current gain and tends to hold the input impedance constant.

15.3.2. *Video peaking by means of collector capacitance*

The upper frequency limit of a gain-compensated CE amplifier may be extended by inserting an inductance in series with the output (L_2 in Fig. 15.3) which is chosen to resonate with the collector capacitance at the frequency f_c given by equation (15.9). The effective collector capacitance at this frequency is approximately

$$C_{\text{eff}} = C_c \frac{(1+\beta_0)+[1+(R_i/R_c)]^2}{1+[1+(R_i/R_c)]^2}. \qquad (15.11)$$

There is a conductance associated with this capacitance but its effect is usually negligible. The coupling capacitor C_2 in Fig. 15.3 is much larger than C_{eff} and does not affect the resonant frequency.

In CB stages the inductance is chosen to resonate with C_c at approximately the frequency $1/2\pi C_c R_l$.

The inductances mentioned in these sections (15.3.1 and 15.3.2) may be applied alone or in combination with other elements (e.g. parallel inductance at the input of a stage to reduce the change of input impedance) to several stages of an amplifier [2]. The design of such arrangements may be attacked by quite elementary methods [4] or by rather advanced techniques of circuit analysis [5]. Lack of space prevents consideration of either procedure but before leaving this subject we must discuss briefly the most generally useful method of improving bandwidth at the expense of gain, viz. the employment of negative feedback.

15.3.3. *High-frequency gain compensation and peaking by means of negative feedback*

The simplest application of negative feedback makes use of an un-by-passed emitter resistor. With this arrangement the current-gain-bandwidth product remains approximately constant for all amounts of feedback, and gain can be exchanged for bandwidth as in the simple CE stage. However, the overall current gain is reduced because of the increase of input resistance with feedback and transducer power gain is probably a better criterion of performance. We may choose the (transducer gain)$^{\frac{1}{2}}$-bandwidth product, which is analogous to equation (8.1), as our figure of merit. A straightforward analysis, using the hybrid-π circuit, for example, then shows that this quantity remains constant provided the source resistance is high compared with the input impedance of the stage with feedback. Its value is

$$(G_T)^{\frac{1}{2}}f_c \simeq \beta_0 f_\beta \sqrt{\frac{R_l}{R_s}}, \qquad (15.12)$$

where R_l is the load and R_s the source resistance. If the low-frequency transducer gain G_T is determined from equation (5.45) with the help of Appendix X, equation (15.12) may be used to estimate the cutoff frequency.

Negative feedback and peaking are sometimes combined as

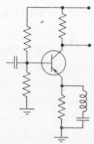

in Fig. 15.5. The emitter resistor introduces negative feedback at all frequencies except those near the resonant frequency of the tuned circuit. This resonant frequency should be close to the cutoff frequency obtained when the resonant circuit is omitted from the amplifier. The effect of adding the resonant circuit is to raise the cutoff frequency by introducing a peak at the upper end of the response curve.

FIG. 15.5. Illustrating peaking by means of negative feedback.

If negative feedback is carried over more than one stage there is usually a small improvement in gain-bandwidth product over the case in which the stages have local feedback. This improvement probably arises because the adverse effect of input impedance on the gain-bandwidth product is diminished for at least one stage within the feedback loop. The application of overall feedback to video amplifiers is governed by the same rules as those outlined in §§ 13.4 and 13.5 for low-frequency amplifiers but, because of the greater effect of distributed capacitance and the larger variations in transistor parameters, an increased effort is required to eliminate positive feedback. Positive feedback, at the high-frequency end of the pass band, is sometimes introduced intentionally to raise the upper frequency limit—a process requiring extremely careful design—but in general the magnitude of the feedback should be negligible at those frequencies at which it has a positive component.

Negative feedback over two or even three stages is often combined with the inductive compensating scheme described

in § 15.3.1 and the video peaking circuit of § 15.3.2 to give a
further increase in bandwidth. The amount of feedback which
may be used in such a compensated amplifier is limited. It is
difficult to assess properly the effects of all the possible sources
of phase shift, and the design is therefore semi-empirical and
will not be considered here.

15.4. The small-signal transient response of video amplifiers

A video amplifier may be used as a small-signal pulse amplifier
whose input consists of a series of rectangular pulses rather than
a smooth continuous wave form. Applications of this type arise
in television and in the detection of nuclear particles and radia-
tions. It is then convenient to describe the performance in terms
of pulse properties such as rise and fall times rather than steady-
state amplitude and phase response. The process is similar to
non-regenerative switching (§ 7.9) except that operation is confined to the active part of the characteristic, i.e. the transistor
is never cut off or saturated. As a result there is no delay time
in the sense of § 7.9.3.2 and the rise and fall times (t_r and t_f) are
equal. As in the large-signal case t_r is the time required for the
output to rise from 10 per cent to
90 per cent of its final value. It is
shown in Fig. 15.6. The fall time
t_f is defined as the time interval
between points that are spaced
from the trailing edge discontinuity (B in Fig. 15.6) by 10 per
cent and 90 per cent of the total
excursion at the trailing edge. This

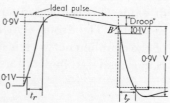

FIG. 15.6. Typical small-signal
output pulse of a video amplifier.

definition is complicated by the presence of pulse droop which
is discussed in the next paragraph. The term 'response time' is
often used to indicate either t_r or t_f.

Since the video pulse amplifier is active under all conditions
of operation, the height of the pulse is not determined by
saturation or by a clamping circuit and the top droops by an
amount which depends on the relation of its length to the

coupling and by-pass (R–C) time constants. When the rise time is short compared with the pulse length t_p, the pulse height at time t is

$$V \simeq V_0 \exp\left\{-t\left(\frac{1}{R_1 C_1} + \frac{1}{R_2 C_2} + \cdots\right)\right\}, \qquad (15.13)$$

where V_0 is the maximum height and $R_1 C_1$, $R_2 C_2$, etc., are the time constants of the coupling and by-pass networks. If the total droop must be small at time t_p, all of the time constants must be large compared with t_p. For example, to limit the droop to 5 per cent when there are two equal time constants, each time constant must be about $40 t_p$. This method of determining coupling or by-pass capacitor size is equivalent to that used in Chapter XI for continuous-signal amplifiers but is more readily applied when pulse length rather than minimum frequency is the pertinent property. The two calculations can be shown to be equivalent by operational or transform methods.

It is also possible to compensate partially for the droop by adding a network whose pulse response is the inverse of that of the coupling circuit. This usually takes the form of a collector decoupling filter, in which a resistor of value R is placed between the collector bias resistor and the power supply, and a capacitor of value C is connected to earth from the junction of the two resistors. The droop is at a minimum when the time constant of the coupling network is equal to CR. This type of compensation is analysed in detail in § 2.3 of Reference [1], Chapter XIV.

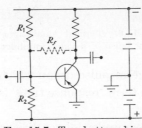

FIG. 15.7. Two-battery bias to eliminate the emitter by-pass capacitor.

For fairly long pulses (e.g. 2 milliseconds) the emitter by-pass capacitors required may be excessively large. It is then common practice to eliminate them by using two power supplies as shown in Fig. 15.7. Base bias current may be supplied from a potentiometer which will not load the preceding stage too heavily. The feedback potentiometer consisting of R_f and R_2 gives slightly better stabilization than the R_1, R_2 arrangement.

15.4.1. *Video pulse-amplifier equivalent circuits*

The performance of a CE video amplifier under pulse conditions may be analysed by means of the simple equivalent circuit of Fig. 7.19. However, in video applications R_l is so small that it absorbs practically all of the output of the current generator. Thus C_c may be neglected and the equivalent circuit takes the form shown in Fig. 15.8, where

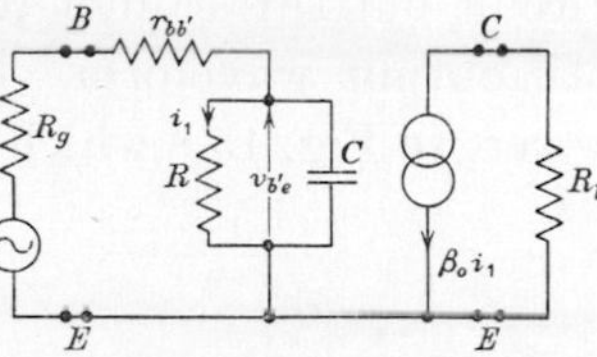

FIG. 15.8. *CE* equivalent circuit for the determination of transient response.

$$R = r_\epsilon/(1-\alpha_0), \qquad C = 0{\cdot}81/r_\epsilon\omega_\alpha,$$

and $\qquad\qquad r_\epsilon = kT/qI_e.$

The following instructive method of deriving this circuit has been given by Cooke-Yarborough [6]: If we substitute the first-order form for β given by equation (7.41) in equation (15.2) we obtain

$$Z_i = (r_{bb'}+r_\epsilon)+\frac{\beta_0 r_\epsilon}{1+j(\omega/\omega_\beta)}. \tag{15.14}$$

As may be seen with the help of equation (7.33) this equation defines an input circuit of the form shown in Fig. 15.8 in which the series resistance is $(r_{bb'}+r_\epsilon)$ instead of $r_{bb'}$, $R = \beta_0 r_\epsilon$ and $C = 1/\beta_0\omega_\beta r_\epsilon = 1/\alpha_0\omega_\alpha r_\epsilon$. These are approximately equal to the components determined from the hybrid-π circuit. The chief difference arises from the fact that the experimentally determined cutoff frequency rather than the true first-order cutoff frequency is used in equation (15.14) (cf. § 7.3.1). The better approximation for C is therefore $C = 0{\cdot}81/r_\epsilon\omega_\alpha$, although the difference is not important in practical work.

For the CC connection the load impedance is in series with r_ϵ and equation (15.14) becomes

$$Z_i = (r_{bb'}+r_\epsilon+Z_l)+\frac{\beta_0(r_\epsilon+Z_l)}{1+j(\omega/\omega_\beta)}. \tag{15.15}$$

If the load is partly reactive ($Z_l = R_l+jX_l$) it is found, after rationalizing, that a term $\beta_0 X_l\omega/\omega_\beta$ forms part of the real term of Z_i. If X_l is a capacitive reactance this term is negative, indicating that a component of negative resistance is reflected into the base circuit by a capacitive load. This negative resistance may cause an overshoot in the pulse output of the amplifier or, in an extreme case, may lead to oscillation.

Equation (15.15) may be represented by a simple equivalent circuit but this cannot readily be applied to the calculation of the output waveform. For the latter purpose it is better to revert to Fig. 15.8 which may be arranged as in Fig. 15.9. This

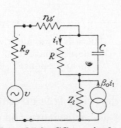

FIG. 15.9. *CC* equivalent circuit for the determination of transient response.

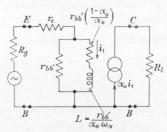

FIG. 15.10. *CB* equivalent circuit for the determination of transient response.

circuit may be applied to the calculation of response time as indicated below.

In the case of a *CB* amplifier whose response is dominated by a change of current gain with frequency, the input impedance rises as the frequency is increased. By an analysis similar to that for the *CE* case [6] we obtain the equivalent circuit of Fig. 15.10 whose component values are indicated on the figure.

15.4.2. *The calculation of response time*

The equivalent circuits of the preceding section may be used in the determination of the transient response of video amplifiers by estimating their time of response to a small-step input of current or voltage. Since the response of each equivalent circuit involves a single time constant T, the response to a step-current input will be of the form

$$i_0 = i_{0s}(1 - e^{-t/T}), \tag{15.16}$$

where i_0 is the change of output current resulting from the application of a sudden step of input current. The final steady state value of i_0 is i_{0s}. The response time $(= t_r = t_f)$ is found from this equation to be $2 \cdot 2T$. The procedure in this section will be to determine the time constants under various operating conditions. The resulting values should be multiplied by $2 \cdot 2$ to give the response times.

15.4.2.1. *The CE response time*

For the CE stage the time constant is determined from Fig. 15.8. If a current source is used the time constant is

$$T_1 = RC \simeq 0 \cdot 81/\omega_\beta.$$

A voltage source causes R to be effectively in parallel with $r_{bb'}$, thus giving a time constant

$$T_2 = \frac{0 \cdot 81}{\omega_\alpha} \frac{r_{bb'}}{(1-\alpha_0)r_{bb'}+r_\epsilon} \qquad (15.17)$$

which may be much shorter than T_1.

The voltage $v_{b'e}$ and the current i_1 in Fig. 15.8 have the form of (15.16) where T is replaced by T_1 or T_2. When a current source is used i_1 reaches a final value equal to the input-current step i_s and the output-current step ultimately reaches $\beta_0 i_s$. When the circuit is driven by a voltage step v_s the output-current step finally attains the value $\beta_0 v_s/(r_{bb'}+R)$.

To illustrate the operation of the CE-connected amplifier under different conditions we consider a transistor for which $r_{bb'} = 300$ ohms, $r_\epsilon = 30$ ohms, $\alpha_0 = 0 \cdot 98$ and $\omega_\alpha = 10^7$ rad/sec. The time constants are:

1. For a current source, $T_1 = 0 \cdot 81/\omega_\beta \simeq 4 \cdot 1$ μsec.
2. For a voltage source, $T_2 \simeq 0 \cdot 7$ μsec.
3. For a source having a resistance of 1,000 ohms: we consider the source resistance to be absorbed into $r_{bb'}$, which therefore becomes 1,300 ohms. Then from equation (15.17) the time constant is found to be $T_3 \simeq 1 \cdot 9$ μsec.

The response times for these three cases are, therefore, $9 \cdot 0$, $1 \cdot 5$, and $4 \cdot 2$ μsec respectively.

15.4.2.2. *The CC response time*

The output of a CC video stage, having a pure resistance load, is determined from the equivalent circuit of Fig. 15.9 to be

$$i_l = \frac{v_s}{R}\left[1-\exp\left(-t\Big/\frac{RC(r_{bb'}+R_g)}{r_{bb'}+R_g+R_l}\right)\right], \qquad (15.18)$$

where i_l is the load current. In the usual case R_g is large compared with R_l and the time constant is approximately $0 \cdot 81/\omega_\beta$.

When a capacitive load is used care must be taken to prevent the output voltage pulse from overshooting too violently because of the reduction of input resistance. This may be done by increasing the value of R_g to provide damping. It has been shown [3] that the output pulse will be critically damped if

$$\left(\omega_\beta + \frac{1}{R'C_l}\right)^2 = \frac{4\omega_\beta\beta_0}{C_l(r_{bb'}+R_g)}, \tag{15.19}$$

where R' is the resistance of $(r_\epsilon + R_l)$ in parallel with $(r_{bb'}+R_g)$ and C_l is the load capacitance. If the l.h.s. of this equation is less than the r.h.s. the response will be underdamped, i.e. there will be an overshoot. If the reverse is true the response will be overdamped and the output voltage will rise exponentially.

15.4.2.3. *The CB response time*

For the *CB* amplifier the time constant is the ratio of the effective inductance L of Fig. 15.10 to the total resistance in parallel with it. A voltage source gives the time constant

$$T_{b_1} \simeq \frac{1}{\omega_\alpha} \frac{r_{bb'}+r_\epsilon}{(1-\alpha_0)r_{bb'}+r_\epsilon} \tag{15.20}$$

while a current source gives the somewhat shorter value

$$T_{b_2} \simeq \frac{1}{\omega_\alpha}. \tag{15.21}$$

The form of the equivalent circuits of Figs. 15.8 and 15.9 suggests that the pulse response of the *CE* and *CC* video amplifiers may be considerably improved if the resistance R_g is by-passed by a capacitor. This method is often used as an alternative to a voltage drive in large-signal switching applications for which design data are given in the next chapter. The procedures there outlined may also be applied to video pulse amplifiers.

This completes our introduction to the properties of video amplifiers. While these properties have been discussed very briefly, the information supplied should be sufficient for preliminary designs which can be modified as a result of experimental work. More detailed design information may be obtained from the references mentioned.

THE APPLICATION OF TRANSISTORS
TO SWITCHING

16.1. Introduction

THE applications of transistors discussed so far in this book
have been of the continuous-signal or steady-state type. There
is another large and rapidly growing area to which transistors
are particularly well adapted. This is the field of switching,
which may be discussed under the following three main headings:

1. Low-level switches, used as linear modulators or 'choppers'.

2. High-level non-regenerative switches, used principally as
components of gating circuits in computers.

3. Regeneratively switched devices such as multivibrators
and blocking oscillators.

In the present chapter we shall make use of the general theory
of switching outlined in Chapter VII in discussions of the properties and design of circuits in these three groups. We begin with
a consideration of low-level switches, which are particularly
useful for the amplification of d.c. signals. This requires a
detailed study of the $V_{CE}-I_C$ characteristic in the region of the
origin, which is undertaken in § 16.4. However, before making
this investigation, the reasons why choppers are necessary and
the general principles of their operation (that apply to other
devices as well as transistors) should be outlined. These subjects
are considered in §§ 16.2 and 16.3. In later sections we present
practical high-level circuits of the non-regenerative and regenerative types mentioned in items (2) and (3) above.

16.2. Drift in transistor and vacuum-tube amplifiers

The variation of transistor parameters with temperature
causes direct-coupled amplifiers to be very susceptible to drift,
i.e. to changes in output current which occur over a long period
of time (of the order of minutes or hours) and which are not due

to applied input signals. The drift is usually expressed as 'equivalent input drift' which is simply the measured change in voltage or current at the output terminals divided by the appropriate gain.

The drift causes an uncertainty in the value of the input voltage and the effect is similar to that of input noise power in that it sets a lower limit to the signal power which can be amplified. Direct-coupled amplifiers which use balanced pairs of germanium transistors, arranged so that temperature-induced variations oppose each other in the output, may have an equivalent input drift of the order of 10 mV. The input resistance is normally in the vicinity of 5,000 ohms and for good power transfer the source resistance must be similar, implying that the minimum useful input power lies between 10^{-7} and 10^{-8} watts. An amplifier of this type using silicon transistors with non-linear temperature compensation at the input has been built [1] in which the equivalent input drift over a period of 12 hours, when the temperature is maintained constant to within $10°$ C, is 60 μV. This amplifier has an input resistance of 140,000 ohms, but the source resistance should be much lower than this, say less than 10,000 ohms, in order to minimize the very low frequency components of flicker noise (§ 10.7.4). The basic sensitivity is therefore in the region of 10^{-12} watts.

This sensitivity, which is close to the maximum attainable at the time of writing, is similar to that of a direct-coupled vacuum-tube amplifier in which the power supplies and the source of heater current have been carefully stabilized. The equivalent input drift in this case is about 1 mV but both input and source resistances may be very high (e.g. between 1 and 10 megohms), so that a basic power sensitivity of from 10^{-12} to 10^{-13} watts is typical.

16.3. Low-level (chopper type) switches

Substantially drift-free amplification of a very low frequency signal is possible if it is first 'chopped' by the regular opening and closing of a switch, which converts it into a series of pulses whose amplitudes are accurately proportional to those of the signal. The pulses may be passed through a band-pass amplifier in which long-term drifts are well outside the pass band and thus have negligible effect. The original signal may be recovered by using a second switch which operates in synchronism with the chopper to form a synchronous rectifier.

Some typical chopping arrangements are shown in Fig. 16.1. A simple half-wave modulation scheme in which the input is

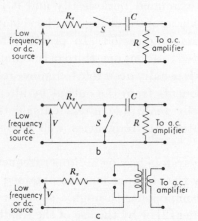

FIG. 16.1. Typical chopping circuits.
(a) Series. (b) Parallel (shunt). (c) Full-wave.

alternately connected to and disconnected from the a.c. amplifier is shown in part a. In part b the input is periodically short-circuited to provide an a.c. signal to the amplifier. Full-wave modulation in which a double throw switch connects the input periodically across opposite halves of a centre-tapped transformer winding is shown in Fig. 16.1 c.

Any periodically operated switch can be used as a chopper. Very good mechanically tuned relays, driven at a fixed frequency which may be as high as 1 kc/sec, are available commercially for this purpose. Transistors are also very good choppers, and they can be operated at considerably higher speeds than the mechanical devices. The upper limit is set by the switching speed of the transistor and with modern transistors a switching frequency of 100 kc/sec is readily attained.

The speed of operation of the switch is one of the fundamental limitations in chopper operation. It is considered, together with other limitations, in the following sub-section.

16.3.1. *Fundamental limitations of choppers*

The switching speed sets the upper limit to the frequency of the signal that may be passed by a chopper amplifier. The chopper is a sampling device by means of which the amplitude of the signal is examined periodically and it is impossible to obtain information about a change in the signal that occurs in less than one sampling period. In practice the upper cutoff frequency is limited to about one-third of the chopping frequency or less because it is usually desirable to remove residual chopping frequency components from the output by filtering. The finite slope of physically realizable filters outside their pass band imposes attenuation at frequencies well below the chopping frequency.

An amplifying system having an upper frequency limit above that imposed by the chopper may be obtained by routing the high-frequency components through a separate (parallel) high-frequency amplifier [2] or by the use of the Goldberg connection described in § 13.5.2. A third system employs a chopper amplifier as an auxiliary channel to provide drift compensation for a wide-band d.c. amplifier [3].

The second important limitation is due to the noise introduced by the switch. This property, which sets a lower limit to the magnitude of the signal that can be amplified, arises from current leakage when the switch is open and from the voltage drop across the switch when it is closed. These effects produce an output voltage, often called the zero offset voltage, when there is no d.c. (or low-frequency) input to the chopper. The noise voltage introduced by a good mechanical switch having precious metal contacts can be kept to about one microvolt in a circuit whose resistance is $100 \text{ k}\Omega$—a power level of 10^{-17} watts. Both the leakage current and the closed-switch voltage (the saturation voltage) are larger for a transistor than for a good mechanical switch, and the minimum voltage that can be modulated (chopped) by a transistor is one or two orders of magnitude higher than the above figure.

16.4. The transistor chopper

The transistor chopper [4] is a special application of the CE switch in which the collector is connected via a series resistor R_l to the source of the voltage V that is to be modulated (Fig. 16.2). An alternating square wave of voltage whose amplitude exceeds $|V|$ is applied to the base of the transistor. Both junctions of a p-n-p transistor, for example, are therefore forward-biased when the base is driven negative and both are reverse-biased when the base is positive. Thus the load R_l is periodically connected across the source, and the output, which is taken from

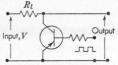

FIG. 16.2. Basic circuit of transistor chopper.

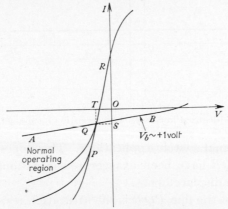

FIG. 16.3. Typical low-level characteristic for a p-n-p transistor.

the collector, is a series of square pulses of amplitude approximately equal to V. The exact amplitude and the effect of changing the sign of V can be determined from a typical switching characteristic which is shown, considerably enlarged, in the neighbourhood of the origin, for a p-n-p transistor in Fig. 16.3. Here the third quadrant is the region of normal operation and PQR is a low-level saturation characteristic. The line AQB is the cutoff characteristic obtained when the base-emitter junction is reverse-biased by a voltage in the range from 1 to 10 volts. This differs from the normal CE cutoff characteristic in that a low-resistance source rather than a high-resistance (current) source is used to supply the base. In our earlier descriptions of the CE characteristic it was implied that the intersection of the saturation and (constant-current) cutoff characteristics occurred at the origin. This is not actually the case for either the usual characteristic or the present switching curves. The displacements QS and QT are, however, of the order of millivolts and microamperes respectively and are negligible in normal amplifiers

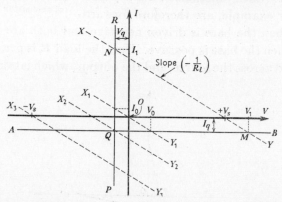

Fig. 16.4. Idealized low-level characteristic of a p-n-p transistor.

or in large-signal switch applications. The slopes of the lines AQB and PQR have been exaggerated intentionally in order to show these displacements.

The slope of the line PQR is the saturation resistance of the transistor which does not usually exceed 10 ohms for a germanium-alloy transistor but may be about 100 ohms for a grown- or diffused-junction type. The cutoff resistance represented by the line AQB is a few megohms or larger. The load resistance R_l is usually much larger than the saturation resistance and considerably smaller than the cutoff resistance so that we may use the idealized characteristic of Fig. 16.4 in which AQB and PQR are parallel to the axes. The operating conditions for an instantaneous applied voltage V_s may then be determined by drawing the 'load' line XY of slope $-1/R_l$ which intersects AQB at the open-circuit point M, whose coordinates are (V_1, I_q), and PQR at the short-circuit point N, whose coordinates are (V_q, I_1). When a square wave of base voltage is applied, the output voltage is a square wave of magnitude $QM = (V_s - I_q R_l - V_q)$, where I_q is the open-circuit collector leakage current and V_q is the short-circuit saturation voltage. For a p-n-p transistor V_q and I_q are negative so that the output is larger than $|V_s|$ when V_s is positive and smaller than $|V_s|$ when V_s is negative. The quantity $(I_q R_l + V_q)$ is the offset voltage referred to above.

As the source of voltage decreases, the load line moves

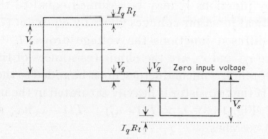

FIG. 16.5. Output waveforms of a p-n-p transistor chopper.

towards the origin, while retaining constant slope, and V_1 and I_1 decrease. When V_s is zero the short-circuit current is I_0 and the open-circuit voltage is V_0. If the applied voltage V_s reverses, the load line moves into the third quadrant and the current and voltage become zero at the point Q. A further decrease in the negative value of V_s leads to a negative output from the switch.

The output waveforms for positive and negative applied voltages are shown in Fig. 16.5. From this we see that if the output is taken from the collector through a capacitor—thereby establishing the zero levels for the outputs at the dashed lines— the phase of the alternating output voltage reverses when the applied d.c. voltage is reversed. This property may be used to establish the correct sign of the output voltage when the chopped wave is rectified or demodulated to recover a reproduction of the original signal.

16.4.1. *The magnitude and temperature dependence of transistor chopper errors*

From Figs. 16.4 and 16.5 we see that the offset error $(I_q R_l + V_q)$ could be removed by subtracting a voltage of this magnitude from V_s. A positive output would be decreased and a negative output increased in magnitude by this amount. One method of doing this is to insert a positive voltage $|I_q|R_l+|V_q|$ in the emitter lead in Fig. 16.2. However, I_q and V_q are functions of temperature and for accurate compensation more complicated methods must be used. Before discussing these we consider in some detail the magnitude and temperature dependence of these errors.

For alloy junctions V_q may be assumed equal to the sum of the theoretical junction voltages given by equation (7.75). For grown or diffused junctions the voltage drops $(I_b+I_c)r_{oe}$ and $I_c r_{oc}$, where r_{oe} and r_{oc} are the ohmic resistances of the emitter and collector bulk semiconductors, must be added to the junction voltages. If the transistor is heavily saturated in the neighbourhood of Q (Fig. 16.3), $I_b \gg I_c(1-\alpha_I) > I_c(1-\alpha_N)/\alpha_N$ and equation (7.75) becomes

$$V_q \simeq \pm \frac{kT}{q}\ln(\alpha_I). \qquad (16.1)$$

Here the positive sign applies to p-n-p transistors and V_q is negative because $\alpha_I < 1$. The value of I_q is found from equation (7.65) to be

$$I_q = \frac{I_{c0}(1-\alpha_I)}{1-\alpha_N\alpha_I}. \qquad (16.2)$$

If the transistor is inverted, i.e. the functions of collector and emitter are interchanged, these equations become

$$V'_q \simeq \pm \frac{kT}{q}\ln(\alpha_N) \qquad (16.3)$$

and
$$I'_q = \frac{I_{e0}(1-\alpha_N)}{1-\alpha_N\alpha_I}. \qquad (16.4)$$

For germanium-alloy transistors, typical current gains are $\alpha_N = 0.98$ and $\alpha_I = 0.75$, giving $V_q/V'_q = 14$ and, using equation (7.64), $I_q/I'_q = 16$. The open- and closed-switch errors are thus reduced by an order of magnitude when the transistor is inverted. Typical values for the coordinates of the point Q are then 0.5 to 1.0 mV and 0.1 to 0.2 μA. For silicon transistors, which are usually of the grown or diffused type, the voltage drop produced by I_b flowing in the bulk semiconductor is usually so much larger when the transistor is inverted that normal operation is preferred. V_q then lies in the range of 2–10 mV while I_q may be less than 0·01 μA.

Equations (16.3) and (16.4) indicate that $|V'_q|$ increases linearly and $|I'_q|$ exponentially with temperature. Both effects contribute to an increase of offset voltage with temperature. The effect of I'_q can be minimized by making R_l as small as possible consistent with the requirement that it must be large compared with the saturation resistance. Optimum values lie between 300 and 1,000 ohms for alloy germanium transistors and between 100 kΩ and 200 kΩ for silicon units.

When the single-transistor chopper of Fig. 16.2 is to be operated at varying temperatures, a transistor having a low I_{c0} or I_{e0} should be chosen and R_l should be at the lower end of the above range. Compensation for V'_q can be introduced by supplying the emitter voltage referred to above from a low-resistance source having a positive temperature coefficient, e.g. a potentiometer whose output section consists of copper wire.

Compensation for V'_q and its variation with temperature is sometimes provided by the addition of a second transistor [5]. However, two transistors whose zero errors are closely matched may be arranged in a bridge to provide compensation for both types of error [6]. Such a circuit for germanium transistors is shown in Fig. 16.6. Adjustments for slight differences between transistors are obtained by varying R_1 and by moving the point

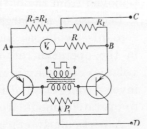

FIG. 16.6. Bridge modulator using two transistors.

P_1 slightly off the centre position. The voltage that can be chopped in this manner is smaller, by a factor of about 10, than the minimum acceptable value for a single uncompensated switch.

Many chopper circuits have been described in the literature [5, 6] but the above examples, which are representative of the more important types, must suffice for our brief survey.

16.4.2. *Demodulators*

As mentioned in § 16.3 the amplified version of the original signal may be recovered by means of a second switch in synchronism with the chopper. Such synchronous switches or 'demodulators' may be obtained by inverting a modulator and operating it at a higher level. In the circuit of Fig. 16.6, for example, the alternating signal is applied to the terminals *C–D* and the output is taken from the terminals *A–B*. Distortion

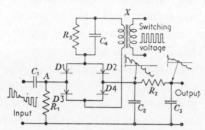

Fig. 16.7. Four-diode demodulator.

arising from rounding of the base and collector 'square waves' and from small differences in phase between them may be removed from the output by filtering.

Because of the large amplitude of the a.c. output signal the zero offset voltages and currents do not play an important part in the operation of demodulators. Also the relatively high voltages used may break down the emitter-base junction of the inverse connection of Fig. 16.6. For these reasons it is desirable to operate demodulator transistors in the normal manner.

A particularly efficient demodulator is shown in Fig. 16.7. This is a bi-directional switch using four silicon junction diodes. All the diodes are switched 'on' and 'off' together, through the isolating transformer X, by the same square wave which drives the chopper. The forward current when the diodes are turned on is controlled by the automatic bias circuit, consisting of C_4 and R_3. During periods of conduction the voltage across C_4 increases, thereby reducing the forward voltage across the diodes. If the time constant $C_4 R_3$ is long compared with the chopping period, only a small part of this charge will leak away while the diodes are not conducting. The bias voltage will reach an equilibrium level soon after the system is turned on, the current in the diodes being limited to the small value required to replenish the charge lost by C_4 between conduction periods.

When the diodes are switched on, a positive pulse at the point A causes current to flow through $D3$, the transformer winding, the bias network $C_4 R_3$, and the diode $D2$ to the output filter capacitor C_2. A negative pulse at A causes current to flow from C_2 through $D1$, the transformer winding, the bias network, and through $D1$ to the point A. Each pulse adds or subtracts an increment of charge to or from C_2 and causes the output voltage to rise or fall in proportion to the amplitude of the pulse. A filter $R_2 C_3$ reduces the level of the chopping-frequency ripple in the output. For maximum output voltage C_2 should be smaller than C_1 but not so small that excessive filtering, with an accompanying reduction of output voltage, will be required.

16.5. High-level non-regenerative transistor switches

So far in this chapter we have considered very low-level non-regenerative switches in which the chief limiting factors are the errors introduced by the transistor. In the present section we consider non-regenerative applications in which considerably larger potentials (of the order of volts) are applied to the switch and the closed-switch currents are correspondingly increased. We shall call these high-level applications but this term does not necessarily imply that the transistors are operated near their maximum power level. The most important consideration in this type of application is usually switching speed and the main applications are to digital computers. Transistors have the advantage over other computing elements such as diodes and magnetic devices that less power is required to 'open' or 'close' them. They have the advantage over vacuum tubes that they can operate at a low power level and do not require standby (filament) power.

Important criteria in the application of these high-level non-regenerative switches include the following:

1. Switching speed.
2. Stability—the ability to produce well-defined levels of output voltage under different loading and temperature conditions.
3. Output impedance, which must be low if the output of one switch is to drive several others.
4. Gain—the ratio of power controlled to power required to control.

All of these factors are interdependent and usually the designer's chief function is to produce the best compromise in a given application.

As mentioned in § 7.9, the most generally useful device is the CE switch which is often called an 'inverter', but in applications requiring a low output impedance the CC or emitter-follower circuit is often used. The CB switch is reserved for exceptionally high-speed circuits in which a high output impedance can be tolerated. We shall confine our remarks to the first two types.

16.5.1. *The CE switch*

In the present section we consider the practical aspects of CE switch operation, discussing the 'off', 'transition', and 'on' states in turn and making use of earlier results where necessary.

16.5.1.1. *The 'off' state*

For the 'off' state the most important requirements are the following:

(i) The current through the transistor, when it is switched off, should not exceed a certain maximum under all operating conditions.

(ii) The method of holding the transistor in the off position should have negligible effect on the switching speed.

These requirements are to some extent contradictory. Thus, in order that the transistor may be turned off under all temperature conditions, a reasonably large reverse voltage must be applied to the base. This causes excess charge to be stored in the emitter transition-region capacitance and increases the turn-on time. A reasonable compromise between the two

requirements is afforded by the arrangement of Fig. 16.8
(omitting the capacitor C_b which will be considered later in
the discussion of switching speed) in which the off bias voltage
V_{b0} is given by

$$V_{b0} = V_{bb} \frac{R_g + R_b}{R_g + R_b + R_{bb}} - I_{b0} \frac{R_{bb}(R_g + R_b)}{R_g + R_b + R_{bb}}, \qquad (16.5)$$

where I_{b0}, the base current in the off state, is the sum of the
currents I'_c and I'_e given by equations (7.65) and (7.66). For

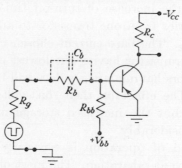

FIG. 16.8. Bias circuit for a non-
regenerative switch.

practical purposes this may be assumed equal to I_{c0} and to vary
in the same manner with temperature. For a low-power transistor I_{b0} may therefore vary from 5 μA to 40 μA when the
temperature rises by 30° C. Using typical values $R_g = 500$ ohms,
$R_b = 1$ k, $R_{bb} = 39$ k, $V_{bb} = 4\cdot5$ volts, V_{b0} is reduced from $0\cdot16$
to $0\cdot11$ volt for this temperature change and the cutoff condition
is maintained. With smaller values of V_{bb} and R_{bb} the change of
V_{b0} could easily become excessive at high temperatures. In the
case of a silicon transistor the small effect of temperature on
I_{b0} makes it possible to use a lower bias voltage, which may be
zero in some non-critical applications.

16.5.1.2. *The 'on' state*

The characteristics of the 'on' state of the transistor switch
are determined by the speed of switching and the extent to
which the 'on' level must be stabilized. The circuit used depends

on the relative importance of these two factors. We consider the following three cases:

1. When speed is of secondary importance but a definite 'on' level must be obtained using a relatively simple circuit, the transistor should be allowed to saturate. The collector will then be clamped at a voltage differing very little from the emitter voltage and the output resistance will be very low—an important consideration when one switch must control several others, as in some computer applications. The most important disadvantage is the increase of turn-off time due to storage. This increase varies from one transistor to another because of variations in h_{FE}. The base current chosen must be sufficient to saturate the transistor having the lowest expected value of h_{FE} and transistors having larger values will therefore saturate more heavily. The effect on their 'on' voltage level will be relatively small but the increased storage may lengthen the turn-off time considerably.

2. When speed of operation is especially important it is necessary to prevent saturation. The most obvious method of doing this is to limit the base current I_b to such a value that the saturated condition will not be reached. The rise and fall times in this case are seen, from equations (7.73) and (7.78) to be at least $2 \cdot 3\tau_e \simeq 2 \cdot 3/\omega_\beta$ and $0 \cdot 6/\omega_\beta$ respectively. These are so large as to nullify the advantage gained from the elimination of storage. In order to decrease the rise time and still prevent the operating point from entering the saturation region, it is necessary to overdrive the base so that $h_{FE} I_{b1} \simeq \beta_0 I_{b1} \gg I_{c1}$, where I_{c1} is the desired 'on' current, and to limit the collector current in some manner when this point is reached. This operation, which is called clamping, makes possible rapid rise and fall times while retaining stabilization of the 'on' level approaching that of a saturated transistor.

3. When a relatively high output impedance (and hence some variation of the on level) can be tolerated, the unsaturated 'on' position may be established by the base current and the over-drive required may be supplied by a series base capacitor.

The first of the above methods (saturated operation) was

described in some detail in § 7.9. The second and third are considered in §§ 16.5.2 and 16.5.3 below.

16.5.1.3. *The 'transition' states*

The transition from the 'off' to the 'on' state and its inverse were discussed in § 7.9 and further discussion of the theory of switching speed is not required. The practical aspects of decreasing the transition time will be considered below in the sections on clamping and capacitor overdrive.

16.5.2. *Clamping methods*

Clamping may be defined quite generally as the stabilization of the output voltage or current of a transistor switch by a sudden change of impedance, produced by an additional circuit device at one of the transistor electrodes. This 'external' control causes the 'on' position to be largely independent of transistor parameters such as h_{FE} and makes heavy base overdrive possible without danger of saturation—although some disadvantages may be introduced by the clamp itself. We shall consider three types of clamp which are in fairly general use.

16.5.2.1. *The collector clamp*

This device, which is sometimes called a catching diode, is illustrated for an n-p-n transistor in Fig. 16.9. (As in Chapter VII we consider n-p-n transistors for convenience in description although most switching transistors are of the p-n-p type. For p-n-p transistors all signs, arrows, and diode connections should be reversed.) When the collector voltage falls below V_{dd} the diode becomes forward-biased and, by virtue of its low resistance, holds the point C close to this potential. If D is a junc-

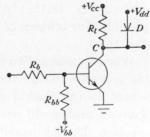

FIG. 16.9. The collector clamp.

tion diode the output resistance will be comparable to that of a saturated transistor and the 'on' state of the switch will be accurately established. However, this arrangement has the following disadvantages:

(i) The diode may show a storage effect similar to that of a transistor.

(ii) If the transistor is driven very hard the collector current continues to increase after clamping and the excess current is drained off through the clamp. In order to produce this excess current the normal stored charge in the base must be increased by the area between the normal unsaturated curve A and the 'clamped' curve B of Fig. 16.10. This increase of stored charge

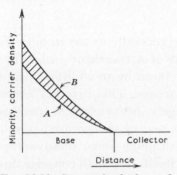

Fig. 16.10. Storage in the base of a transistor in the clamped (B) and unclamped (A) conditions.

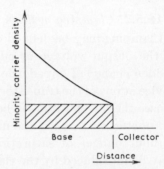

Fig. 16.11. The stored charge in a saturated transistor.

differs from the excess stored charge in a saturated transistor which was discussed in § 7.9.3.3 and is represented by the shaded area of Fig. 16.11. In effect, this type of clamping makes possible the exchange of the shaded area of Fig. 16.11 for that of Fig. 16.10.

When an attempt to turn off the clamped transistor is made, the collector voltage remains clamped until the charge represented by the shaded area of Fig. 16.10 has been removed. Turn-off proper will not commence until the curve A has been reached. There is usually a net reduction of storage time when this type of clamp is used but in many cases it is insufficient to warrant the addition of a diode and an extra power-supply tap.

16.5.2.2. *The base or degenerative clamp*

A more useful arrangement than the above is the base clamp [7] of which examples are shown in Figs. 16.12 and 16.13. This circuit introduces a large amount of negative feedback between collector and base and is therefore sometimes called a degenerative clamp. The principle of its operation may be described with the help of Fig. 16.12 ignoring, for the moment, the presence of R_3 and the bias source $-V_{bb}$. A drive current I_1, which may be much larger than the base current required to saturate the transistor, is applied to turn the transistor on very rapidly. When the collector voltage has fallen to a pre-set limit, determined by the value of R_2, the diode $D1$ conducts. This limit is $(V_{cc}-I_{l1} R_l)$, where I_{l1} is the value of I_l at the onset of clamping.

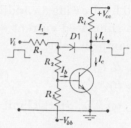

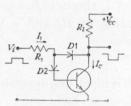

FIG. 16.12. Base or degenerative clamping circuit.

FIG. 16.13.   Baker degenerative clamp.

For $I_l < I_{l1}$, I_l and I_c are equal. Any input current in excess of the value I_{l1}/h_{FE} required to maintain I_{l1} is diverted into the collector circuit by the diode. An alternative way of viewing the circuit action is to regard the diode as a switch which closes a low-resistance d.c. negative feedback loop of the operational type. The transistor gain is therefore suddenly reduced so that a considerable increase in base current is required to raise I_c when the clamp has closed.

The clamped value of the collector voltage is

$$V'_{ce} = V_{be}+I_b R_2-V_d, \tag{16.6}$$

where V_d is the forward voltage drop of the diode. If the diode and the transistor are germanium junction devices, the diode may be chosen so that $V_d \simeq V_{be}$, whence

$$V'_{ce} \simeq I_b R_2. \tag{16.7}$$

Also, when the clamping point is just reached, we have

$$V_{cc} = V'_{ce}+h_{FE} I_b R_l = V'_{ce}\left(1+h_{FE} \frac{R_l}{R_2}\right), \tag{16.8}$$

whence $$V'_{ce} = V_{cc} \frac{R_2}{R_2 + h_{FE} R_l}. \qquad (16.9)$$

This formula may be used to determine the value of R_2 to establish a desired unsaturated 'on' state.

In order that the clamped voltage V'_{ce} be small, R_2 must be small compared with $h_{FE} R_l$. Equation (16.9) therefore indicates that the 'on' voltage of this simple base-clamping circuit depends markedly on h_{FE}. A transistor having an unusually high value of h_{FE} may saturate while one having a low value of h_{FE} may suffer a rather large dissipation in the 'on' state. This strong dependence on h_{FE} may be diminished by drawing an additional current I_3 through R_2 by means of a simulated current source consisting of R_3 and $-V_{bb}$. The clamped value of V_{ce} then becomes

$$V''_{ce} \simeq \frac{R_2(V_{cc} + h_{FE} R_l I_3)}{R_2 + h_{FE} R_l}, \qquad (16.10)$$

which is much less dependent than V'_{ce} on h_{FE}. In the limit when I_3 is large we have $$V''_{ce} \simeq R_2 I_3. \qquad (16.11)$$

The circuit of Fig. 16.12 requires an additional power supply and wastes a rather large amount of power. A more efficient arrangement [8] is shown in Fig. 16.13, in which a forward-biased silicon diode $D1$ is used as a low-resistance source of output 0·6–0·7 volt. The transistor and the diode $D1$ remain germanium devices. If the forward voltage drop across $D1$ is approximately V_{be}, the clamped value of V_{ce} is nearly equal to the drop across $D2$ which is high enough to keep the transistor out of saturation.

The properties of the diodes in the circuits of Figs. 16.12 and 16.13 are important. $D1$ is forward-biased when the switch is fully on and must be reversed before turn-off can commence. It must therefore be a high-speed (low-storage) diode. It must also have a high back resistance at full power supply voltage to prevent the introduction of negative feedback with accompanying loss of gain and switching speed. The silicon diode $D2$ should also have minimum storage for rapid turn-off.

A silicon transistor may be clamped by connecting a high-conductance germanium diode between collector and base in such a direction that the diode conducts when the forward collector-base voltage rises to about 0·2 volt. The collector junction is thus clamped at this forward voltage which is well below the 0·6 volt required for appreciable injection in a silicon junction. The amount of excess charge storage obtained with this arrangement is therefore negligible.

16.5.2.3. *The emitter clamp or current switch*

A method of clamping the emitter is used in the non-saturating current switch or 'current-mode' switch [9] which is one of the

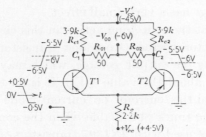

FIG. 16.14. Non-saturating current switch.

fastest transistor switches available at present. Its competitors are the complementary switches described in §§ 16.5.4 and 16.5.5. In this case the clamping results from the turn-off of a second transistor which is arranged with the first to form a long-tail pair. A typical circuit using p-n-p transistors is shown in Fig. 16.14. Both collectors are connected to constant current power supplies produced by the large negative voltage $-V'_{cc}$ acting through the resistors R_{c1} and R_{c2}. The low output impedance required at very high operating speeds is obtained by means of an auxiliary low voltage supply $-V_{00}$ and the output resistors R_{01} and R_{02}. The total emitter current is also supplied by a large voltage $(+V_{ee})$ acting through the resistor R_e and therefore remains constant. The circuit operates as follows: The base of $T1$ is connected to the source and that of $T2$ to a reference point which in the present case is earth. When the source voltage is $+0·5$ volt, for example, $T1$ is cut off and a current I_c flows in $T2$. A well-defined 'off' level is established at C_1 by the current flowing between $-V_{00}$ and $-V'_{cc}$. Reversal of the input to -0.5 volt causes $T1$ to conduct and its collector current rapidly reaches I_c while that of $T2$ drops almost to zero. When $T2$ reaches cutoff the emitter current of $T1$ is clamped by the large amount of degeneration introduced by the emitter resistor R_e. A decrease of source voltage beyond this point has very little effect as long as V_{ee} and R_e are reasonably large. The total collector current thus remains approximately constant throughout and a well-defined 'on' level is established in $T1$. Alternatively, we may consider that the input impedance of $T1$ increases suddenly when $T2$ is cut off so that a further change of source voltage has a very small effect.

It is seen that the switching action in this circuit transfers a constant collector current from one transistor to the other, thereby varying the output voltage, which may be taken from either C_1 or C_2, about the value $-V_{00}$. It is for this reason that it is often called the 'current' or 'current-mode' switch.

The switching times obtainable when the component values in Fig. 16.14 are used with 2N1307 transistors ($f_\alpha = 12$ Mc/sec, $h_{FE} = 100$) have been given by the transistor manufacturer (Texas Instruments). For input rise and fall times of 20×10^{-9} sec and a generator resistance of 50 ohms the output times defined in Fig. 7.21, and expressed in units of 10^{-9} sec, are: $t_{d1} = 20$, $t_r = 140$, $t_{d2} = 20$, $t_f = 140$. The value of τ_e for this transistor, expressed in the same units, is about $1,300$ so that a considerable improvement over the normal CE switching speed is obtained. With the above component values the circuit is, of course, very heavily overdriven and provides no power gain since its source and output resistances are equal. Its chief application is in the performance of computer logic (§ 16.5.6) where many circuits are coupled together to perform counting operations.

In the high-speed region in which the complexity of the current switch is worth while, direct coupling between stages is desirable to eliminate the stray capacitance to earth of bias networks and coupling capacitors. Because of the difference between input and output levels, which in the present case is 6 volts, two current switches using the same types of transistors cannot be directly cascaded. However, p-n-p and n-p-n current switches can be direct-coupled if the ($T2$ base) reference voltage of one pair of transistors is properly adjusted.

In many computer circuits several inputs are combined to produce one output. When a current switch is used, one transistor (e.g. $T2$ in Fig. 16.14) may act as an emitter clamp for several input transistors whose emitters and collectors are connected in parallel while their bases are fed from separate sources.

In view of the above rather detailed descriptions of computer circuits it should be emphasized that the current switch may be used in any CE switching application. However, the added expense and circuit complication that it introduces can usually be justified only when high-speed operation is the chief consideration. The advantage that it holds over other circuits in this field results from the following properties:

(i) Saturation is avoided.

(ii) Well-defined 'on' and 'off' levels are produced.

(iii) There are no auxiliary devices such as diodes to contribute to storage.

(iv) The transistors can be operated in a region where f_α is high and C_c is low [9].

16.5.3. *Capacitor overdrive*

The third method of driving transistor switches mentioned in § 16.5.1 employs a series capacitor in the base lead as shown by the dashed connections in Fig. 16.8. During the early part of the turn-on process the capacitor allows a large amount of charge to enter the transistor and thus furnishes an initial overdrive which shortens the rise time considerably. When the series and transistor capacitances are charged up and the steady state is reached, the base current is set by R_b at a value which prevents saturation. An alternative view is that the capacitor by-passes R_b during part of the turn-on process and allows the switch to be nearly voltage-driven. During the turn-off process C_b performs a similar function in removing charge rapidly from the transistor base.

The value chosen for C_b is a compromise between the conflicting requirements that sufficient initial overdrive current should be supplied to shorten the rise time appreciably and that the turn-off time should not be increased by the production of excess storage in the base. A good estimate of the capacitance required may be obtained with the help of the equivalent circuit of Fig. 7.19, omitting C_c on the assumption that the load resistance is low and $\tau_c \ll \tau_e$. The complete input equivalent circuit, which is

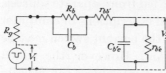

shown in Fig. 16.15, may be made aperiodic (i.e. capable of passing all frequencies equally and hence able to reproduce any pulse shape) provided $(r_{bb'} + R_g)$ is negligible compared with the larger of R_b and $r_{b'e}$. The required condition, which

Fig. 16.15. Equivalent input circuit of a transistor with capacitor overdrive.

is used in the construction of wide-band attenuation networks, is that the time constants $R_b C_b, r_{b'e} C_{b'e}$, be equal. Hence, using the relations of § 7.6, we have $R_b C_b \simeq 0.81/\omega_\beta$.

The value of R_b is decided by the following two conditions:

(i) The maximum base current

$$I_b = V_1/[R_g + R_b + r_{bb'} + (1 + \beta_0)r_\epsilon],$$

where V_1 is the applied pulse voltage, must be small enough that saturation is avoided.

(ii) R_b or $r_{b'e}$ must be large compared with $(r_{bb'} + R_g)$.

When the value of R_b has been chosen, C_b is determined from the above relation.

If the circuit of Fig. 16.15 were an exact representation of the transistor under all conditions of operation it would be possible by this method to produce an exact replica of the input pulse regardless of its rise time. This ideal state cannot be reached for the following reasons:

(a) The equivalent circuit does not take account of the delay times t_{d1} and t_{d2} (§ 7.9).

(b) The effect of the input circuit can be represented by the simple time constant $r_{b'e} C_{b'e}$ only for rise or fall times of the order of $1/\omega_\alpha$ or larger.

(c) Perfect aperiodic response cannot be obtained because of the presence of $(r_{bb'} + R_g)$.

These effects limit the improvement in rise time to a factor lying between 10 and 20. In practice it is therefore unnecessary to make R_b exceed $(r_{bb'}+R_g)$ by more than twenty times.

It may appear at first glance that the time constant

$$\tau_c = (1+\beta_0)R_l C_c$$

should also affect the response of the circuit to higher frequencies when the effect τ_e has been removed by compensation. However, as long as $\tau_c \ll \tau_e - C_{b'e}r_{b'e}$, this is not the case since τ_c decreases with β in the same manner as τ_e. In most switching applications this condition $\tau_c \ll \tau_e$ is satisfied, but for some modern transistors of the mesa type the reverse may be the case. The same compensation method may then be used with $R_b C_b \simeq \tau_c$.

The above remarks are illustrated by the experimental results listed in Table 16.1. The transistors were tested in the circuit of Fig. 16.8 using a load resistor R_c of 100 ohms and an input pulse whose magnitude was not large enough to saturate the transistor. The pulse generator, whose internal resistance R_g was 50 ohms, supplied pulses having rise times less than 0.02 μsec. Other relevant constants are mentioned in the table.

TABLE 16.1

Transistor	CE time constant τ_e ($= 0.81/\omega_\beta$) μsec	R_b ohms	C_b $\mu\mu F$	Collector current turn-on time† μsec
2N369	5·6	8,200	0	8·0
,,	,,	0	0	1·4
,,	,,	8,200	1,000	0·3
,,	,,	330	0	2·0
,,	,,	330	4,700	1·3
2N1307	0·6	8,200	100	0·14
,,	,,	1,000	820	0·14

† Time to reach $(1-1/e)$ of final value.

The following aspects of the results should be noted:

1. The first two lines give approximate time constants for current and voltage drive respectively.

2. The third line gives the best rise time obtained for the

2N369. Similar results could be obtained with a larger R_b and a smaller C_b but the current gain would be decreased.

3. The drive in the fourth and fifth lines is intermediate in type. The value of R_b is not large compared with $R_g + r_{bb'}$ ($\simeq 300$ ohms) and the compensation is incomplete. The experimentally determined value of $R_b C_b$ differs considerably from $1/\omega_\beta$.

4. For the 2N1307, $r_{bb'} \simeq 50$ ohms so that R_b is much larger than $(r_{bb'} + R_g)$ for both cases. When a 100 ohm load is used with these higher-speed transistors, τ_c is of the same order as τ_e. In addition, the delay times form larger fractions of the rise and fall times. The compensation is therefore not as effective.

As mentioned earlier, the above discussions also apply to the turn-off process and the improvement in fall time obtained experimentally by means of capacitor overdrive is very similar to that obtained for the rise time.

16.5.4. *The complemented inverter*

An approach to the clamping different from that of § 16.5.2 is used in the complemented inverter shown in Fig. 16.16. Here

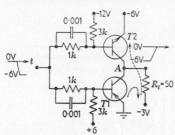

FIG. 16.16. The complemented inverter.

$T1$ is initially turned off while $T2$ is saturated. A negative input pulse applied to both bases through a capacitor overdrive circuit turns on $T1$ and drives it to saturation. The point A is therefore driven from -6 V to earth. The storage of $T2$ prevents it from turning off as rapidly as $T1$ is turned on, but this is not important because the hard drive lowers the resistance of $T1$ very rapidly. The rise and fall times of the output pulse are thus equal to the rise times of $T1$ and $T2$ respectively. Saturation is used for clamping but the long storage time associated with it is avoided. In addition, none of the power output is wasted in low-value collector bias resistors. The interval between pulses must, of course, be somewhat longer than the storage time of $T1$ and the pulse length greater than the storage time of $T2$ but often these are not serious disadvantages.

It is seen from Fig. 16.16 that, in order to saturate $T1$, the load resistor must be connected to a source of negative voltage. The correct choice of the other power-supply voltages makes the 'on' currents of the two transistors equal. Equal but opposite currents, shown by the dashed lines, then flow through the load in the two states of the circuit.

The 90 per cent turn-on time of this circuit is about 0·05 μsec when the complementary alloy transistors 2N1306 and 2N1307 are used. This is considerably smaller than the value of about 0·3 μsec ($\simeq 0.14 \times 2.3$) obtained from Table 16.1. The improvement is apparently due to the fact that the low saturation resistance of the transistor $T2$ allows the collector capacitance of $T2$ to charge up rapidly, thus reducing its effect on the turn-on time. This is one of the few cases in which storage is advantageous. Because of this feature the complemented inverter is particularly well adapted to transistors whose rise-time is determined by collector capacitance and whose saturation resistance is reasonably low. Some mesa transistors are in this category.

16.5.5. *The CC (emitter-follower) switch*

The emitter-follower switch, which is shown in Fig. 16.17, is used to change impedance levels in the same manner as its continuous signal counterpart. Its input and output voltages differ only by V_{be} ($\simeq 0.15$ volt) and, if desired, this difference may be reduced (provided R_2 is large) by the addition of an emitter bias voltage V_{ee} (positive for a p-n-p transistor).

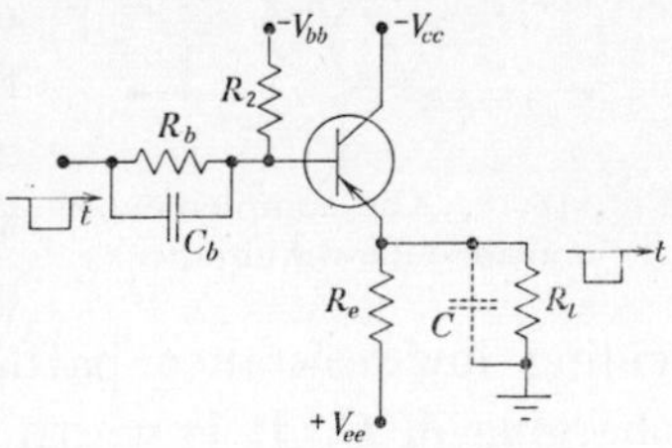

FIG. 16.17. The emitter-follower switch.

The CC switch is much less dependent on transistor parameters than the CE circuit and the position of the operating point is controlled by the input pulse. Clamping is usually unnecessary. Switching times, which were given for a constant current drive in § 7.9, may be improved by techniques similar to those used with the CE switch. We will mention two possibilities:

(i) Use of a voltage drive. In equation (15.19) we then have $R_g \ll R_l$ and a close approximation to the input pulse can be obtained. However, this improvement is of doubtful value since the emitter follower is usually required only when R_g exceeds R_l by a considerable margin.

(ii) Capacitor overdrive. From equation (15.19) we see that the external base time constant should be approximately $\tau_e = RC$ as in the CE case. This circuit has the advantage that the series base resistance (R_b in Fig. 16.17) may be used to compensate for the negative input resistance mentioned in Chapter XV [9].

The transient response of the emitter follower is complicated by the presence of stray capacitance (C in Fig. 16.17) at the emitter terminal. When the transistor is turned on, this capacitance is charged very rapidly through the low output impedance of the CC stage and the increase in the rise time produced by it is small. During turn-off, on the other hand, the transistor is inactive and the effective output resistance is R_e. For low-impedance loads with large associated cable capacitance the turn-off time may therefore be quite long. This effect may be eliminated by means of the complemented emitter-follower circuit of Fig. 16.18. In this circuit, one transistor turns on at the leading edge of the pulse and the other at the trailing edge, thus providing low-resistance paths for both the charging and discharging of C. It is worth noting that this phenomenon also arises in vacuum-tube circuitry and that, because there is no 'complement' to the vacuum tube, a simple solution is not possible.

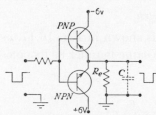

FIG. 16.18. The complemented emitter-follower circuit.

16.5.6. *The use of switches in logic circuits*

As mentioned above, one of the main fields for non-regenerative switching is in the performance of logical operations in computers. Many industrial control applications are of a similar nature and transistors seem destined to play an important part in this field also. Some mention of these basic 'logic' processes and of the methods of performing them by transistors is therefore desirable. In the following we will treat three examples, introducing them from the transistor circuit viewpoint.

(i) Consider a group of n emitter followers, using p-n-p transistors, connected to a common load resistor. If all n transistors are cut off the output terminal will be at its most positive value. If any one transistor is turned on, the output terminal goes negative. If we now define the most positive value of the output to represent a 'one' and the most negative value a 'zero' in a binary system of arithmetic (the positive logic system) the emitter followers form an 'AND' gate, i.e. all n inputs must be 'one' if the output is to be 'one', and if any single input goes to 'zero', so does the output.

(ii) If the emitter followers are changed to n-p-n transistors, then a 'zero' output can only be obtained if all inputs are 'zero'; if any single input becomes 'one', the output will change to 'one'. This type of gate is called an 'OR' gate.

These two gates can be interchanged by changing to negative logic, i.e. defining the most negative signal to represent a one.

The above results may be most easily summarized for two transistors with two inputs A and B in the form of so-called truth tables, two of which are shown below:

Truth Tables

AND			OR		
A	B	OUT	A	B	OUT
0	0	0	0	0	0
1	0	0	1	0	1
0	1	0	0	1	1
1	1	1	1	1	1

(iii) If 'one' is fed to a CE inverter the output is 'zero'. If two or more n-p-n inverters are connected in parallel to a common load the output will be positive only if all inputs are negative, i.e. all transistors are cut off. A 'one' fed to any input will cause the output to go negative. This circuit is called a 'NOT OR' gate for positive logic. Parallel p-n-p inverters form a 'NOT AND' gate, for which all inputs must be one to maintain a zero output. Truth tables may be constructed for these circuits also, using both positive and negative logic.

Many special gates, useful in both computer circuits and industrial relaying, may be built up from combinations of CE and CC switches. Also, series switch arrangements, rather than the parallel circuits described above, may be used to perform logic operations if advantage is taken of the low saturation voltage of germanium alloy transistors.

16.6. Regenerative switches

It was indicated in § 7.10 that switches having well-defined 'on' and 'off' positions and a high switching speed may be obtained by the introduction of positive feedback or regeneration between output and input. Such regeneration may be regarded as an extreme case of the overdrive mentioned in the preceding sections of this chapter. It is this hard drive that reduces the rise time from $1/f_\beta$ to the value of order $1/f_\alpha$ mentioned in § 7.10.

The current-voltage characteristics of the open-circuit stable and short-circuit stable regenerative switches were illustrated in Chapter VII and the process in which the open-circuit stable type is switched from one state to another was described in detail. Regenerative switches that make use of junction transistors are almost invariably of this type. In this section we shall consider a few basic examples and describe the operation in greater detail than in the earlier chapter.

16.6.1. *Classification of regenerative junction transistor switches*

There are two ways of closing the positive feedback loop in a CE amplifier while maintaining a high value of current gain: in the first, which is called the multivibrator, the correct phase relation is produced by means of a second CE stage. In the second, a single transistor and a phase-inverting transformer are used, thus producing a transformer-coupled multivibrator or a blocking oscillator. The mechanisms that decide pulse length or operating frequency may differ from one circuit to another but all such regenerative circuits may be included in a broad classification containing bistable, monostable, and astable groups which are defined as follows:

1. The bistable circuit has two stable states separated by an

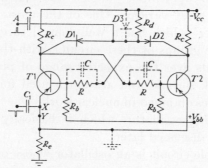

Fig. 16.19. Symmetrical bistable multivibrator.

unstable (regenerative) region. An input pulse causes it to switch from one state to another and a second pulse is required to return it to the initial state. In order that two stable states may exist, both the forward and backward (positive feedback) coupling arrangements must carry d.c. and a transformer coupling cannot be used. Hence bistable circuits must either be of the multivibrator type using CE-connected junction transistors or must make use of one of the devices possessing internal regeneration mentioned in Chapter VIII.

The basic junction-transistor bistable circuit is the symmetrical multivibrator shown in Fig. 16.19. This is called the Eccles–Jordan Trigger Circuit or 'flip-flop'. It can be used to store digits in computers and to divide by two since two input pulses are required to produce one output pulse of a chosen polarity. A variant of it, known as the latch, is an asymmetric bistable multivibrator which switches upon receipt of one trigger pulse but requires a different pulse at the same point or a similar pulse at some other point to cause it to reset. The operation of these circuits is described in some detail below.

2. The monostable circuit has one stable and one temporarily stable (metastable) state. An input pulse causes it to switch from the stable to the metastable state but after a definite interval it returns to the stable state. It can thus be used to generate a single pulse of predetermined duration for each input or trigger pulse. For this reason it is often called a 'one-shot'. Both resistance-capacitance coupled and transformer-coupled forms exist in great variety. One of the most popular is the 'Schmitt trigger' which has a well-defined threshold of input voltage. Large groups of these circuits, with thresholds set at regular intervals over the expected range of pulse amplitude, are called 'kick sorters' and are much used for sampling the pulse amplitudes obtained in nuclear work. The Schmitt trigger and the blocking oscillator, which is basically a monostable circuit, will be discussed later.

3. The astable circuit is an oscillator whose output is a flat-topped wave rather than a sine wave. It is often called a free-running multivibrator or, in some cases, simply a multivibrator. We will reserve the single word multivibrator for the whole class of circuits having two states and describe the astable circuit as a free-running multivibrator.

Free-running multivibrators are applied chiefly as static-power inverters which convert direct to alternating current at high efficiency. Their power output ranges from a few milliwatts to several kilowatts. Because of the absence of moving parts they have largely replaced rotating machines in low-power applications, particularly in aircraft. They are considered in § 16.6.5.

16.6.2. *Analysis of regenerative circuit characteristics*

Before discussing in detail the circuits mentioned above we will describe how the characteristic of Fig. 7.22 arises from a regenerative connection of two junction transistors and the methods of choosing the operating conditions for the three types of operation.

As an example consider the symmetrical multivibrator of Fig. 16.19 and imagine the circuit to be broken at some point to produce input terminals for the derivation of a volt-ampere curve [10]. Thus the emitter lead of $T1$ may be opened between the points X and Y and a current I_e forced into the emitter from an external source whose voltage V_e is recorded. If we assume that the emitter junction of $T1$ is initially cut off the resistance seen from X and Y is very high. This is indicated by the line AB

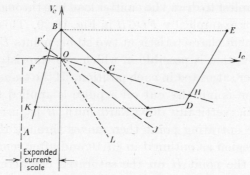

Fig. 16.20. Emitter characteristic of a multivibrator.

of Fig. 16.20, which is displaced from the zero voltage axis because of the reverse bias $+V_{bb}$ on the base of $T1$. If V_e is now increased, i.e. the reverse voltage on the junction is decreased, the point B, at which the emitter junction of $T1$ becomes forward-biased, is eventually reached. $T1$ then conducts, thus applying a positive voltage to the base of $T2$ which begins to turn off. The resulting negative voltage at the collector of $T2$ increases the negative bias on the base of $T1$, causing it to turn on more rapidly and accelerating the process of turning off $T2$. Because of this regeneration, the 'forcing' voltage V_e must actually be reduced as the current I_e increases and the characteristic in this region represents a negative resistance. The next discontinuity occurs when transistor $T2$ turns off at the point C thus removing the regeneration. The precise path followed in the unstable region BC is not important for the present purpose and we may assume that B and C are joined by a straight line.

In the region CD, transistor $T1$ continues to turn on and the resistance seen at its emitter is its CC output resistance. At the point D, $T1$ becomes saturated and the resistance becomes that of the collector bias resistor R_c.

The emitter characteristic of Fig. 16.20 is the same in its essentials as that of Fig. 7.22 and the external emitter resistance corresponds to the load resistance in that figure. In the present case the characteristic may be displaced vertically by means of the bias voltage $+V_{bb}$ and in studying the different types of operation it is simplest to draw the emitter load line through the origin as shown, for example, by $FOGH$ in Fig. 16.20. This line intersects the circuit characteristic at two stable points F and H and bistable operation is possible in which one transistor is cut off and the other saturated in each position. If the transistor under consideration is initially cut off a pulse is applied to shift the characteristic vertically downward until B is just below the origin. The operating point then moves through the negative resistance region as outlined in § 7.10 and after removal of the pulse is at the point H on the saturated characteristic. If a non-saturated 'off' position is required, an emitter load of higher resistance, which intersects the region CD, should be used. In this case some care is necessary to make sure that the operating point does not move into the saturated region before reaching its final position in CD.

We have so far assumed that the emitter-load resistance is associated with one transistor. In practice it is usually common to both transistors, as indicated by R_e of Fig. 16.19, to increase the switching speed. The shape of the circuit characteristic may be somewhat modified but the essentials are the same.

We see from the figure that bistable operation is also obtained when the emitter load is reduced to zero since the load line then coincides with the current axis. In order to obtain unsaturated operation under these conditions, a larger positive bias $+V_{bb}$ must be applied to make CD intersect with the current axis and a larger trigger pulse is necessary. Also, if the CC output resistance represented by CD is low, the range of bias voltage over which unsaturated operation is possible is small. In general

a certain amount of emitter resistance is desirable for unsaturated operation.

The bistable circuit will function if the base capacitors in
Fig. 16.19 are omitted, but some capacitance is usually desirable
to provide overdrive during the switching process. It is usually
advisable to make RC equal to the input time constant of the
transistor unless a 'recovery time' (for the circuit to settle down
between operations) of the order of τ_e cannot be tolerated.

The operation of the monostable circuit may also be explained
by means of the emitter diagram of Fig. 16.20. We assume that
the emitter load line is OJ and the stable operating point is F'.
A triggering pulse from a voltage source is applied to the emitter
through a large capacitance C_1 and moves the operating point
to B thus starting the regenerative process. During the rapid
changes that follow, the capacitor acts as a short-circuit and the
load line is parallel to the current axis. The operating point
therefore moves rapidly via the dotted line to E and transistor
$T1$ is saturated. The capacitor now charges up through $T1$
until the point C is reached. Here it again acts as a short-circuit
during the regenerative process and the operating point jumps
to K. It then moves slowly to the stable position F' as the
charge on C_1 approaches its rest value.

The length of the pulse generated by the monostable action
depends on the length of time to charge up the capacitor in
section EDC while the time for the circuit to reset in preparation
for another pulse is decided by the time to discharge along the
path KF'.

In practice the monostable circuit is usually triggered by a
pulse applied to the base or collector rather than the emitter.
Also, the pulse length is usually controlled by means of one of
the base capacitors, the resistance in parallel with it having been
removed. The method of calculating the pulse length of a typical
circuit is discussed later in this chapter.

Astable operation of the circuit whose characteristic is shown
in Fig. 16.20 is obtained if the circuit is biased so that the point B
is below the current axis, and a high-resistance emitter load, in
parallel with a capacitor, is used with each transistor. Provided

that the load line, which is represented by OL, is steeper than the negative resistance region BC the 'equilibrium' position of the operating point will fall in the negative resistance region. Since it is impossible to establish a stable operating point in this region, a steady-state oscillation is maintained. The motion of the operating point in this case may be followed if we assume that it is initially in the region AB and is moved by some disturbance to the point B. Because of the effect of the emitter capacitor, it moves to E and follows the path $EDCKB$. One may consider that it is continually attempting to reach the intersection of OL and the (displaced) line BC but can never do so. As with the monostable multivibrator the length of pulse and the period is decided by the rates of charge and discharge of the capacitors. If the emitter time constants are different, the lengths of the positive and negative parts of the output wave will be unequal.

In the usual method of producing free-running multivibrators the emitters are earthed and base capacitors are used to control the period and the waveform. It is then necessary to consider an operating-point diagram similar to that of Fig. 16.20 but referred to the base terminal. The procedure for choosing the base bias resistors and coupling capacitors is similar to that used in the present case for the emitter circuit.

The analysis of regenerative circuits outlined in this section may be applied to the open-circuit stable regenerative devices mentioned in Chapters VII and VIII. It has also been developed into a technique for the design of regenerative circuits which is given in detail in references [10] and [11].

16.6.3. *Triggering and steering circuits*

Before describing examples of the three types of regenerative circuit mentioned above, a few remarks concerning methods of starting the switching process are necessary. A detailed study of these 'triggering' methods [12] leads to intricate discussions which would be out of place in this book. We shall therefore restrict ourselves to the following brief qualitative description of trigger-pulse characteristics and methods of applying them.

1. Before regenerative action begins the transistor being triggered behaves as a non-regenerative CE switch. For rapid turn-on the trigger-pulse source should therefore have a low resistance. If the source is the collector of a saturated or clamped transistor of the same type as those in the regenerative circuit its impedance will be lower when it is turned on. The pulse thus supplied (e.g. a positive pulse from a p-n-p transistor) is suitable for turning off the conducting transistor of the multivibrator. Conversely, if the trigger source is an emitter follower or the collector of a complementary transistor, the 'off' unit should be turned on. Special circuits, in which the collector of the source transistor is clamped in the off, rather than the on, position may also be used if a negative triggering pulse is required.

2. The trigger pulse should be long enough to ensure that changeover is properly started. A pulse length somewhat larger than $1/\omega_\alpha$ is suitable.

3. In order to lower the trigger-pulse power requirement, the pulse is usually applied to the base of the transistor which is being switched or to the opposite collector. Emitter triggering is used only in special applications. Base triggering requires the least power of the three methods but the pulse amplitude must be accurately controlled to prevent distortion of the multivibrator output by 'trigger break-through'. Collector triggering is really a form of base triggering in which there is a buffer network (e.g. C, R, and R_b in Fig. 16.19) between the point of trigger application and the base concerned.

4. To determine the trigger-pulse power it is usually sufficient to assume that the source must supply, in a time $1/\omega_\alpha$, the base charge required to establish the final collector current. For the unsaturated case we may use equation (4.19) to give an estimate of the charge stored as a function of the emitter current. Then, assuming that $I_e \simeq I_c$, we find from equation (7.27) that the base charge is $1{\cdot}22I_c/\omega_\alpha$. If the transistor is saturated we must also take into account the excess stored charge Q_s which may reach a maximum value of

$$Q_s \simeq \frac{\omega_\alpha + \omega_I}{\omega_\alpha \, \omega_I (1 - \alpha_N \, \alpha_I)}\left(I_{b1} - \frac{I_c}{h_{FE}}\right), \qquad (16.12)$$

where I_{b1} is the base current initially chosen to drive the transistor into saturation.

5. In monostable circuits the triggering process is relatively simple since the same type of trigger, applied at the same point, is needed for each operation. In many bistable circuits, on the other hand, trigger pulses of opposite polarity must be used alternately ('set, re-set' operation) or pulses of one polarity must alternately be switched from one collector or base to another. The latter process, which is usually performed by diodes or auxiliary transistors, is called steering. Diodes $D1$ and $D2$ in Fig. 16.19 perform this function. The cathode of the diode connected to the transistor that is off is biased negatively and a positive pulse applied at A will pass through it. The other diode will be reverse-biased because the transistor to which it is connected is turned on. The input pulse is therefore steered to the collector of the 'off' transistor.

Steering diodes may be used in a similar way at other electrodes and for other circuits than the simple bistable one.

6. Trigger pulses may be coupled directly from a source at a suitable d.c. level or supplied through a capacitor. In the latter case the capacitor must be large enough to transfer the required charge but not so large that the recovery time is excessive. A diode such as $D3$ in Fig. 16.19 may be used to speed recovery. If $D3$ were not present, the capacitor C_2 would recover its original charge through the resistor R_d after completion of the switching process. The value of R_d should therefore be low if recovery is to be rapid but it should be high to avoid wasting power in the triggering circuit. The diode $D3$ removes the necessity for compromise by acting as a very low-resistance recovery path.

16.6.4. *Multivibrator circuits*

In this section we will describe some basic multivibrator circuits and give some simple design information. Variations of the basic circuits that are particularly useful are also discussed.

16.6.4.1. *The bistable multivibrator*

The operation of this circuit (Fig. 16.19) following application of a positive emitter-trigger pulse to $T1$ was described in § 16.6.2. In the more usual case a positive pulse is applied to the collector of $T1$, and hence to the base of $T2$. The negative-going pulse at the collector of $T2$ is transmitted to $T1$ and starts to turn it on. From this point the process continues as previously described.

The time constant of the switching process may be determined by setting up an equation of the form (7.68) for each transistor and making use of the linear relations between I_{b1} and I_{c2} and between I_{b2} and I_{c1}. The equations are then solved simultaneously to give currents that increase exponentially. If there is sufficient overdrive through the base capacitors, $\Delta I_{b1} \simeq \Delta I_{c2}$, etc., and the solution [13, 14] is found to have a term proportional to $\exp[2(\alpha_0-1)\omega_\alpha t] \simeq \exp(\omega_\alpha t)$, indicating that two regeneratively coupled CE stages will change state at about the speed of a current-driven CB switch. The required overdrive cannot be used in all cases, however, since the base capacitor limits the pulse repetition rate. The time $1/\omega_\alpha$ is therefore a lower limit which may not always be reached in practice.

The simplest bistable multivibrator is one in which definite stable states are obtained by allowing the 'on' transistor to saturate and the 'off' transistor to reach cut-off. These two conditions, which decide the values of the resistors in Fig. 16.19, may be combined with relations determining the switching and repetition rates to produce a formal design procedure [7]. We shall not describe such a procedure in detail but will present two relations from which the values of the resistors R, R_b, and R_c may be determined by trial. The first of these relations is decided by the condition that the 'off' transistor must remain off for the highest expected value of I_{c0} and may be expressed in the form

$$\frac{R}{R_b} \geqslant \frac{0 \cdot 1 + V_s + I_{c0}\, r_{bb'}}{V_{bb} - 0 \cdot 1 - I_{c0}(R_b + r_{bb'})}, \qquad (16.13)$$

where V_s is the saturation voltage of the 'on' transistor and the $0 \cdot 1$ volt arises from the requirement that the net voltage at the base of the 'off' transistor be not less than this value. Note that this analysis assumes that $R_e = 0$.

The second relation, which is determined by the condition that the 'on' transistor must saturate for the lowest anticipated value of h_{FE}, is

$$h_{FE} \geqslant \frac{R+R_c}{R_c} \frac{1-(V_{bb}/V_{cc})\{R_c/(R+R_b)\}}{1-(V_{bb}/V_{cc})\{(R+R_c)/R_b\}}. \quad (16.14)$$

This expression is obtained by an analysis of Fig. 16.19 (with $R_e = 0$) with the following assumptions:

(i) $I_c \leqslant h_{FE} I_b$.

(ii) $V_{cc} \gg V_s$ and $V_{bb} \gg V_s$.

(iii) $V_{bb} \gg V_{bes}$ where V_{bes} is the base voltage to produce saturation.

(For the case in which bias is supplied by an emitter resistor R_e rather than by V_{bb} the value of R_e is determined by the procedure outlined below.)

In order that the 'on' and 'off' voltages and the trigger sensitivity of the bistable multivibrator be independent of temperature the following additional conditions should be met:

(a) The current in the bias network should be five to ten times the maximum value of I_{c0}.

(b) The voltage drop $I_{c0} R_b$ should be a small fraction, say one-fifth, of V_{bb}.

A simple design procedure which makes use of the above relations and conditions is the following:

1. Choose V_{cc}, which is determined by the required output voltage.

2. The value of the collector current at saturation V_{cs} is chosen. It will be decided by the required output current and the transistor characteristics. Then $R_c \simeq V_{cc}/I_{cs}$.

3. Choose V_{bb} in the range $0 \cdot 1 V_{cc} \leqslant V_{bb} \leqslant 0 \cdot 4 V_{cc}$. The upper limit may be raised above $0 \cdot 4 V_{cc}$ if desired but the range given represents common practice. If an emitter resistor is to be used to provide bias, the value of V_{cc} should be increased by V_{bb}. Then $R_e \simeq V_{bb}/I_{cs}$. To ensure saturation, R_e should be by-passed by a small capacitor ($\simeq 0 \cdot 02 \ \mu F$). This will eliminate voltage changes across it during the switching processes.

4. Choose R and R_b to satisfy conditions (a) and (b). As a first choice we may make $R_b \simeq 2R$.

5. Ascertain if the design satisfies equations (16.13) and (16.14). If it does not, some readjustment of the chosen values will be necessary.

The basic saturated bistable multivibrator discussed above may be simplified for some applications by omission of the bias supply and bias networks, thus producing the simple and

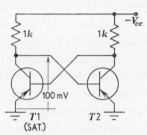

FIG. 16.21. Direct-coupled multivibrator.

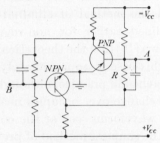

FIG. 16.22. Complementary bistable latch.

economical circuit of Fig. 16.21. This circuit requires a transistor whose saturation voltage is lower than the emitter-base voltage to turn it on. Germanium alloy transistors are suitable from this point of view. However, because of the absence of reverse bias, the circuit is sensitive to changes in I_{c0} and should be operated only at low temperatures. Operation at higher temperatures should be possible with silicon-alloy transistors and some silicon graded-base (mesa) transistors.

The simplicity of the positive feedback loops in this circuit and the resulting reduction in stray capacitance help to maintain switching speed, thus making it possible to operate at a repetition rate of 10^7 pulses per second with high-frequency transistors $(f_\alpha \simeq 300 \text{ Mc/sec})$. The circuit is a member of a class of circuits known as the direct-coupled transistor logic (DCTL) group.

In the above circuits a transistor is 'on' in each stable state. Some applications require that a bistable circuit remain in one of the stable states for long periods of time and it is then advantageous to use an asymmetrical circuit in which both transistors are 'off' in the standby position and both are 'on' in the other position. A complementary latch which demonstrates this type of operation is shown in Fig. 16.22. Here both transistors are assumed to be off initially. A positive pulse at B will turn both on regeneratively while a (reset) positive pulse at A will turn them both off.

It is possible to operate multivibrators so that the transistors do not saturate in the 'on' position and thus obtain higher switching speed. The disadvantages of unsaturated operation and the method of eliminating them are the same as those outlined earlier for non-regenerative switches. It has been shown [10] that the theoretical maximum frequency of operation in this case is approximately $\sqrt{(f_\alpha f_\beta)}$. This value may be approached in practice, although at frequencies close to this limit the change-over occupies nearly one-half of the period so that the waveforms seen at the collector are nearly triangular.

The simplest method of preventing saturation is to use a large un-by-passed emitter resistor. During the switching process the sum of the emitter currents remains approximately constant and the resistor introduces little degeneration. When one transistor is turned off the amount of degeneration suddenly increases. The emitter is then clamped and saturation is prevented in the same manner as in the current switch. If more definite clamping and low output impedance is desired one of the diode clamping methods mentioned earlier or two current switches (four transistors) may be used.

The design of a reliable unsaturated symmetrical multivibrator, which is quite intricate, will not be discussed here. It has been reduced to a formal tabulated process by the staff of the (U.S.) General Electric Company [7, 11].

To close this section on the bistable multivibrator we will consider an application that is of major importance in experimental physics—the counting circuit. It has been noted earlier that two triggering pulses must be applied to a bistable circuit to restore it to its initial condition. The number of output pulses of a bistable multivibrator is therefore one-half of the number of input pulses so that the circuit may be used as a binary (scale of two) counter. If n stages are used, operation of the final stage indicates the passage of 2^n pulses, operation of the penultimate stage indicates 2^{n-1} pulses, etc. Thus if a pilot light is used on each stage to indicate when it is in one of the two states, the total number of pulses passed will be given by $(a_1 + a_2 2 + a_3 2^2 + \ldots + a_n 2^{n-1})$ where the a's may, for example, have the value 0 when the corresponding light is out and 1 when it is on.

In most cases, decade (scale of ten) counting is preferred and this may be obtained by the following method: If the output of the penultimate stage is fed back to the input, a complete operation of the output stage will be obtained for each $(2^n - 1)$ input pulses. If a similar extra pulse is returned to the second stage input as well, a complete output pulse will be obtained for $(2^n - 3)$ input pulses. When this procedure is followed for a 3-stage (scale of 8) chain the number of output pulses is one-fifth of the number of input pulses. Combining such a scale of five counter with an additional binary stage gives a decade counter.

16.6.4.2. *The monostable multivibrator*

As mentioned in § 16.6.2 the most popular form of monostable multivibrator is derived from the symmetrical bistable circuit of Fig. 16.19 by omitting one of the collector-to-base coupling resistors (R). The associated capacitor and its bias resistor R_b now determine the pulse length. The resulting circuit and appropriate waveforms are shown in Fig. 16.23. The bias voltage V_{bb} is adjusted so that, in the stable state, $T1$ is off and $T2$ is on. The pulse length or lifetime of the metastable state is then determined by the time taken to discharge the timing capacitor C through the d.c. resistance of $T1$ and the resistor R. The timing capacitor should be placed in the base circuit of the transistor which is turned off when the metastable state is reached so that the influence of the base current $(\simeq I_{c0})$ on the time of discharge of the capacitor will be small.

The operation of the circuit, which is analogous to that of the emitter-triggered monostable circuit mentioned in § 16.6.2, is as follows: A positive trigger pulse applied to point A turns off $T2$

and thus brings $T1$ into conduction. Assuming that $T1$ is rapidly driven to saturation the voltage at its collector rises in a step from $-V_{cc}$ to the saturation value $-V_s$. This step is transferred through C to the base of $T2$ which therefore rises from the normal bias voltage $-V_{be}$ by the height of the step to the value $+(V_{cc}-V_s-V_{be})$. The capacitor at once starts to discharge, and,

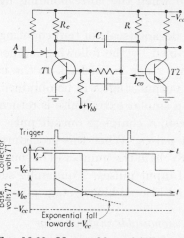

FIG. 16.23. Monostable multivibrator
and associated waveforms.

neglecting the effect of I_{c0}, the voltage at the base of $T2$ falls exponentially with time constant CR towards an ultimate value $-V_{cc}$. This voltage, which is often called the aiming voltage, is the value which would be reached if $T2$ were removed from the circuit. It is convenient to refer all circuit voltages to this aiming point as origin so that the initial voltage V_0 at the base of $T2$ becomes

$$V_0 = 2V_{cc}-V_s-V_{be}. \qquad (16.15)$$

The voltage at time t after the start of the pulse is

$$v = V_0 \exp(-t/CR). \qquad (16.16)$$

When v drops to within a few millivolts of earth, $T2$ begins to conduct, the discharge is arrested, and the circuit reverts to the stable state. This occurs when v becomes approximately equal to V_{cc} (with respect to the new origin $-V_{cc}$), at a time T after the start of the pulse, where

$$T = CR \ln \frac{2V_{cc}-V_s-V_{be}}{V_{cc}}. \qquad (16.17)$$

When the effect of I_{c0} is taken into account this time is decreased somewhat, the corrected expression being

$$T = CR \ln \frac{2V_{cc}-V_s-V_{be}+I_{c0}(R-R_c)}{V_{cc}+I_{c0}R}. \qquad (16.18)$$

If accuracy of pulse length is important it is essential that both R and R_c should be small. For example, assuming that

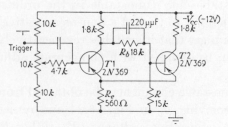

FIG. 16.24. The Schmitt trigger.

$V_{cc} = -12$ V, $V_s = V_{be} = -0.25$ V, $R = 10$ kΩ, and $R_c = 1$ kΩ; a tenfold increase in I_{c0} from 5 μA to 50 μA will shorten the pulse length by about 2·5 per cent. If R and R_c are made 100 kΩ and 10 kΩ respectively the same variation in I_{c0} will cause a 23 per cent decrease in T.

A useful first approximation when the pulse length is not critical may be obtained by neglecting V_s, V_{be}, and I_{c0} to give $T \simeq 0.69CR$.

The above monostable circuit may probably be regarded as the basic type but many other circuits that perform a similar function have been developed. An important example is the Schmitt trigger mentioned earlier in which one of the collector-base couplings of the symmetric multivibrator is replaced by emitter coupling, as shown in Fig. 16.24. In the rest state of this circuit, $T1$ is off and both emitters are at approximately -5.0 volts owing to the bias on the base of $T2$. If the base of $T1$ is moved from the cutoff position to a level that is slightly negative with respect to the emitters, $T1$ conducts and $T2$ is switched off. The circuit remains in this second state as long as the input voltage remains at this negative value. However, when the input voltage is altered in the positive direction, $T1$ starts to turn off and the emitter current is switched regeneratively from $T1$ to $T2$. There is a small hysteresis effect in that the two critical levels differ slightly but this may be minimized by careful design. An excellent discussion of the design problems, which has been given by Williams [15] for the vacuum-tube version, may also be applied to the transistor circuit.

It may be seen from this description that the Schmitt trigger is neither bistable nor monostable in the ordinary sense. Its behaviour is similar to that of a non-regenerative switch but it has the advantages that it switches regeneratively at very high speed and can be designed with an accurate adjustable trigger threshold.

A true monostable circuit may be obtained from the Schmitt trigger by removing R_b in Fig. 16.24 and returning the base resistor R to a negative voltage $-V_{bb}$ rather than to earth. A stable condition then exists in which $T1$ is off and $T2$ is on. Upon application of a negative pulse to $T1$ the circuit may operate in one of two modes. In the first, the base of $T1$ is returned to a source of bias voltage which allows the transistor to saturate when the circuit current is switched from $T2$ to $T1$. The change of voltage at the collector of $T1$, which is transferred to the base of $T2$, is therefore a positive step whose height is $(V_{cc}-V_s-R_e I_{sat})$, where V_s is the voltage drop and I_{sat} the emitter current when the collector is saturated. The base voltage has little effect on the value of I_{sat}, which is principally determined by the resistors in series with the collector and the emitter. The pulse length is determined by the time required to re-establish the initial charge on the collector-base coupling capacitor, through the circuit consisting of R_e, the emitter to collector path of $T1$, and the resistor R in series, and is almost independent of the value of the base bias voltage. If the base bias is such that $T1$ cannot saturate when $T2$ is turned off, the operation is in the second mode. The height of the positive voltage step at the collector of $T1$ is now almost proportional to the base bias voltage, and hence, to a good approximation, so is the pulse length. The circuit is useful as a variable delay generator; in this application the trailing edge of the generated pulse is used to form a fresh trigger pulse which follows the original trigger by a variable delay, equal to the pulse length. In this mode $T1$ is essentially emitter clamped in an unsaturated condition and the circuit may be used to generate very short pulses. The circuit also has the advantage that the load may be connected to the free collector of $T2$, in which case it has little effect on the multivibrator action.

These multivibrators are formally very similar to their vacuum-tube counterparts except that the circuit impedances are all at a much lower level. This suggests that the timing capacitor could be replaced by an inductance which could be put in series with one of the collector returns to $-V_{cc}$. Hamilton [16] has analysed the effects of I_{c0} on the pulse width of an inductance-timed monostable multivibrator and has shown that they may be made much smaller than in the circuits discussed above.

The monostable version of the complementary latch (in which, for example, R of Fig. 16.22 is removed) is particularly important, as both transistors may be off in the rest position and may turn on together to give a large pulse when triggered. This type is used chiefly in unattended locations as a switch for such low duty-cycle devices as radio beacons, 'on demand' marine radio buoys, etc., where battery economy is of paramount importance.

16.6.4.3. *The astable multivibrator*

Astable versions of all of the above circuits exist but the most popular is the simple symmetric a.c. coupled type mentioned in § 16.6.2 and shown in Fig. 16.25. This simple circuit exhibits an appreciable variation of frequency with temperature but this may be reduced if the transistors are bias-stabilized by one of the methods given in Chapter IX. In most applications there is little advantage in using other types of feedback loop to

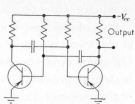

FIG. 16.25. Symmetric astable multivibrator.

produce frequency stability, although it should be noted that two monostable circuits can be coupled to provide a free-running oscillator whose frequency is quite constant. If a square wave of accurately known frequency is required, however, it is more usual to derive it from a stable sine-wave oscillator followed by a Schmitt trigger.

16.6.5. *Transformer-coupled regenerative switches*

In the regenerative switches so far discussed positive feedback has been obtained by resistive or capacitive networks. The majority of regenerative applications are of this type. However, as mentioned earlier, monostable and astable regenerative circuits may also be obtained by transformer coupling. To close this chapter we describe two of the more important—the transformer-coupled multivibrator or power converter and the blocking oscillator.

16.6.5.1. *The transformer-coupled multivibrator or power converter*

For many years vibrating mechanical switches have been combined with transformers to form d.c. to a.c. converters capable of producing high a.c. voltage outputs from low-voltage d.c. supplies. A high-voltage d.c. source may then be obtained by rectification. The contact troubles that beset mechanical switches can be avoided if they are replaced by transistors. Also, high-efficiency operation can be obtained if the transistors are alternately cut off and saturated and if the switching process is made very rapid by regeneration. The transistor converter thus takes the form of a transformer-coupled astable multivibrator or square wave oscillator.

One of the best-known examples of the transistor converter is the two transistor push-pull oscillator shown in Fig. 16.26. *CE*-connected transistors are used in this case although the matching provided by the transformer also makes it possible to obtain regeneration in the *CB* connection. The *CE* converter is, in general, the more efficient but the *CB* version is less sensitive to variations between transistors and may be preferred for operation at high ambient temperatures.

In order to explain the operation of the circuit of Fig. 16.26, we assume that the transistor $T1$ has just begun to switch on. The collector current starts to increase and, because of the transformer coupling between collector and base circuits, positive feedback is applied to the base. The rise of collector current produces a large voltage drop across the transformer winding in the collector circuit and the transistor saturates. This transformer winding, which is one-half of the total primary winding, has an inductance L_p and a linear component of magnetizing

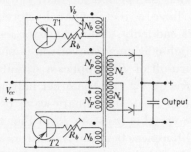

FIG. 16.26. Transformer-coupled push-pull oscillator.

current given by the relation $V_{cc} \simeq L_p(dI_c/dt)$ flows into it. There is, in addition to this magnetizing current, a constant component of collector current which supplies the load. However, the fluxes produced by the primary and secondary load currents cancel each other in the usual manner and these currents do not affect the qualitative discussion which follows.

During this magnetizing process the voltage across the transformer and hence across the load remains constant. Similarly a constant voltage is applied to the base and the resulting base current furnishes the driving force to increase the collector current. The linear rise of collector current continues until one of the following processes occurs:

(i) The total collector current (magnetizing plus load) reaches the value $h_{FE} I_b$. When this happens the collector current cannot increase further because of the lack of additional base drive. The voltage $L_p(dI_c/dt)$ across the transformer therefore decreases and the transistor comes out of saturation. The decrease of transformer voltage reduces the base drive and, since the transistor is now active, the collector current decreases regeneratively and the transistor switches off.

(ii) Before the total collector current reaches the value $h_{FE} I_b$ the transformer may saturate, producing a decrease of L_p. An increase of dI_c/dt is therefore required and the magnetizing current must rise more rapidly. It soon reaches the stage at which $h_{FE} I_b$ is insufficient to maintain the total current and the transformer switches off regeneratively as before. If this method of determining the 'on' period is used, the transformer core material should have a rectangular hysteresis loop so that saturation occurs suddenly. The transistor losses can then be minimized and high-efficiency conversion is possible.

The sudden turn-off of $T1$ supplies a stimulus via the transformer which turns on $T2$ and the other half of the a.c. output wave is generated. A steady square-wave oscillation is thus maintained. The variable resistors R_b in Fig. 16.26 are used to compensate for differences between transistors and thus to make their 'on' periods equal when the switch-off process is not decided by transformer saturation.

On the assumption that the resistance and leakage reactance of the transformer windings are negligible the output voltage of this converter is $(N_s/N_p)(V_{cc}-I_c R_s)$, where R_s, the saturation resistance of the transistor, is very small for good high-power switching transistors. The circuit may therefore have very good output-voltage regulation.

The collector junction of the 'off' transistor in this circuit is positively biased and the emitter is negatively biased. The transistor is thus capable of operating in the inverse direction and returning power to the d.c. source. This process occurs if the loading is light and helps to maintain high efficiency of operation under these conditions.

The optimum frequency of operation of the circuit is governed by the following factors:

(*a*) The transformer core loss increases rapidly with frequency (approximately as f^2).

(*b*) The transformer copper loss decreases with frequency

since a smaller inductance and thus fewer turns are needed for a high-frequency transformer.

(c) The transistor loss is almost exactly proportional to frequency because the switching time, which is constant, represents an increased fraction of each cycle as the frequency is increased.

(d) Rectifier losses, which are added when a d.c. output is required, are constant except at very high frequencies.

The operating frequency should be chosen so that the sum of these quantities is a minimum. When iron cores of standard

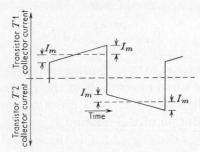

FIG. 16.27. Collector currents in the push-pull oscillator.

lamination thickness ($\simeq 0 \cdot 014$ inch) are used, it is usually sufficient to make (a) lie between 50 per cent and 100 per cent of (b). The optimum frequency is then in the neighbourhood of a few hundred cycles per second. Ferrite cores make possible the use of higher frequencies and the chief frequency-dependent loss then arises from the transistor, which limits the best operating frequency to a few kilocycles per second.

From our knowledge of the processes described above we may devise a simple design procedure for this type of converter. This may not produce the most efficient design immediately but a satisfactory result should be obtained after a few trials. The criteria leading to the design and the resulting procedures are the following:

1. A linear change of magnetizing current of the type mentioned earlier takes place during each half of the generated square wave. In a symmetrical circuit, such as that of Fig. 16.26, this requires that the collector currents have the form shown in

Fig. 16.27 where the magnetizing component of the total current varies linearly from $-I_m$ to $+I_m$. To a first approximation the load current does not affect the flux in the transformer core. The magnetizing components in the two halves of the wave produce opposing effects in the core so that the flux increases from $-\phi_m$ to $+\phi_m$ in one half-cycle and decreases again during the next half-cycle. During each half-cycle the voltage across the transformer winding connected to the conducting transistor is $-V_{cc}$. Hence

$$V_{cc} = N_p \frac{d\phi}{dt} \times 10^{-8} \qquad (16.19)$$

or

$$V_{cc} = \frac{N_p \, 2\phi_m}{1/2f} \times 10^{-8} \qquad (16.20)$$

since the flux changes by $2\phi_m$ during the period $1/2f$. Here N_p is the number of turns in one-half of the primary winding and ϕ_m is in maxwells. If m.k.s. units are used the factor 10^{-8} is omitted. Substitution of the relation $\phi_m = B_m A$, where B_m is the maximum flux density and A is the area of the core, gives

$$AN_p = \frac{V_{cc} \times 10^8}{4f B_m}. \qquad (16.21)$$

The value of V_{cc} in this equation should be somewhat less than one-half of the maximum allowable V_{ce} for the chosen transistor. B_m may be determined from manufacturers' data for core materials. For transformer steel a value of 10,000 gauss is probably suitable. An operating frequency of 200 c/sec is then a good starting-point.

A trial value of core area should now be chosen and the value of N_p determined from equation (16.21).

2. The load component, I_l, of the collector current may be determined from the relation

$$I_l \simeq \frac{W}{0 \cdot 75 V_{cc}}, \qquad (16.22)$$

where W is the required output power and the factor 0·75 is an assumed value for the overall efficiency.

3. The magnetizing current is normally about 10 per cent of I_l so that the maximum required base current is $I_{bm} = 1 \cdot 1 I_l / h_{FE}$

and the induced base voltage is $V_b = (h_{IE} + R_b)I_{bm}$. The number of turns in the base winding is $N_b = N_p V_b/V_{cc}$.

In order to balance transistor characteristics R_b should be at least equal to h_{IE} but should not exceed it by a factor larger than two or three if high switching speed is to be maintained.

4. The open-circuit voltage V'_0 of the square wave a.c. output is

$$V'_0 = \frac{(V_{cc} - V_s)N_s}{N_p}, \qquad (16.23)$$

where V_s is the saturation voltage of the transistor. In order to allow for voltage drops in the resistances and leakage inductances of the primary and secondary windings V'_0 should be about 10 per cent larger than the required load voltage V_0. Equation (16.23) may then be used to determine N_s.

5. The cross-sections of the primary and secondary conductors may be determined using a current density of 1,200 amperes per sq. in. (This figure should be decreased for transformers of output in excess of 150 watts. Suitable empirical formulae may be obtained from radio handbooks.) Since the core area and the numbers of turns are fixed, the mean length per turn and the total winding resistance may be estimated. The total copper loss may then be obtained.

6. If a steel core is used, the core losses of the completed design should be determined from published data and compared with the total copper loss. If the ratio of the losses is not as indicated above, a new core size should be chosen and the design repeated.

Since oscillations in a circuit of this type are self-sustaining but not self-starting, some provision should be made for initiating them. The simplest method makes use of a push button which supplies a temporary negative bias to the base of one transistor and thus turns it on.

The push-pull circuit is the most widely used in transformer-coupled power converters. For low-power applications, however, a single-transistor arrangement equivalet to one-half of Fig. 16.26 is sometimes used. In this case, to secure efficient operation, it is necessary to remove energy from the transformer during the off period and to return it to the power supply—a procedure requiring an auxiliary transformer winding and a diode. This arrangement, which is almost as complicated as the push-pull circuit, will not be discussed further.

Another type of transformer-coupled multivibrator which is useful for high-voltage low-current d.c. applications, is the so-called ringing-choke converter shown in Fig. 16.28. This circuit

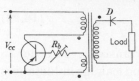

operates in a manner fundamentally different from that of the push-pull circuit. During the part of the cycle in which the transistor is on, the secondary of the transformer is disconnected from the load by the half-wave rectifier D.

FIG. 16.28. The ringing choke converter.

The growth of collector current during this period and the subsequent switching off takes place in the same manner as in the push-pull converter but the constant load current is absent. Following turn-off the energy stored in the transformer inductance is switched to the load by means of the output diode. During this process the transistor base is driven to cutoff by the transformer voltage and is held there until the energy has been released. The magnitude and period of the secondary voltage are then determined by the following factors:

1. The transformer-turns ratio, whose useful upper limit is about 10:1. For larger ratios the increased transformer leakage inductance nullifies the effect of the increase in turns ratio.

2. The transformer inductance L_{eff} and distributed capacitance C_{eff} seen from the secondary terminals. For large values of $L_{\text{eff}}/C_{\text{eff}}$ the output voltage is many times that expected on the basis of transformer ratio alone.

3. The time constant L_{eff}/R_l, which decides the length of the off period of the transistor. The latter need not be equal to the on period but in most applications they will be of the same order.

To complete this summary of the properties of the ringing choke converter we add the following observations:

(i) In contrast to the push-pull converter, the ringing choke converter has poor voltage regulation, i.e. it is a high-resistance source and should be used to supply constant loads.

(ii) Its efficiency may be made very high by proper design.

(iii) Its mode of operation is such that it can only supply d.c. loads. For a.c. loads, e.g. small induction motors, either the push-pull or the single-ended converter mentioned above should be used.

(iv) As with the other transformer-coupled converters, some means of initiating oscillations should be provided. A simple push-button scheme is satisfactory.

16.6.5.2. *The blocking oscillator*

The second basic transformer-coupled regenerative oscillator that we shall consider is the blocking oscillator. As the name implies this originally took the form of a resonant oscillator in which the input and output circuits were strongly overcoupled. A bias voltage developed in an auxiliary CR circuit during the first half-cycle of oscillation cut off the active element and limited the output to a half-cycle pulse. This type of blocking oscillator is still used occasionally, but more general modern practice is to replace the resonant circuits by a transformer having a magnetic core which produces a sharp rise of the pulse by regenerative action similar to that in the power converter. As with the power converter the matching introduced by the transformer makes CB or CE operation possible and we shall consider examples of both types.

A typical CB circuit, in which the transistor is used as an unsaturated clamped switch, is shown in Fig. 16.29. Here the diode $D1$ clamps the collector to a voltage $-V'_{cc}$ while $D2$ prevents the collector voltage from becoming more negative than $-V_{cc}$ and allows the transformer to discharge its stored energy through R_1. The resulting output waveform is also shown in the figure.

On the assumption that the transformer has negligible core loss and winding capacitance Linvill and Mattson [17] have shown that the time constant of the regenerative build-up in this case may be as short as $1/2\omega_\alpha$ if the correct transformer ratio (which normally lies between 5 and 10) is chosen.

The length of time that the transistor is on is determined for the blocking oscillator by the same mechanism as in the transformer-coupled multivibrator, and is approximately $(n-1)L_2/R_i$, where n is the turns ratio n_1/n_2, L_2 is the secondary self-inductance, and R_i is the input resistance of the transistor. Following turn-off, a reverse bias is applied to the emitter-base junction by the transformer secondary acting through the capacitor C. The length of time that this bias is maintained

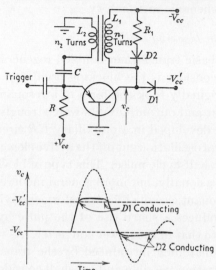

FIG. 16.29. Unsaturated CB blocking oscillator.

depends on the larger of the two time constants L_1/R_1 and RC. Thus, in the astable version of the blocking oscillator, as in the single-transistor converter, the lengths of the positive and negative parts of the wave are determined by different mechanisms. In monostable operation, which is obtained when V_{ee} is sufficient to cut off the transistor and a positive trigger pulse is applied, the recovery time between pulses depends similarly on L_1/R_1 or RC.

The CB blocking oscillator is used chiefly when high-voltage pulses are required. It has the advantage over the CE version that a higher collector supply voltage can be used.

A simple saturating CE blocking oscillator is shown in Fig. 16.30. This is similar to Fig. 16.29 except for the removal of the clamping diode and the addition of the triggering transistor

$T2$. The latter prevents the violent changes produced by the blocking oscillator from reacting on the input source and leads to more reliable operation. The circuit can be made monostable or astable, in a manner analogous to that employed with the CB circuit, by control of the base bias voltage. The RC network, which can be chosen to determine the recovery time in a monostable circuit and the period in an astable circuit, may

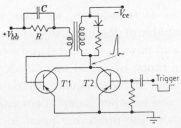

FIG. 16.30. Saturating CE blocking oscillator.

be inserted in the emitter lead if desired. Incidentally, for a monostable circuit, the time constant RC should be considerably larger than the trigger-pulse length if multiple firings are to be avoided. The transformer ratio is generally lower than for the CB oscillator, values in the range from 2 to 5 being suitable.

The design of a blocking oscillator to meet a given set of specifications has been thoroughly discussed by Narud and Aaron [18]. Excellent discussions of the properties of transformer-coupled regenerative switches are contained in references [19], [20], and [21].

16.7. Conclusion

Some indication of the usefulness of the transistor as a switch will be given by the variety of circuits discussed in this chapter. There seems to be no doubt that this is potentially the most important field for transistor applications. Lack of space prevents a more comprehensive survey but the subjects considered should give the reader a reasonable picture of the breadth of the field and a suitable grounding for the study of circuits in the references and other literature.

TRANSISTOR SINE-WAVE OSCILLATORS AND SWEEP GENERATORS

17.1. Introduction

IN the applications of transistors, we have so far considered linear amplifiers capable of dealing with small or large continuous signals (low-level and power amplifiers) and switching amplifiers covering a similar range of signal magnitudes. The switching applications have also included square-wave or non-linear oscillators. There remains another group of circuits which make use of large excursions of the operating point in the active region but which depend upon the property of the transistor as a linear amplifying device. This group includes two important classes of circuit, sine-wave oscillators and linear-sweep generators. We shall consider their operating principles and describe some typical circuits in the present chapter.

17.2. General remarks concerning sine-wave oscillators

We have shown in the preceding chapter that non-linear multivibrator oscillations can be obtained if positive feedback is applied from output to input. In such applications the transistor is continually driven between cutoff and saturation and no upper limit need be placed on the amount of positive feedback. It should, in fact, be made as large as possible in order to increase the switching speed.

The sine-wave oscillator also requires positive feedback but in this case a limit must be placed on the amount if distortion is to be avoided. The reason for this may be seen by considering the oscillator as a feedback amplifier of the type depicted in Fig. 13.1. If the open-loop voltage gain is A, and the feedback network has an attenuation B, the voltage returned to the input is ABv_i, where v_i is the applied input signal of angular frequency ω. If the phase angle of AB is a multiple of $360°$ and if $|AB| = 1$, the source may be removed. The amplifier will then continue to function by supplying its own input signal and will thus become an oscillator. However, if $|AB|$ is not exactly unity the oscillations will either die out or build up in amplitude until the amplifier is overloaded and the waveform is distorted. In practical circuits the following requirements must be met if the oscillator is to produce a sine-wave output that is stable in amplitude and frequency:

(i) The gain must decrease with amplitude. Then if AB exceeds unity for small outputs the output will grow until the condition $AB = 1$ is met. In order for the output to approach a sine wave as closely as possible the small-signal value of AB should be just large enough to ensure that it can never be less than unity and, in order to minimize the generation of harmonics, the gain should decrease smoothly as the amplitude is increased.

(ii) The change of amplitude with frequency (the Q factor) in the feedback network should be as large as possible. This implies a high rate of change of phase with frequency in the vicinity of the oscillator frequency.

(iii) The feedback network should present a high impedance to harmonics of the frequency of oscillation. This condition usually follows automatically if (ii) is satisfied.

Condition (ii) is imposed for the following reason: if the overall phase shift changes (e.g. as a result of a change of power-supply voltage and the resulting variation of transistor capacitance) the frequency will move to a new value at which the total phase shift is again a multiple of $360°$. If (ii) is satisfied the required change in frequency will be small and the circuit will have good frequency stability. Condition (iii) is required because the non-linear amplifier characteristic causes the harmonics to beat with each other and with the fundamental frequency, thus producing intermodulation products having the same frequency as the fundamental. If not reduced by filtering of the harmonics, these modulation products will produce an appreciable change of phase angle at the fundamental frequency. The frequency will then move to a new value at which the phase shift again becomes an exact multiple of $360°$.

It is worth remarking that the sine-wave oscillator is in general self-starting. The transient current produced when it is switched on contains a component at the frequency of oscillation which is selectively amplified and continues to build up until a constant amplitude of oscillation is established. As long as AB exceeds unity for signals below the normal amplitude the oscillator will start.

In an oscillator which operates at a frequency whose value is well below that of the transistor cutoff frequency, the required 360° phase shift is usually obtained by a combination of about 180° in an amplifier stage added to a similar shift in a passive network. The passive network may consist of combinations of resistance and capacitance elements, in which case the frequency is that at which the R-C combinations produce approximately 180° phase shift, or it may be a resonant circuit, often called the 'tank' circuit, containing inductance and capacitance and a transformer to bring the total phase shift close to 360°. Since the phase of the current or voltage in a resonant circuit varies rapidly near the resonant frequency, a total shift of 360° is obtained when the oscillator frequency differs but slightly from that of the resonant circuit. If the oscillation frequency is well above the cutoff frequency of the transistor it may be necessary to compensate for the phase shift in the transistor by adding an extra phase shift in the system. Otherwise the frequency of oscillation may differ considerably from the resonant frequency of the tank circuit, thus reducing the effective Q and the frequency stability.

It is theoretically possible to build oscillators which do not contain resonant circuits in which the required phase shift is obtained by combinations of inductance and resistance rather than R-C networks. These are, however, more expensive than R-C oscillators and are seldom used.

In the remainder of the oscillator section of this chapter we shall consider examples of both the phase shift and resonant circuit types but before describing them we shall outline briefly a general method of analysis that may be applied to all oscillator circuits.

17.3. The analysis of oscillating circuits

The analysis of an oscillator circuit is normally divided into two parts: the development of the condition for oscillation to occur and the determination of the frequency. There are several ways in which these problems may be attacked and the preferred method depends on the type of circuit. A general procedure which often provides a useful short cut may be derived as follows:

We consider the closed-loop gain, which has the form $A/(1-AB)$. In the present case $AB = +1$, the positive sign denoting positive feedback, and the gain has a zero in the denominator. It was shown for a simple circuit in Chapter V that the expression for the gain contains the circuit determinant Δ in the denominator and this result can easily be extended to more general circuits which include feedback. A necessary condition for oscillation is, therefore, that $\Delta = 0$. Equating the real part of Δ to zero gives the condition imposed on the gain, while the imaginary part, which must be separately equal to zero, gives the frequency.

17.4. The phase-shift oscillator

The simplest type of oscillator in which $R\text{-}C$ networks are used to provide the required phase shift employs a CE amplifier with CR phase-advance networks or RC phase-lag networks connected between collector and base. Phase-advance networks are usually more convenient since they automatically produce d.c. isolation between the two electrodes. An oscillator of this type, which uses the compound connection of two transistors to give a large current gain, is shown in Fig.

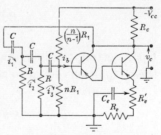

Fig. 17.1. Phase-shift oscillator.

17.1. At least three CR networks are required since the phase shift from a single network must be appreciably less than 90° if a reasonable feedback current is to be obtained.

In the present case all the resistance arms of the three networks are assumed to be of equal value R in order to simplify the analysis, although in practice they may be different. The input resistance r_i of the amplifier and the equivalent resistance R_1 of the base bias network can be considered to be incorporated into one of the shunt resistance arms by choosing R_1 so that the value of R_1 and r_i in parallel is equal to R. The values of the two resistors which make the bias network can be expressed as nR_1 and $nR_1/(n-1)$, the parameter n being chosen to give the correct d.c. bias voltage. The value of the load resistor R_c is assumed to be much less than R and the collector voltage is therefore

$$v_c = -h_{fe} i_b R_c = -h_{fe} i_3 \frac{R R_c}{r_i}. \qquad (17.1)$$

The transistor output circuit may be represented by a voltage generator of voltage v_c in series with a resistance R_c. When this is applied to the input network the following equations are obtained:

$$i_1\left(R + R_c + \frac{1}{j\omega C}\right) - i_2 R \qquad + i_3 h_{fe} \frac{R R_c}{r_i} \qquad = 0, \qquad (17.2)$$

$$-i_1 R \qquad + i_2\left(2R + \frac{1}{j\omega C}\right) - i_3 R \qquad = 0, \qquad (17.3)$$

$$-i_2 R \qquad + i_3\left(2R + \frac{1}{j\omega C}\right) = 0. \qquad (17.4)$$

Upon setting the imaginary part of the circuit determinant of these equations equal to zero, we obtain

$$\omega = \omega_0 = \frac{1}{RC\sqrt{(6 + 4R_c/R)}} \qquad (17.5)$$

and substituting this value of ω into the real part, which is also equated to zero, gives

$$R^3 h_{fe}\left(\frac{R_c}{r_i}\right) = (5R + R_c)(6R^2 + 4R R_c) - R^2(R + 3R_c). \qquad (17.6)$$

Neglecting R_c in comparison with R we obtain

$$\omega_0 \simeq \frac{1}{RC\sqrt{6}}, \qquad h_{fe}\left(\frac{R_c}{r_i}\right) \simeq 29. \qquad (17.7)$$

Equation (17.7) indicates that the circuit will just oscillate if the open-loop voltage gain is 29. A very large value of h_{fe} is required since R_c is small compared with r_i. It is for this reason that the compound connection is used. The un-by-passed emitter resistance R'_e is inserted to control r_i and hence the voltage gain, which should just exceed 29 if distortion of the output is to be prevented.

17.5. Bridge oscillators

A second type of oscillator employs a resistance-capacitance bridge which provides two feedback paths between output and input of the amplifier. One of these paths supplies positive and the other negative feedback. A well-known example is the Wien bridge oscillator shown schematically in Fig. 17.2. In this circuit negative feedback is available at all frequencies via the resistance arms R_1 and R_2. Positive feedback is

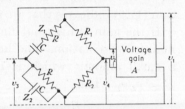

Fig. 17.2. Schematic diagram of Wien bridge oscillator.

applied through the reactive arms Z_1 and Z_2 which are frequency selective. The circuit oscillates at the frequency at which the phase shift in the positive feedback loop is an integral multiple of 360°.

Another way in which the bridge type of network can be used is to have frequency-independent positive feedback, while the negative feedback is through a null network such as a bridged T or a twin T. The circuit then tends to oscillate at the null frequency of the network.

In order to demonstrate the design of this type of circuit we consider a Wien bridge circuit in which the R and C components in the frequency-dependent arms (Fig. 17.2) are equal. Then, assuming that the bridge impedances are large compared with the output resistance of the amplifier and small compared with its input resistance, and using the symbols shown in the figure, we have

$$v_2 = v_3 - v_4, \tag{17.8}$$

$$v_4 = \frac{R_2}{R_1 + R_2} v_1 \quad \text{(negative feedback)}, \tag{17.9}$$

$$v_3 = \frac{Z_2}{Z_1 + Z_2} v_1 \quad \text{(positive feedback)}, \tag{17.10}$$

where $\quad Z_1 = R - \dfrac{j}{\omega C} \quad$ and $\quad Z_2 = \dfrac{R(1 - j\omega CR)}{1 + \omega^2 C^2 R^2}.$ $\tag{17.11}$

If the bridge were perfectly balanced v_2 would be zero and v_3 would equal v_4 in amplitude and phase. The tangents of the two phase angles are $1/\omega CR$ and ωCR and these are equal at the balance frequency $\omega_0 = 1/CR$. At this frequency we also have $Z_1 = R(1-j)$, $Z_2 = R(1-j)/2$ so that $v_4 = v_3 = v_1/3$ and equation (17.9) indicates that we should make $R_1 = 2R_2$.

If the gain is high but finite, a small voltage is required to maintain oscillation. The bridge must then be unbalanced by a small amount which is indicated by the feedback factor $B = v_2/v_1$. Thus

$$B = \frac{v_3 - v_4}{v_1} = \frac{Z_2}{Z_1 + Z_2} - \frac{R_2}{R_1 + R_2}. \tag{17.12}$$

This equation states that B is precisely the amount by which the bridge must depart from perfect balance. Since $AB = 1$ the fractional unbalance is $1/A$. This quantity expresses the difference between the frequency of oscillation and that for perfect balance of the bridge as a fraction of the frequency of oscillation. It is negligible if A is large.

The circuit thus described is unstable because no attempt has yet been made to obtain the gradual non-linearity of gain mentioned in § 17.2. The oscillation will either die out or it will build up until some part of the amplifier saturates and produces waveform distortion. In order to produce a smooth decrease in gain, R_2 is replaced by an incandescent lamp which is operated at a dull-red heat. Its resistance is then a strong function of the current passing through it and if R_1 is correctly chosen the bridge will be unbalanced by just the required amount to maintain a constant amplitude of oscillation.

The circuit of an oscillator of this type is shown in Fig. 17.3. With the component values shown the frequency is 1,100 c/sec and the output is a good sine wave of about 1 volt r.m.s. across the 1 kΩ load resistor. The resistive arms of the bridge consist of the lamp R_2 and the variable resistor R_1. If the amplifier gain increases, more current is fed back to the emitter of the first

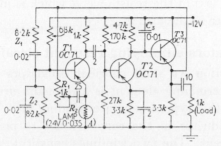

FIG. 17.3. Practical Wien bridge oscillator circuit.

stage and the lamp temperature rises, increasing both the lamp resistance and the negative feedback. The thermal time constant must be very long compared with the period of oscillation, and at very low frequencies (e.g. $f < 10$ c/sec) other means of amplitude stabilization must be adopted. In one such system the oscillator output is rectified and the resulting d.c. is smoothed in a low-pass filter. The output of the filter is used as a gain-control bias, exactly as in the AGC system discussed in Chapter XIV.

In order to secure a reasonable voltage gain the relatively low impedance bridge in this circuit is fed from an emitter follower. The output is taken from the same point to minimize the effect of load variations on the frequency. The open-loop gain is reduced by the degeneration introduced into the first stage by the lamp but is sufficient to bring the oscillation frequency to within 3 per cent of the balance frequency of the bridge. The capacitor C_3 is required to supply a dominant time constant in one stage and thus prevent a high-frequency oscillation from occurring because of the presence of three similar transistor time constants in the system.

This oscillator may also be analysed in an entirely different way which, however, yields identical results. It can be shown [1] that the amplifier with the elements R and C in the positive feedback loop behaves as if a positive inductance and a negative resistance were placed in series across the input terminals. The equivalent inductance can be imagined to be in resonance with the capacitance in the arm Z_2 of the bridge; oscillation will occur if the negative resistance supplies sufficient power to overcome the loss in the resistance R which is in parallel with the capacitance in the arm Z_2.

17.6. Oscillators employing resonant circuits

In this section we shall consider oscillators in which the frequency determining element is a resonant circuit. In some oscillators of this type a separate winding may be coupled to the tuning inductor in the correct sense to provide positive feedback current. The two windings constitute a transformer and advantage may be taken of the possibility of impedance matching to build an oscillator using a single transistor in any of the three connections. The situation is analogous to that arising with regenerative circuits where the introduction of inductive coupling makes single-stage regeneration possible. In other versions of the circuit described below the two-winding transformer is replaced by a tapped coil (auto-transformer), or a capacitance divider is used to produce an a.c. tap.

In order to secure good frequency stability it is desirable that the resonant circuit be loaded as lightly as possible by the transistor output impedance. For this reason the CB and CE connections are preferred in most applications.

There are many useful oscillators of the resonant type whose circuits are adapted directly from vacuum-tube versions. Most of them contain a single parallel-tuned LC circuit and the frequency of oscillation is given, very nearly, by $\omega_0^2 = 1/LC$. The condition for oscillation, which depends on the constants of the resonant circuit and the gain of the transistor, may be obtained from the circuit determinant or from the fact that the closed-loop current gain must exceed unity. Because of the excellent filtering introduced by a high Q tuned circuit, the gain may exceed unity by a considerable margin without introducing appreciable distortion.

The following are typical examples of this type of circuit:

1. *The tuned-collector CB oscillator*, which is shown in Fig. 17.4. The loading on the resonant circuit is minimized by means of the following procedures:

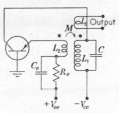

FIG. 17.4. Tuned-collector *CB* oscillator.

(a) The resonant circuit is placed in series with the collector.

(b) The *CB* connection, which has the highest output impedance, is used.

(c) The external load is connected to a loosely coupled transformer winding as shown in the figure or, in series with a very small capacitor, to the collector.

Under these conditions the frequency stability and purity of waveform can be very good. The frequency is given by $\omega_0^2 = 1/L_1 C$, and the condition for oscillation, when the coupling between collector and emitter is very loose, is $\omega_0 M > r_i/Q\alpha$. Here M is the mutual inductance between windings, r_i is the effective input resistance of the transistor (including any un-by-passed external emitter resistance), and $Q = r_p/\omega_0 L_1$, where r_p is the effective resistance in parallel with the tuned circuit. This includes the reflected resistance of the load and the effective parallel resistance of the coil (determined as in Chapter XIV). If the windings L_1 and L_2 are tightly coupled this condition becomes $A_v n_2/n_1 > 1$, where A_v is the voltage gain of the transistor.

2. *The Hartley oscillator*, of which a *CE* version is shown in Fig. 17.5. The frequency of oscillation is given by $\omega_0^2 \simeq 1/CL$, where $L = L_1 + L_2 + 2M$ is the inductance of the tank circuit coil. The condition for oscillation, in the loosely coupled case, is $\omega_0 M > r_i/Q\beta$, where r_i is now the total *CE* input resistance. In the more general case this expression has the form

$$A_v(L_2+M)/(L_1+M) > 1,$$

which in the limit of large mutual inductance (tight-coupling) again becomes the condition $A_v n_2/n_1 > 1$.

3. *The Colpitts oscillator*, which is shown in Fig. 17.6. In this case a capacitance potentiometer is used to create an a.c. earth part-way along the inductance and thus provide a base signal that is $180°$ out of phase with that at the collector. The frequency of oscillation is given by $\omega_0^2 = 1/LC_s$, where $C_s = C_1 C_2/(C_1+C_2)$ and the condition for oscillation is approximately $A_v C_1/C_2 > 1$.

4. *The Clapp oscillator* [2, 3] which may be derived from

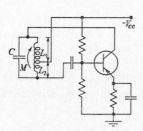
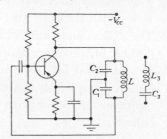
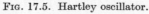

FIG. 17.5. Hartley oscillator.   FIG. 17.6. Colpitts oscillator and modification to give a Clapp oscillator.

the Colpitts oscillator of Fig. 17.6 by replacing the inductance L by a series resonant arm consisting of L_3 and C_3. At a frequency ω_0 slightly above its resonant frequency ω_s this arm has a small net inductance. The capacitors C_1 and C_2 are chosen so that C_s resonates with this inductance at frequency ω_0 and this is the frequency of oscillation. This circuit has the following advantages:

(i) The change of phase with frequency in the neighbourhood of ω_0 is very large (the circuit has a high effective Q) and its frequency stability is very good.

(ii) In order that C_s may resonate with the small net inductance of the series arm, C_1 and C_2 must be large and hence the tank circuit has a low impedance. Variations in the transistor output capacitance therefore have a comparatively small effect on the oscillation frequency.

17.7. Crystal-controlled oscillators

A crystal-controlled oscillator may be derived from the Clapp oscillator if the tank circuit (Fig. 17.6) consisting of C_1, C_2, C_3, and L_3 is replaced by a thin wafer of single-crystal quartz which is cut in a special direction relative to the crystal axes. Metal electrodes placed on the flat surfaces of the crystal form the terminals of the tank circuit. Under the influence of an applied alternating electric field the crystal vibrates (the piezo-electric effect) and its electrical behaviour is described by the equivalent circuit of Fig. 17.7. Representative values for a crystal whose fundamental resonance is about 1 Mc/sec are $L \simeq 0{\cdot}1$ henry, $C \simeq 0{\cdot}1$ $\mu\mu$F, $C_p \simeq 10\,\mu\mu$F, and $r \simeq 20$ ohms. The crystal has two resonant frequencies [4]

Fig. 17.7. Equivalent circuit of a quartz crystal.

$$\omega_s = 1/\sqrt{(LC)} \quad \text{and} \quad \omega_p = \omega_s(1+C/2C_p),$$

which are very close together.

The Q values of quartz crystals of this type are determined by their mechanical properties and are exceedingly large—normally greater than 20,000 and sometimes in excess of 100,000. The rate of change of phase angle with frequency is therefore very high and fulfils the condition for good frequency stability. Further, the crystal can be cut in such a manner that the effect of temperature on the components of the equivalent circuit is very small. However, when extremely good stability is required the crystal temperature should be controlled, and the crystal itself should form one of the bridge elements in an oscillator similar to the Wien bridge circuit described previously [5].

17.8. Power oscillators

When a large amount of oscillator power of good frequency stability is required the simplest procedure is to use one of the stable low-power oscillators described above to drive a Class B or Class C tuned amplifier. However, if some frequency drift can be tolerated it may be possible to incorporate the amplifier and oscillator into a single circuit to form a power oscillator. This should be designed for Class C operation and may be regarded as a power amplifier from whose output sufficient energy is diverted to the input to maintain oscillation. Design details have been given by Roach [6].

The low-frequency power obtained from an oscillator of this type may be several times the collector dissipation of the transistor. The total a.c. power output from the collector circuit can be as high as $P\eta/(1-\eta)$, where η is the collector efficiency and P the collector dissipation. Of this power output, a fraction $1/G$ (where G is the operating power gain) must be returned to the input to maintain oscillation and the useful power output is $P\eta(G-1)/(1-\eta)G$. At frequencies above the cutoff value for the chosen transistor connection (CB or CE), the power gain falls as $1/f^2$ and the power output decreases rapidly. In this region the internal phase shift in the transistor must be taken into account in the design of the feedback circuit. For the CE connection, for example, this phase shift approaches $90°$ at $f \simeq 0\cdot1f_\alpha$. At very high frequencies, when G approaches unity, all of the power output is required to maintain oscillation. The limiting frequency is a little below the theoretical maximum (Chapter VIII).

The circuit diagram of Fig. 17.4 may be taken to represent a CB power oscillator. The network consisting of C_e and R_e provides automatic bias which enables the oscillator to start under the nearly Class A conditions that exist immediately following the application of the power-supply voltage. As the oscillation builds up, rectification in the emitter circuit produces the required d.c. bias for efficient Class C operation. The time constant $C_e R_e$ must be large compared with the oscillation period.

The automatic bias built up in this way helps to compensate for load variations. If more power is taken from the oscillator the circulating tank current is reduced, thus decreasing the current transferred to the emitter circuit. The reverse bias voltage therefore decreases and emitter current flows for a larger fraction of each cycle, increasing the power output.

17.9. Linear-sweep generators

We shall conclude this chapter with a description of another large-signal non-switching application of the transistor, namely the linear-sweep generator which produces an output voltage varying almost linearly with time. Most of the circuit arrangements were developed originally for use with vacuum tubes and many types are available. We shall describe transistor versions of two of them, the Bootstrap Sweep Generator and the Miller Integrator.

17.9.1. *The bootstrap sweep generator*

The simplest sweep voltage is obtained by suddenly applying a d.c. voltage V to a resistor R and a capacitor C in series and taking the voltage across the capacitor as the output. The resulting voltage obeys the equation

$$v_0 = V[1 - e^{-t/CR}], \qquad (17.13)$$

and the deviation from a linear sweep $v_0 = Vt/CR$ is less than 5 per cent if the maximum value of t is less than $0 \cdot 1 CR$, or if the maximum output voltage v_0 is not more than about $0 \cdot 1$ V. Since $dv_0/dt = i/C$ the linear range may be extended considerably if the current flowing into the capacitor can be kept constant. One method of doing this is to use the constant-current collector characteristic of a transistor whose input current is fixed. However, a better method, when a highly linear sweep is required, is to use a large amount of negative feedback. When this feedback is applied in such a manner that the voltage across the series resistor, and hence the current into the capacitor, is kept constant the circuit is called a 'bootstrap generator' or 'bootstrap integrator'.

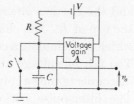

The basic arrangement is that of Fig. 17.8. The output of the amplifier, whose gain is A, is applied in series with the power-supply voltage V to produce a voltage $(V + Av_0)$ with respect to earth at the top of R. If q is the charge on the capacitor at time t after the switch S has been opened, we then have $v_0 = q/C$ and

FIG. 17.8. Schematic diagram of bootstrap integrator.

$$R\frac{dq}{dt} + \frac{q}{C} = V + Av_0, \qquad (17.14)$$

or
$$\frac{dq}{dt} = \frac{V}{R} + (A-1)\frac{q}{RC}, \tag{17.15}$$

and, if $A = 1$,
$$q = \frac{1}{R}\int V \, dt. \tag{17.16}$$

Since V and R are constant the charge on the capacitor, and hence the voltage across it, rises linearly with time. The circuit is a true integrator whose name arises from its ability to 'pull itself up by its own bootstraps'.

A practical version is shown in Fig. 17.9. The alloy-junction

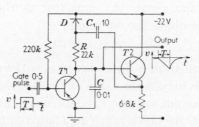

FIG. 17.9. Practical bootstrap sweep generator.

transistor $T1$, which is saturated in the quiescent condition, replaces the switch S. The amplifier $T2$ is an emitter follower whose voltage gain is within about 1 per cent of unity, and the floating battery has been replaced by a large capacitor C_1. When $T1$ is turned off by an input (gating) pulse, C begins to charge and the rise in voltage across it is transferred via $T2$ and C_1 to the top of R. The charging current for C is thus supplied by C_1 which can simulate a constant-voltage battery as long as $C_1 \gg C$. The fall in voltage at the top of R turns off the diode D and disconnects the supply line for the remainder of the sweep time. The inter-pulse period must be long enough to allow C_1 to replenish its charge before another sweep begins.

The design of bootstrap integrators is discussed in detail in references [7] and [8].

17.9.2. *The Miller integrator*

A second circuit by which a linear rise of potential may be produced is the Miller integrator, which is shown schematically in Fig. 17.10. In this case a phase-inverting d.c. amplifier of voltage gain $(-A)$, where A is a positive quantity,† provides negative feedback to increase the effective applied voltage. Thus $v_0 = -Av_i$ and the voltage across the capacitor C is

$$(v_0 - v_i) = v_0(1 + 1/A).$$

The current flowing into the capacitor is

$$i_c = C\frac{d}{dt}\left[v_0\left(1 + \frac{1}{A}\right)\right]. \tag{17.17}$$

The current in R is $(V - v_i)/R = (V + v_0/A)/R$ and, neglecting

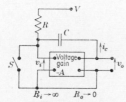

FIG. 17.10. Schematic diagram of Miller integrator.

FIG. 17.11. Equivalent circuit of Miller integrator.

loss of current to the input terminals of the amplifier, the sum of this and i_c must be zero. Hence

$$C\left(1 + \frac{1}{A}\right)\frac{dv_0}{dt} + \frac{v_0}{RA} + \frac{V}{R} = 0,$$

or

$$RC(1 + A)\frac{dv_0}{dt} + v_0 = -AV. \tag{17.18}$$

This equation is represented by the equivalent circuit of Fig. 17.11 and its solution is

$$v_0 = -AV[1 - \exp\{-t/RC(1 + A)\}]. \tag{17.19}$$

When the amplifier has a finite input resistance R_i, equation (17.18) is modified. The effective applied voltage is reduced to $VR_i/(R + R_i)$ and the effective discharge resistance becomes

† In restricting A to positive values, so that the gain of an amplifier which inverts the signal is written $-A$, we have followed the common practice when discussing the Miller effect. (Cf. page 291 of reference [2], Chapter XIII.) This is in contrast to the more general arguments of Chapter XIII in which A is allowed to take either sign.

$R_2 = RR_i/(R+R_i)$. The equation for v_0 is then

$$v_0 = -\frac{AVR_i}{R+R_i}[1-\exp\{-t/R_2 C(1+A)\}]. \qquad (17.20)$$

Equations (17.19) and (17.20) indicate that the effective supply voltage and the effective capacitance are both increased by the gain factor. This increase of effective capacitance, which results when a capacitor is placed between output and input of an amplifier, has been known for many years as the Miller effect, so that this circuit is appropriately named.

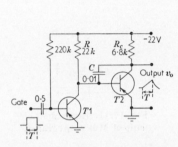

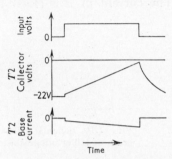

Fig. 17.12. Simple practical Miller
integrator.

Fig. 17.13. Waveforms of the
circuit of Fig. 17.12.

By expanding the exponential term in equation (17.20) we obtain

$$v_0 = -AV\left[\frac{t}{RC(1+A)} - \frac{t^2}{2R^2C^2(1+A)^2}\frac{R+R_i}{R_i} + ...\right]. \qquad (17.21)$$

If A is large and if $R_i \gg R$ the rate of rise of voltage in the linear section (the first term) is the same as in the simple case described by equation (17.13) but the linear range is greatly extended.

A simple circuit of this type is shown in Fig. 17.12. The stage $T1$ is 'on' in the quiescent condition and is gated 'off' by a low-level incoming pulse. For manual operation this stage could be replaced by a normally closed switch between the base of $T2$ and earth. The stage $T2$, which is initially cut off, is the integrator proper. Application of a negative current pulse to its base by $T1$ causes $T2$ to conduct and a small positive step appears at its collector, as shown in Fig. 17.13. As soon as $T2$ becomes active the negative feedback through capacitor C opposes the increase of collector current and produces the voltage rise given by equation (17.20).

In the case of a transistor for which $\beta_0 = 50, r_i$ (average) $= 1\,\text{k}\Omega$, assuming a load resistor of value $6\cdot8\,\text{k}\Omega$, $A = 50 \times 6\cdot8 = 340$; the second term of equation (17.21) is 1 per cent of the first for $v_0 \simeq 0\cdot30V$, i.e. the error is approximately 1 per cent when the

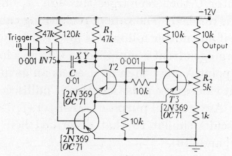

FIG. 17.14. Self-gating Miller integrator or phantastron.

output voltage is 30 per cent of V. For the simple RC circuit, equation (17.13) gives $v_0 \simeq 0\cdot02V$ for the same error. The single-stage Miller integrator has thus extended the linear sweep output voltage available from the same power supply by a factor of 15 while giving approximately the same rate of rise. This advantage could be increased considerably by the addition of an emitter follower between $T1$ and $T2$ to increase the effective value of r_i, or by increasing the gain of the amplifier.

To complete this section we describe the self-gating Miller circuit or phantastron shown in Fig. 17.14. This is a monostable circuit which is derived from its vacuum-tube counterpart by replacing a pentode by a series CE–CB (cascode) transistor connection ($T1$ and $T2$ in the figure). The cascode arrangement combines with capacitor C to form a high-gain Miller integrator and the voltage across $T1$ is used to control the pulse length. The operation is as follows: in the rest state $T2$ is 'off' and $T1$ and $T3$ are operating in their active regions. A short positive trigger pulse to the base of $T1$ or $T3$, or a negative pulse to the emitter of $T3$, turns $T3$ off and $T2$ on, but the sudden increase of potential at the collector of $T2$ acts through capacitor C and $T1$ to reduce the current flowing through $T1$ and $T2$ initially to a few microamperes. However, as C discharges, the base of $T1$ goes negative and $T1$ and $T2$ are gradually turned on. Eventually the collector of $T1$ becomes sufficiently positive to turn $T3$ on and $T2$ completely off by regenerative action.

The capacitor C then recharges through R_1 until the initial rest position is reached. The rate of recharging can be increased considerably if an emitter follower is inserted between X and Y so that recharging current is supplied to C from a low impedance source. The point X may then be used as an output terminal.

Component values for a pulse length of 1 millisecond are shown in the figure. Any general purpose transistor $(f_\alpha \geqslant 500$ kc) may be used. Circuits similar to that described here are given in references [9] and [10].

In addition to its application as a monostable linear-sweep generator this circuit is used for the production of pulses of accurately controlled length. Because the charging of the capacitor is a linear rather than an exponential process, the monostable Miller integrator is much superior in this respect to the simple monostable multivibrator.

NON-LINEAR CONTINUOUS-SIGNAL APPLICATIONS OF TRANSISTORS

18.1. Introduction

IN several of the circuit chapters of this book we have described amplifiers and oscillators that may be used as elements of radio transmitters or receivers. While it is not our intention to discuss the synthesis of circuits to form such communication systems, it does seem worth while to describe briefly the parts that remain. These include modulation, demodulation or detection, and frequency-conversion circuits which all have in common the property that they depend on the non-linearity of a device characteristic. They are readily derived from the vacuum-tube equivalents which are described in detail in many standard works [1, 2]. We shall therefore confine our remarks to brief discussions of theory and descriptions of a few basic circuits.

18.2. Modulation of amplitude, frequency, and phase

In all but the most rudimentary communications systems it is necessary to convey intelligence by suitably controlling some property of a continuous sinusoidal current, or of a train of pulses. The control process is called modulation and may vary the amplitude, frequency, or phase of the continuous current, which is then called the carrier frequency current, or it may vary the width or spacing of the pulses. Because of their excellent switching characteristics, transistors are well adapted to pulse modulation but this method has so far been confined to rather special telemetering applications and we shall not discuss it further. In this section we shall give equations for the total current in continuous modulation systems and indicate how the properties of other parts of the systems are affected by the method used. Circuit details will be considered later.

In an amplitude modulation (AM) system the modulating

current of angular frequency ω_m is made to control the amplitude of a carrier wave of angular frequency ω_c. The resulting current is of the form

$$i = i_0(1+m \sin \omega_m t)\sin \omega_c t, \tag{18.1}$$

where m is the modulation ratio and $0 \leqslant m \leqslant 1$. If the modulating current is larger than the carrier $(m > 1)$ distortion of the transmitted information due to 'overmodulation' occurs.

In a frequency modulated (FM) system the frequency of the carrier current is changed by the modulating process, the resultant current being of the form

$$i = i_0 \sin\left(\omega_c t + \frac{\delta\omega}{\omega_m} \sin \omega_m t\right). \tag{18.2}$$

Here $\delta\omega = 2\pi\,\delta f$ is the frequency deviation, which depends upon the *amplitude* of the modulating current and normally has an assigned peak value which represents maximum or full modulation.

Phase modulation (PM) is quite similar to frequency modulation, and the same equipment can often be adapted to either type. The expression analogous to equations (18.1) and (18.2), for a phase modulated current, is

$$i = i_0 \sin(\omega_c t + \phi M \sin \omega_m t), \tag{18.3}$$

where ϕ is a constant and M is proportional to the amplitude of the modulating component but is independent of its frequency.

It is apparent from these equations that the modulator, which adds the intelligence to the carrier in the transmitter, and the demodulator or detector, which removes the intelligence in the receiver, are fundamentally different in the AM and FM (or PM) systems. Another important difference is found in the bandwidths of the tuned radio-frequency amplifiers used in the two systems. These bandwidths are determined as follows:

(i) For the AM system, equation (18.1) may be written in the form

$$i = i_c\{\sin \omega_c t + \tfrac{1}{2}m \cos(\omega_c - \omega_m)t - \tfrac{1}{2}m \cos(\omega_c + \omega_m)t\}. \tag{18.4}$$

The components whose angular frequencies are the sum and difference of ω_c and ω_m are known as the upper and lower sidebands and both are needed to reproduce the original modulating wave. The AM receiver thus requires a bandwidth equal to twice the highest modulating frequency. Sometimes one sideband is suppressed at the transmitter, to give a bandwidth *over the transmission link* of half the normal value. However, the missing sideband must be replaced at the receiver, whose effective bandwidth is therefore unaltered.

(ii) In the FM and PM cases, the expansion of equations (18.2) and (18.3) leads to infinite series of terms which extend above and below the carrier frequency. However, it can be shown [2] that a channel bandwidth of approximately three times the peak frequency deviation δf will accommodate all sidebands except those whose amplitude is less than 1 per cent of that of the carrier.

The magnitude of δf determines the ratio of the maximum to the minimum signal (the dynamic range) that can be transmitted with negligible interference from external sources. The actual value chosen is a compromise because the amount of the frequency spectrum available for any one transmitter is limited. The generally accepted value for δf is 75 kc/sec and a high-quality receiver should therefore have a bandwidth of about 225 kc/sec. This is about ten times the bandwidth of a comparable AM receiver.

For low-fidelity communication links using portable equipment a narrow-band FM system, in which the carrier-frequency deviation is much less than the highest modulating frequency, may be used. The required bandwidth is then only about three times the modulation frequency. This is also larger than the corresponding AM bandwidth but the greater immunity to interference of the FM system makes its use worth while.

18.3. Amplitude modulation circuits

Circuits performing amplitude modulation include three common types which we shall call square-law, linear low-level, and high-level modulators. Their modes of operation are the following:

(*a*) The ideal square-law modulator produces an output which

varies as the square of the input. If the characteristic of the
modulating device does not conform closely to this ideal it may
be expanded in a power series, which for a transistor takes the
form:

$$I_c = a_0 + a_1(V_1 + V_2) + a_2(V_1 + V_2)^2 + a_3(V_1 + V_2)^3 + ..., \quad (18.5)$$

where V_1 and V_2 are the base-emitter voltages at the carrier and
modulating frequencies. The third term on the r.h.s. contains

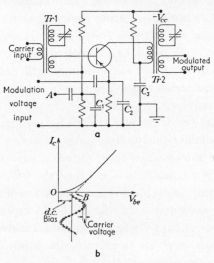

FIG. 18.1. A square-law modulator.
(a) Circuit. (b) Device characteristic.

the product $2a_2 V_1 V_2$. Other combinations of the two frequencies
and their harmonics are also present but, provided they are well
removed in frequency from the desired components (the carrier
and sidebands), they may be reduced to insignificant proportions
by filtering. This condition requires that the third- and higher-
order terms be small. Fortunately this is the case for the
transistor characteristic.

Fig. 18.1 a shows a circuit which is suitable for square-law
modulation. The carrier voltage is applied to the base and the
emitter is the modulating terminal. Capacitors C_1 and C_3 are
large enough to by-pass currents of both frequencies ω_c and ω_m
to earth while C_2 is only effective as a by-pass capacitor at the
higher frequency ω_c.

The operation of the circuit may be described with the help of Fig. 18.1 *b* which shows the transfer characteristic. The d.c. bias is such that in the absence of either signal the collector current is quite small, e.g. 100 μA. The modulating voltage is considerably larger than the carrier and the effective transconductance at the carrier frequency therefore varies with the instantaneous value of the modulating voltage. The modulated component of the collector current is selected by the tuned transformer $Tr2$. Because of the high load impedance and the effect of C_2, the voltage gain in the pass-band centred on ω_c is very high and the output may be quite large. However, the circuit is classed as a low-level modulator since the modulation and carrier voltages are applied to the input.

The modulating voltage could be inserted at A if C_1 were reduced to make it effective as a by-pass at the carrier frequency only and C_2 were increased to form a by-pass for both frequencies. Alternatively, with analogous changes, both voltages could be fed to the emitter terminal.

(*b*) The second device referred to above is the linear low-level modulator. In this circuit, as in the square-law modulator, the carrier and modulating voltages are applied to the input and operation is described in terms of the transfer characteristic. However, in this case the ideal characteristic consists of a horizontal section followed by a linearly rising part as shown in Fig. 18.2. The carrier and modulation frequencies are applied to one or both of the input electrodes as before and a d.c. bias is added to bring the a.c. zero to the neighbourhood of the point B. The input is thus rectified and pulses at carrier-wave frequency whose magnitudes are linear functions of the modulating voltage are applied to a resonant circuit in series with the collector. These pulses, which are plotted on the horizontal axis in Fig. 18.2, excite the resonant circuit thus producing an a.c. output (also shown in the figure) proportional to the magnitudes of the pulses.

An approximation to the ideal characteristic of Fig. 18.2 may be obtained from the transistor characteristic of Fig. 18.1 *b* by projecting the linear section back to the point B, as shown by

the dashed line. Operation at a higher level than in the case of
the square-law modulation diminishes the effect of the curvature
of the characteristic and the ideal two-section characteristic is
approached.

As might be expected from the above description the circuit
of Fig. 18.1 a may be used as a linear low-level modulator if
suitable adjustments, which include the following, are made:

(i) The modulation voltage should be applied by means of a

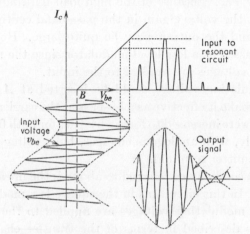

FIG. 18.2. Characteristic and output of the
low-level linear modulator.

transformer in series with the base or the emitter, or through
a capacitor to the point A.

(ii) The capacitor C_2 and its accompanying resistor should
be omitted to prevent undesirable biasing due to rectification
through the emitter-base junction. The capacitor C_1, which
should by-pass the carrier but not the modulating frequency,
may be used to supply a d.c. bias in the base circuit to compensate
for variations in carrier voltage. If the carrier voltage is well
regulated, fixed bias may be used and C_1 should then be removed.

(iii) The carrier voltage should exceed the modulation voltage.
A suitable ratio lies between two and three to one.

(iv) The Q factor of the collector resonant circuit must be
high enough so that this circuit will act as a flywheel and generate

an alternating output proportional to the magnitude of the carrier-frequency pulses that it receives from the transistor. The Q factor must, however, be low enough to allow the circuit to respond to the most rapid variations in the modulating voltage.

(c) In the high-level modulator, which is shown in Fig. 18.3 a,

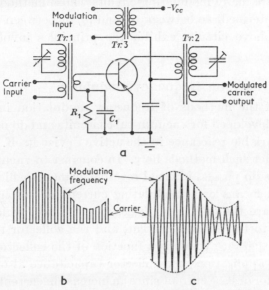

FIG. 18.3. High-level modulator. (a) Circuit. (b) Transistor current output. (c) Modulator output.

the modulation signal is applied in the collector circuit and a carrier-frequency signal, which switches the transistor between saturation and cutoff, is applied to the base. The modulation signal may then be regarded as part of the power-supply voltage and if the load were a pure resistance the collector voltage would have the appearance of Fig. 18.3 b. If the collector load is a resonant transformer tuned to the carrier frequency, it will be excited by the half-wave carrier-frequency pulses and produce a modulated sine-wave output of the form of Fig. 18.3 c. For full modulation the modulation transformer $Tr3$ must have a peak-to-peak output voltage equal to $2(V_{cc}-V_s)$, where V_s is the saturation voltage, and it must be capable of supplying full collector power. An automatic bias circuit consisting of R_1 and C_1, where $1/\omega_c \ll R_1 C_1 \ll 1/\omega_m$, may be used to compensate for fluctuations in carrier voltage.

This high-level circuit produces less distortion than the low-level methods but requires expensive equipment when large amounts of power are involved.

There are many modulating circuits whose method of operation are intermediate between (a) and (b) or between (b) and (c) but the above circuits exhibit the principles involved most readily.

18.4. A transistor frequency modulator

Most of the methods of frequency modulation in common use were developed for vacuum-tube circuits and do not depend upon a variable reactance in the active device itself. We shall not consider such methods here. In contrast to vacuum tubes, transistors do possess internal reactive elements which may be varied by means of a modulating current or voltage. These elements are the emitter diffusion capacitance, which is proportional to the emitter current, and the collector transition-region capacitance which is a function of the collector voltage. In circuit applications the collector capacitance also increases with emitter or base current since an increase in current produces a lowering of collector voltage through the collector load impedance and thus leads to an increase in collector capacitance.

A typical transistor frequency-modulation circuit [3] is shown in Fig. 18.4. Here the transistor input capacitance between terminal A and earth is connected (through the large capacitor C_1) in parallel with a coil L to form a circuit whose resonant frequency is varied by the modulating signal. An additional fixed capacitance C is used to tune the circuit to the desired carrier frequency. The resonant circuit forms the tank circuit of an oscillator which is not shown in the figure.

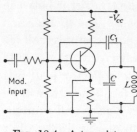

FIG. 18.4. A transistor frequency modulator.

The effective input capacitance of this circuit, which is most readily determined from the hybrid-π equivalent circuit, is approximately $(C_{b'e}+A_v C_c)$, where A_v is the voltage gain from base to collector of the transistor (i.e. neglecting external input resistance). The term $A_v C_c$ is often called the Miller-effect capacitance and this type of circuit is sometimes called a Miller-effect modulator. The term is not strictly correct since $C_{b'e}$ is of the same order as, and often exceeds, $A_v C_c$.

The variation of capacitance with modulating voltage, produced by this circuit, is linear over a relatively small range and the useful frequency deviation is, therefore, small. It may be increased by modulating a sub-multiple of the carrier frequency and using a frequency-multiplying circuit to increase both the carrier and deviation frequencies. An unusually wide frequency deviation may be obtained by beating a high-frequency FM signal with an auxiliary signal and extracting the difference frequency.

Phase modulation can be obtained from a variable reactance device in exactly the same way as frequency modulation, provided that the modulating signal is first passed through a filter whose output is directly proportional to frequency. It can be seen from equation (18.2) that frequency modulation of a carrier by a signal whose amplitude is proportional to ω_m results in a wave which is described by an expression similar to equation (18.3)—i.e. in which the coefficient of the term $\sin \omega_m t$ is independent of ω_m.

18.5. Frequency changing or mixing

The simplest radio receiver having a reasonable sensitivity consists of a radio-frequency (r.f.) amplifier to increase the strength of the modulated carrier followed by a detector which removes the carrier and an audio-frequency (a.f.) amplifier which further increases the power level of the modulation before it is fed to a loudspeaker or a recording device. Such receivers have poor selectivity—and thus cannot separate the signals of transmitters whose carrier frequencies are close together—because it is difficult to construct an r.f. amplifier that can be tuned over a wide range of frequencies and also has a sharply defined pass band. Accordingly it has become standard practice with both AM and FM systems to change the incoming frequency to a new, fixed, value called the intermediate frequency (i.f.) and to carry out the bulk of the amplification and bandpass filtering at this frequency. The i.f. frequency is the difference frequency obtained by beating or 'heterodyning' the r.f. signal of frequency f_s against the output of a local oscillator of adjustable frequency f_0 and the equipment is usually referred to as a 'superheterodyne' receiver. The circuit which produces the fixed i.f. frequency $f_i = (f_0 - f_s)$ or $(f_s - f_0)$ is called the mixer or frequency changer. The choice of f_0 is usually a matter of convenience. In ordinary low-frequency or broadcast-band radio reception the ratio of maximum to minimum oscillator frequency is considerably smaller if $f_0 > f_s$ than if the reverse is true. The smaller frequency range simplifies the tuning problem and f_0 usually exceeds f_s.

It should be mentioned that some narrow-band amplification of the incoming signal is still desirable in superheterodyne receivers for the following reasons:

(i) Two signal frequencies, one above and one below the local oscillator frequency can mix with f_0 to produce f_i. The unwanted r.f. signal, which is called the image frequency signal, may be eliminated by the use of a bandpass amplifier centred on the desired r.f. frequency.

(ii) The local oscillator frequency beats with any signal frequency that reaches it. Some of the difference components that result from unwanted input frequencies may beat together to produce noise components of i.f. frequency. Such noise is most easily reduced by the use of one or more tuned r.f. stages.

In both of these cases the r.f. pass band need not be nearly as sharply defined as in the case of the non-heterodyning receiver and it is still advantageous to obtain the required selectivity by the use of an intermediate frequency.

The operation of the frequency changer is identical in principle to that of a modulator and any of the three AM modulators previously described could be used for mixing. In practice the low-level (linear) modulator is found to be most useful at all but the highest frequencies. The arrangement of Fig. 18.1 may be used if the modulating voltage is replaced by the incoming r.f. signal and the carrier is replaced by the local oscillator. The output filter is tuned to the i.f. frequency and the oscillator frequency is varied in such a way that $f_0 - f_s = f_i$. For efficient mixing the amplitude of the local oscillator signal should be large compared with that of the r.f. signal.

The required combinations of a large oscillator signal and a

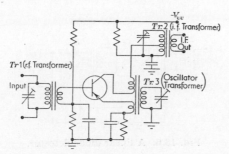

FIG. 18.5. A self-oscillating mixer or converter stage.

small r.f. input signal may be obtained by injecting the r.f. signal into a transistor oscillator, thus combining the two functions of oscillation and mixing in a single stage. An example of such a circuit which is called a self-oscillating mixer or a frequency converter stage, is shown in Fig. 18.5. In this case the incoming signal is coupled to the base via the tuned transformer $Tr1$. The secondary winding offers a low impedance at the local oscillator frequency and the transistor forms a CB oscillator whose positive feedback from collector to emitter is supplied by the tuned transformer $Tr3$. The emitter current is varied, at oscillator frequency, over a peak amplitude of the order of 1 mA, which is very large compared with the amplitude of the base signal. Mixing occurs and the difference (i.f.) frequency is selectively coupled to the succeeding stage by the tuned transformer $Tr2$. This circuit has the disadvantage, when compared with arrangements which employ separate transistors for mixing and for oscillation, that the gain cannot be controlled by AGC bias.

It can be shown that frequency changing may also be used in FM receivers without introducing distortion of the transmitted information [1] and the principle is almost invariably applied in this case also. The circuits are similar to those used in AM receivers and we shall not consider them further.

18.6. Detection of amplitude modulated signals

The removal of the modulation from a carrier or i.f. signal is called demodulation or detection. It is essentially a rectifying

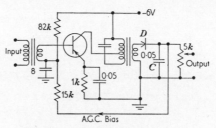

FIG. 18.6. A linear diode detector.

or switching process which may be carried out by a diode or a transistor. We first consider diode detectors.

The most generally useful diode detector is a half-wave recti-fier, such as D in Fig. 18.6, whose output is fed into an R–C filter having a time constant that is long compared with the period of the i.f. (or r.f.) wave. The capacitor therefore maintains a value approaching the peak i.f. voltage. In addition the time con-stant should be small compared with the period of the highest frequency component in the modulation. Under these condi-tions the output voltage will follow the modulation envelope on one side of the axis in Fig. 18.3 c and an accurate reproduction of the modulated signal will be obtained.

Because the non-linearity of the forward characteristic of the diode is negligible, this type of demodulator is usually called a linear detector. The name is unfortunate in some respects since the rectification process on which the action depends approaches the ultimate in non-linearity.

Fig. 18.6 also shows a typical automatic gain control. This makes use of the mean rectified signal, which is proportional to the average magnitude of the i.f. signal, to control the overall gain and thus compensate for variations in the magnitude of the incoming r.f. signal. The magnitudes of the filter components shown are typical of good practice for a broadcast-band receiver when the input resistance of the first a.f. stage is almost 50 kΩ— a value which may be obtained by negative feedback or by the use of an emitter follower, or an audio-frequency coupling transformer.

One of the requirements of the linear diode detector is a relatively large i.f. signal—of the order of 1 volt if a germanium diode is used and larger for silicon diodes. This requires several stages of i.f. amplification. Simpler a.f. stages could be substituted for some of these if detection could be carried out at a lower level. The tunnel rectifier or backward diode shows considerable promise in this respect since the transition to a low forward resistance is very sharp and occurs at a very low voltage. Linear detection should be obtained at one-tenth or less of the voltage required by a germanium point contact or junction diode. The tunnel rectifier also has the advantage that it can rectify at very high frequencies. It should therefore be useful in radar applications.

A second type of detector, which can demodulate lower amplitude signals than the linear detector is the 'square-law' diode detector. This makes use of the curvature of the forward characteristic of the diode at very low voltages to produce an asymmetric output signal and thus acts as a rather poor rectifier. The output contains an appreciable amount of second harmonic of the modulation frequency, and this type of detector is not used in high-fidelity communication equipment. It is useful in some measuring equipment where a d.c. output depending on a modulated signal is required. In its ideal form this method gives a d.c. output proportional to the square of the modulated signal. Many diode characteristics approach this ideal parabolic form at very low voltages.

In some communications uses, the variations in the magnitude of the incoming signal are very large and a diode detector cannot supply sufficient power for effective automatic gain control. A d.c. amplifier may then be added to supply an AGC bias of the required magnitude but if the resulting cost and complication must be avoided a transistor detector may be used. In this circuit rectification takes place in the E-B junction whose bias

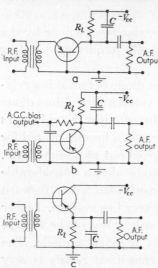

voltage should approach OB in Fig. 18.1 b. (For germanium transistors OB is small and zero bias voltage is sometimes used.) In the CE and CB versions shown in Fig. 18.7, d.c. amplification is provided in the collector circuit. In the CC version there is no voltage amplification but the low output impedance may be an advantage in some applications. An AGC circuit is shown in the case of the CE detector only, but may be readily adapted to the other connections. The distortion introduced in these detectors is usually greater than that produced by a linear diode detector. In principle the sudden change of resistance at saturation instead of that at cutoff can also be used for detection but an accurate current bias source is required and this method is seldom employed.

FIG. 18.7. Transistor detectors. (a) Common base. (b) Common emitter. (c) Common collector.

18.7. A diode FM detector

The most common type of frequency-modulation detector, the discriminator, was developed originally for vacuum-tube receivers. It is described in references [1] and [2]. Transistor versions can be devised but it would take us too far afield to describe them. We shall, however, consider briefly a simple integrating frequency-to-amplitude converter which can be used to recover the modulation from an FM carrier. Such integrators usually employ a low intermediate frequency—perhaps 100 kc/sec—which is normally produced by two frequency conversions in order to maintain good image rejection. This frequency-modulated i.f. signal is used to trigger, once per cycle, a mono-stable circuit whose output pulses are of a constant duration and amplitude independent of the trigger voltage. These pulses may be added or 'integrated' in a capacitor to produce the original modulation. A suitable integrator is the 'diode-pump' shown in Fig. 18.8. Between pulses the capacitor C_1 is charged to the zero level of the pulse-generator output through the diode $D1$ and the interval between pulses must be long enough for this purpose. During the application of the positive pulse, $D1$ is

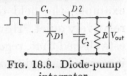

FIG. 18.8. Diode-pump integrator.

effectively disconnected and C_1 discharges through diode $D2$ with C_2. During this period an amount of charge proportional to the amplitude of the pulse is transferred to C_2 and increases its voltage. If the pulse amplitude and length are kept constant a fixed amount of charge per cycle reaches C_2 and its voltage is proportional to frequency. The time constant RC_2 is long compared with the carrier period, but short compared with the shortest period of the modulation. The output is therefore a faithful reproduction of the modulation voltage and frequency.

18.8. Conclusion: the outlook for transistors

This chapter completes our outline of junction transistor circuits. In this outline, as in the first part of the book, we have emphasized those aspects that are of permanent value and are unlikely to be changed in the next few years. In the writers' opinion those years will form a period of consolidation in which the main advances will be due to refinements in device construction and circuit applications. The 'epitaxial diffused transistor' [4] and the 'binistor' [5], a p-n-p-n switching device, are recent examples of such refinements.

Some of the major developments of the next decade will probably take place in the field of 'solid state circuits' in which resistors, capacitors, diodes, and transistors are formed in a single block of semiconductor. If they can be mass-produced such circuits should revolutionize computer and military electronics. Another contributor to the revolution in computer circuits is the tunnel diode. The extremely high speed and small power consumption of this inherently inexpensive device should make miniature high-speed computers a reality within a short period.

These predictions do not take into account the possibility of a radically new device or of a 'breakthrough' in some area, for example, the field of unipolar transistors, that is at present relatively quiet. However, the junction transistor is now so well established that, regardless of present and future developments, it seems destined to occupy a prominent position for many years to come.

APPENDIX I

SYSTEMS OF UNITS AND VALUES OF CONSTANTS

The electrical units used in the body of this book are the so-called practical units which include the volt, ampere, ohm, henry, and farad. The units of mass and length are the gramme and the centimetre and the unit of energy is the erg or the electron volt (1 eV $= 1 \cdot 602 \times 10^{-12}$ erg). It is therefore possible to follow common usage and to express field strength in volts/cm, resistivity in ohm cm, and diffusion coefficient in cm²/sec.

In Appendixes III and IV a complete system of units such as the Gaussian or rationalized m.k.s. system must be used. Poisson's equation is there expressed in the form required by the Gaussian system in which the dielectric constant *in vacuo* is unity. Rationalized m.k.s. units can be used in this equation if ϵ, the ratio of the dielectric constant of the material to that of a vacuum, is replaced by $4\pi\epsilon\epsilon_0$, where ϵ_0 is the vacuum dielectric constant in the rationalized m.k.s. system.

The following table gives the required constants in both systems.

Constant	Symbol	Value in Gaussian system	Value in rationalized M.K.S. system
Boltzmann's constant	k	$1 \cdot 380 \times 10^{-16}$ erg deg⁻¹	$1 \cdot 380 \times 10^{-23}$ joule deg⁻¹ $8 \cdot 614 \times 10^{-5}$ eV
Planck's constant	h	$6 \cdot 626 \times 10^{-27}$ erg sec	$6 \cdot 626 \times 10^{-34}$ joule sec
Electron mass	m	$9 \cdot 110 \times 10^{-28}$ gramme	$9 \cdot 110 \times 10^{-31}$ kilogramme
Electron charge	q	$4 \cdot 803 \times 10^{-10}$ e.s.u.	$1 \cdot 601 \times 10^{-19}$ coulomb
Dielectric constant *in vacuo*	ϵ_0	1	$8 \cdot 854 \times 10^{-12}$ farad/metre

APPENDIX II

SOLUTIONS OF THE DIFFUSION EQUATION UNDER D.C. CONDITIONS

THE diffusion equation (2.7) governing the density of positive holes in the n-type material of a junction rectifier or the base of a p-n-p transistor under d.c. conditions is

$$D_p \frac{d^2p}{dx^2} = \frac{p - p_n}{\tau_p}. \tag{A2.1}$$

The solution of this is

$$p - p_n = C_1 e^{-x/\sqrt{(\tau D)}} + C_2 e^{+x/\sqrt{(\tau D)}}, \tag{A2.2}$$

where the subscripts on τ and D have been omitted for convenience in writing. We now consider the final form of (A2.2) under the following conditions:

1. The n-type region extends from $x = 0$ to $x = W$.

2. The density of holes p_1 at $x = 0$ is greater than p_n, the equilibrium density in the n-type material. Positive holes therefore diffuse into the n-type material from the left.

3. At $x = W$ positive holes are removed rapidly by one of the following processes:

3.1. Recombination at a metal electrode. This occurs at the ohmic connection of a p-n junction and it may be assumed that any excess of holes at $x = W$ will be immediately reduced to p_n which is the equilibrium density with energies above the bottom of the full band, for both semiconductor and metal.

3.2. Withdrawal of holes by an electric field. This process takes place in a transistor whose base-collector boundary occurs at $x = W$. Holes reaching the boundary are removed rapidly by the negative electric field of the collector junction. It may be assumed in this case that $p = 0$ at $x = W$.

Substitution of conditions 2 and 3.1 into equation (A2.2) allows evaluation of C_1 and C_2 and the equation becomes

$$p - p_n = \frac{(p_1 - p_n)\sinh[(W - x)/L]}{\sinh(W/L)}, \tag{A2.3}$$

where we have replaced $(\tau D)^{\frac{1}{2}}$, which has the dimensions of length, by the symbol L.

It is seen by inspection that this equation satisfies the above boundary conditions. We now consider versions of (A2.3) for two cases:

(a) $W \gg L$. Upon writing the equation in terms of the exponential and ignoring terms of order $\exp(-W/L)$ we then obtain

$$p - p_n = (p_1 - p_n)\exp(-x/L). \tag{A2.4}$$

The excess of injected holes thus decays by a factor $1/e$ in the length L and the density of holes in the n-type material drops to p_n at some value of x less than W. This is the case considered in the discussion of the p-n junction in Chapter IV.

(b) $W \ll L$. In this case, since $x \leqslant W$ we may expand the hyperbolic functions of (A2.3) and neglect all but the first terms. Then

$$p - p_n = (p_1 - p_n)\left(\frac{W-x}{W}\right). \tag{A2.5}$$

The number of positive holes stored in a region of unit cross-section and length $W \ll L$, obtained by integration of either (A2.3) or (A2.5), is $W(p_1 + p_n)/2$.

The solution of equation (A2.2) with the boundary condition 3.2 above is

$$p - p_n = \frac{1}{\sinh(W/L)}\left[(p_1 - p_n)\sinh\frac{W-x}{L} - p_n\sinh\frac{x}{L}\right], \tag{A2.6}$$

and for $W \ll L$ this gives

$$p = p_1\frac{W-x}{W}. \tag{A2.7}$$

This equation, which differs only slightly from (A2.5) may be used to calculate the density of minority carriers in the base region of a transistor.

APPENDIX III

THE FUNDAMENTAL EQUATIONS FOR THE FLOW OF ELECTRONS AND HOLES

THE equations for the flow of electrons and holes in a homogeneous semiconductor may be written [1]

$$\mathbf{I}_p = q\mathbf{J}_p = q\mu_h p\mathbf{F} - qD_p \nabla p, \qquad (A3.1)$$

$$\mathbf{I}_n = -q\mathbf{J}_n = q\mu_e n\mathbf{F} + qD_n \nabla n, \qquad (A3.2)$$

$$\frac{\partial p}{\partial t} = g - \frac{p}{\tau_p} - \nabla . \mathbf{J}_p = -\left(\frac{p-p_0}{\tau_p}\right) - \mu_h \nabla . (p\mathbf{F}) + D_p \nabla^2 p, \quad (A3.3)$$

$$\frac{\partial n}{\partial t} = g - \frac{n}{\tau_n} - \nabla . \mathbf{J}_n = -\left(\frac{n-n_0}{\tau_n}\right) + \mu_n \nabla . (n\mathbf{F}) + D_n \nabla^2 n. \quad (A3.4)$$

In these ∇, $\nabla .$, and ∇^2 are symbols for the gradient, divergence, and Laplacian operators. All other symbols with the exception of p_0 and n_0 are defined in Chapters I and II. p_0 and n_0 are the equilibrium densities of holes and electrons respectively. The neutral subscript 0 is used because, in contrast to the cases considered in Chapter II and Appendix II, we are considering both majority- and minority-carrier flow and the conductivity of the material may be n-type, p-type, or intrinsic.

The currents, field strength, and carrier densities contained in these equations are, in general, all functions of time and distance. Equations (A3.1) and (A3.2) define the currents flowing under the influence of electrical and diffusion forces. Equations (A3.3) and (A3.4) are the continuity equations which indicate how the carrier densities change with time under the influence of generation, recombination, electric field, and diffusion. In the one-dimensional case the four equations become

$$I_p = q\mu_h pF - qD_p \frac{\partial p}{\partial x}, \qquad (A3.5)$$

$$I_n = q\mu_e nF + qD_n \frac{\partial n}{\partial x}, \qquad (A3.6)$$

$$\frac{\partial p}{\partial t} = -\left(\frac{p-p_0}{\tau_p}\right) - \mu_h \frac{\partial}{\partial x}(pF) + D_p \frac{\partial^2 p}{\partial x^2}, \qquad (A3.7)$$

$$\frac{\partial n}{\partial t} = -\left(\frac{n-n_0}{\tau_n}\right) + \mu_e \frac{\partial}{\partial x}(nF) + D_n \frac{\partial^2 n}{\partial x^2}. \qquad (A3.8)$$

These equations are supplemented by Poisson's equation

$$\nabla^2 V = -\nabla\mathbf{F} = -\frac{4\pi q}{\epsilon}(p-n+N_d-N_a) \qquad (A3.9)$$

or, in one dimension,

$$\frac{d^2 V}{dx^2} = -\frac{dF}{dx} = -\frac{4\pi q}{\epsilon}(p-n+N_d-N_a). \qquad (A3.10)$$

Here ϵ is the dielectric constant and N_d, the density of ionized donors, and N_a, the density of ionized acceptors, may be functions of distance. For the semiconductors considered in this book, germanium and silicon, N_d and N_a will not usually be affected appreciably by injected carriers [1]. When N_d and N_a are constant they may be put equal to n_0 and p_0 respectively and equation (A3.9) becomes

$$\nabla^2 V = -\frac{4\pi q}{\epsilon}[(p-p_0)-(n-n_0)]. \qquad (A3.11)$$

Equations (A3.3) and (A3.4) are based on the assumptions of constant lifetime and negligible trapping. As pointed out in Chapter II the lifetimes in practical cases are decided by the presence of traps in the forbidden energy regions. For many cases, however, the number of carriers trapped at any instant is very small even though most recombination processes take place through the traps [2]. In junction rectifier and transistor calculations the above equations are almost invariably used.

REFERENCES

1. VAN ROOSBROECK, W. (1950). *Bell Syst. Tech. J.* **29**, 560–607.
2. SHOCKLEY, W., and READ, W. T. Jr. (1952). *Phys. Rev.* **87**, 835–42.

THICKNESS AND CAPACITANCE OF THE
p-n JUNCTION TRANSITION REGION

(a) The graded junction

In the first section of this appendix we show how two important properties of the transition region of a graded p-n junction can be calculated. The positive-hole energy diagram and the impurity-centre distribution for this device are shown in Fig. A4.1. It is assumed that $N_A \gg N_D$ for the p-type region and $N_D \gg N_A$ for the n-type region. Capital subscripts are used here to indicate the constant concentrations of acceptors and donors that occur for $x < -T$ and $x > +T$. For $-T \leqslant x \leqslant +T$ the concentrations are designated by N_a and N_d and it is assumed that $(N_d - N_a)$ varies linearly in this region. Since donors are positively charged and acceptors negatively charged the net impurity-centre charge density is therefore

$$q(N_d - N_a) = qax, \qquad \text{(A4.1)}$$

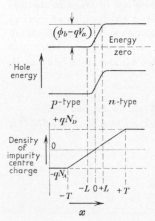

Fig. A4.1. Positive-hole energy diagram and impurity-centre charge distribution for a graded p-n junction.

where a is a constant whose units are cm^{-4}.

From the symmetry of the problem it is apparent that the boundaries of the space-charge (transition) region must be equidistant from the point $x = 0$, the point at which the total impurity charge is zero. They are therefore given the coordinates $x = \pm L$. In order to obtain the potential distribution in the region $-L \leqslant x \leqslant L$ we must then solve the one-dimensional Poisson equation

$$\frac{d^2 V}{dx^2} = -\frac{4\pi qax}{\epsilon}, \qquad \text{(A4.2)}$$

in which ϵ is the static dielectric constant. We have here assumed that there are no free electrons and holes in the space-charge region. For the rectifying p-n junctions considered in this book Shockley [1] has shown that this assumption is valid except in the immediate neighbourhood of $x = -L$ and $x = +L$.

Integration of (A4.2) gives

$$\frac{dV}{dx} = -\frac{2\pi qax^2}{\epsilon} + C. \qquad \text{(A4.3)}$$

The slope of the potential is small for $x = \pm L$ and may be taken equal to zero without sensible error. Evaluation of the constant C then leads to

$$\frac{dV}{dx} = \frac{2\pi qa}{\epsilon}(L^2 - x^2), \qquad (A4.4)$$

whence
$$V = \frac{2\pi qa}{\epsilon}\Big(L^2 x - \frac{x^3}{3}\Big) + D. \qquad (A4.5)$$

Since potential differences are the important quantities in problems of this nature we may choose the potential or energy zero, for convenience, at the bottom of the barrier as shown in Fig. A4.1. We then find that $D = (V_0 - V_a)/2$, where $V_0 = \phi_b/q$ and, on substituting $V = (V_0 - V_a)$ at $x = L$, obtain
$$L^3 = \frac{3\epsilon(V_0 - V_a)}{8\pi qa}. \qquad (A4.6)$$

For large negative (reverse) values of the applied voltage V_a we see that the transition-region thickness increases as $|V_a|^{\frac{1}{3}}$ approximately. Substitution of numerical values in (A4.6) shows that for germanium or silicon with $V_a \simeq 10$ volts, $aL^3 \sim 10^8$ so that $L \ll T$ for most cases of interest. For example, if $N_D = N_A = 10^{17}/\mathrm{cm}^3$ and $T = 10^{-3}$ cm, $a \simeq 10^{20}$ and $L \simeq 10^{-4}$ cm. The transition region then falls well within the region over which the impurity-centre concentration is changing and as the voltage is increased the transition region extends at the same rate into the p and n regions. For a very large ($\geqslant 10^{24}$) the above condition does not hold. The abrupt junction described below may then be a better approximation.

When the reverse voltage is increased by an increment $-\delta V_a$ the width of the transition region is increased by an amount δL which may be obtained by differentiation of (A4.6). Thus

$$3L^2 \delta L = -\frac{3\epsilon\,\delta V_a}{8\pi qa}. \qquad (A4.7)$$

From equation (A4.1) the charge density at $x = \pm L$ is $\pm qaL$ so that the increment of charge produced by the removal of holes or electrons from opposite ends of the transition region is $\pm\delta Q = \pm qaL\,\delta L$. From equation (A4.7) we have

$$\delta Q = qaL\,\delta L = -\epsilon\,\delta V_a/8\pi L$$

and, substituting for L from (A4.6) the transition-region capacity becomes
$$C_T = \frac{\delta Q}{\delta V_a} = -\epsilon[8\pi qa/3\epsilon(V_0 - V_a)]^{\frac{1}{3}}/8\pi, \qquad (A4.8)$$

or
$$C_T \propto (V_0 - V_a)^{-\frac{1}{3}}. \qquad (A4.9)$$

(b) *The abrupt junction*

The positive-hole energy diagram and the impurity-centre distribution for the abrupt junction are shown in Fig. A4.2. The point at which the impurity-centre charge distribution changes suddenly from $-qN_A$ to $+qN_D$ is chosen as the origin of the x-coordinates and, in order to simplify the mathematical development, the corresponding position on the energy diagram is chosen as the point of zero energy or potential. In this device the transition region extends into the n- and p-type regions by amounts that depend on the magnitudes of N_D and N_A so that its boundaries, here designated $x = -L_1$ and $x = +L_2$, are not necessarily equidistant from $x = 0$.

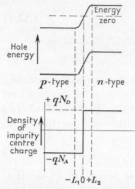

FIG. A4.2. Positive-hole energy diagram and impurity-centre charge distribution for an abrupt p-n junction.

We now have two Poisson equations

$$\frac{d^2V}{dx^2} = +4\pi qN_A/\epsilon \quad \text{for } x \leqslant 0, \quad (A4.10)$$

$$\frac{d^2V}{dx^2} = -4\pi qN_D/\epsilon \quad \text{for } x \geqslant 0. \quad (A4.11)$$

Using the conditions $dV/dx = 0$ at $x = -L_1$ and $x = +L_2$ these equations may be integrated to give

$$\frac{dV}{dx} = A(L_1+x) \quad (x \leqslant 0), \quad (A4.12)$$

$$\frac{dV}{dx} = D(L_2-x) \quad (x \geqslant 0), \quad (A4.13)$$

where $\qquad A = 4\pi qN_A/\epsilon \quad \text{and} \quad D = 4\pi qN_D/\epsilon.$

Since the integral of a step function is continuous these derivatives must be equal at $x = 0$, giving

$$AL_1 = DL_2. \quad (A4.14)$$

We now put $L_1+L_2 = W$, the total width of the transition region, and with the use of (A4.14), obtain

$$L_1 = DW/(A+D), \qquad L_2 = AW(A+D). \quad (A4.15)$$

Integration of (A4.12) and (A4.13), with the condition $V = 0$ at $x = 0$, gives

$$V = A(L_1x+x^2/2) \quad (x \leqslant 0), \quad (A4.16)$$

$$V = D(L_2x-x^2/2) \quad (x \geqslant 0). \quad (A4.17)$$

The potentials at $x = -L_1$ and $x = +L_2$ are

$$V_1 = -AL_1^2/2, \quad (A4.18)$$

$$V_2 = DL_2^2/2. \quad (A4.19)$$

Now $\qquad (V_0-V_a) = V_2-V_1 = (AL_1^2+DL_2^2)/2 = DL_2(L_1+L_2)/2$

or, using (A4.15),

$$(V_0-V_a) = ADW^2/2(A+D) = W^2/2(1/D+1/A), \quad (A4.20)$$

or $\qquad W = [2(1/D+1/A)(V_0-V_a)]^{\frac{1}{2}}. \quad (A4.21)$

In this case the transition region thickness increases as $|V_a|^{\frac{1}{2}}$ approximately for large reverse voltages. Using (A4.15) again, we obtain

$$L_1^2 = 2D(V_0-V_a)/A(A+D), \qquad L_2^2 = 2A(V_0-V_a)/D(A+D), \qquad \text{(A4.22)}$$

and
$$L_1/L_2 = D/A = N_D/N_A. \qquad \text{(A4.23)}$$

The conductivities of the n- and p-type materials are proportional to $\mu_e N_D$ and $\mu_h N_A$ respectively, so that

$$\frac{L_1}{L_2} \propto \frac{\sigma_n}{\sigma_p}\frac{\mu_h}{\mu_e}. \qquad \text{(A4.24)}$$

For an alloy junction, to which this abrupt junction theory applies, $\sigma_p \gg \sigma_n$ so that the transition region is almost entirely contained in the high-resistance n-type region.

To obtain an expression for the capacitance we again determine the change in charge δQ, at one boundary of the transition region, resulting from an increase $-\delta V_a$ in applied reverse voltage. At the boundary $x = +L_2$ we have

$$\delta Q = qN_D\,\delta L_2 = -qN_D[2A/D(A+D)(V_0-V_a)]^{\frac{1}{2}}\,\delta V_a/2$$

and
$$C_T = -\delta Q/\delta V_a = qN_D[AD/2(A+D)(V_0-V_a)]^{\frac{1}{2}}/D, \qquad \text{(A4.25)}$$

or
$$C_T = \frac{\epsilon}{4\pi W}. \qquad \text{(A4.26)}$$

For this case
$$C_T \propto (V_0-V_a)^{-\frac{1}{2}}. \qquad \text{(A4.27)}$$

REFERENCE

1. SHOCKLEY, W. (1949). *Bell System Tech. J.* **28**, 435–89.

APPENDIX V

DERIVATION OF THE *CE* AND *CC*
T-EQUIVALENT CIRCUITS

THE *CE* *T*-equivalent circuit may be derived from the *CB* circuit of Fig. A5.1 by expressing the input voltage v_{be} and the output voltage v_{ce}

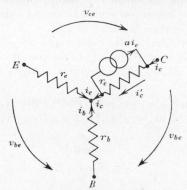

FIG. A5.1. *CB* *T*-circuit.

in terms of i_b and i_c. (Note that i_c is now shown reversed for convenience in analysis.) Thus

$$i_b + i_c + i_e = 0, \tag{A5.1}$$

$$v_{be} = i_b r_b - i_e r_e = i_b r_b + (i_b + i_c) r_e. \tag{A5.2}$$

Also $\qquad\qquad i_c' = i_c + a i_e.$

Therefore
$$v_{ce} = (i_c + a i_e) r_c - i_e r_e$$
$$= i_c r_c - (i_b + i_c)(a r_c - r_e)$$
$$= i_c r_c (1 - a) - i_b a r_c + (i_b + i_c) r_e$$
$$= \left(i_c - \frac{a i_b}{1-a} \right) r_c (1-a) + (i_b + i_c) r_e. \tag{A5.3}$$

Equations (A5.2) and (A5.3) are satisfied by the circuit of Fig. 5.8. The equations for the *CC* case become

$$v_{bc} = i_b r_b - (i_c + a i_e) r_c$$
$$= i_b r_b + (i_b + i_e) r_c - a i_e r_c$$
$$= i_b r_b + i_b r_c + i_e (1 - a) r_c$$
$$= i_b r_b + \left(\frac{i_b}{1-a} + i_e \right)(1-a) r_c$$
$$= i_b r_b + \left(i_b + i_e + \frac{a}{1-a} i_b \right)(1-a) r_c, \tag{A5.4}$$

$$v_{ec} = -v_{ce} = -i_c r_c - a i_e r_c + i_e r_e$$
$$= (i_b + i_e) r_c - a i_e r_c + i_e r_e$$
$$= i_b r_c + i_e (1-a) r_c + i_e r_e$$
$$= \left(\frac{i_b}{1-a} + i_e \right) (1-a) r_c + i_e r_e$$
$$= \left(i_b + i_e + \frac{a}{1-a} i_b \right) (1-a) r_c + i_e r_e. \tag{A5.5}$$

Equations (A5.4) and (A5.5) are satisfied by the circuit of Fig. 5.9.

APPENDIX VI

RELATIONS BETWEEN z-, y-, AND h-PARAMETERS

IN the following table the circuit representations are given in matrix form and Δ is the corresponding determinant. Thus $[z] = \begin{bmatrix} z_{11} & z_{12} \\ z_{21} & z_{22} \end{bmatrix}$ and $\Delta_z = z_{11}z_{22} - z_{12}z_{21}$, etc.

Circuit matrix or determinant	Expressed in terms of		
	z-parameters	y-parameters	h-parameters
$[z]$		$\begin{matrix} \dfrac{y_{22}}{\Delta_y} & -\dfrac{y_{12}}{\Delta_y} \\[2mm] -\dfrac{y_{21}}{\Delta_y} & \dfrac{y_{11}}{\Delta_y} \end{matrix}$	$\begin{matrix} \dfrac{\Delta_h}{h_{22}} & \dfrac{h_{12}}{h_{22}} \\[2mm] -\dfrac{h_{21}}{h_{22}} & \dfrac{1}{h_{22}} \end{matrix}$
$[y]$	$\begin{matrix} \dfrac{z_{22}}{\Delta_z} & -\dfrac{z_{12}}{\Delta_z} \\[2mm] -\dfrac{z_{21}}{\Delta_z} & \dfrac{z_{11}}{\Delta_z} \end{matrix}$		$\begin{matrix} \dfrac{1}{h_{11}} & -\dfrac{h_{12}}{h_{11}} \\[2mm] \dfrac{h_{21}}{h_{11}} & \dfrac{\Delta_h}{h_{11}} \end{matrix}$
$[h]$	$\begin{matrix} \dfrac{\Delta_z}{z_{22}} & \dfrac{z_{12}}{z_{22}} \\[2mm] -\dfrac{z_{21}}{z_{22}} & \dfrac{1}{z_{22}} \end{matrix}$	$\begin{matrix} \dfrac{1}{y_{11}} & -\dfrac{y_{12}}{y_{11}} \\[2mm] \dfrac{y_{21}}{y_{11}} & \dfrac{\Delta_y}{y_{11}} \end{matrix}$	
Δ_z		$1/\Delta_y$	h_{11}/h_{22}
Δ_y	$1/\Delta_z$		h_{22}/h_{11}
Δ_h	z_{11}/z_{22}	y_{22}/y_{11}	

APPENDIX VII

THE APPLICATION OF CRAMER'S RULE IN THE ANALYSIS OF CIRCUITS

THE equations governing the operation of linear circuits of the type considered in this book may usually be expressed in the form:

$$a_{11}x_1 + a_{12}x_2 + a_{13}x_3 = y_1, \tag{A7.1}$$

$$a_{21}x_1 + a_{22}x_2 + a_{23}x_3 = y_2, \tag{A7.2}$$

$$a_{31}x_1 + a_{32}x_2 + a_{33}x_3 = y_3. \tag{A7.3}$$

The value of the unknown x_1 in terms of the known quantities y_1, y_2, y_3 and the constant coefficients (a's) is given by

$$x_1 = \frac{X_1}{\Delta},$$

where

$$\Delta = \begin{vmatrix} a_{11} & a_{12} & a_{13} \\ a_{21} & a_{22} & a_{23} \\ a_{31} & a_{32} & a_{33} \end{vmatrix} \tag{A7.4}$$

is the determinant of the coefficients and X_1 is obtained from Δ by replacing the coefficients $a_{11}, a_{21},$ and a_{31} of x_1 by $y_1, y_2,$ and y_3 respectively.

Thus

$$X_1 = \begin{vmatrix} y_1 & a_{12} & a_{13} \\ y_2 & a_{22} & a_{23} \\ y_3 & a_{32} & a_{33} \end{vmatrix}. \tag{A7.5}$$

x_2 and x_3 are obtained in a similar manner and the process may be extended to any number of equations and unknowns.

DETERMINATION OF THE RELATIONS BETWEEN h-PARAMETERS FOR THE CB, CE, AND CC CONNECTIONS

A GENERAL schematic diagram applicable to all transistor connections is shown in Fig. A8.1.

From this we have

$$i_b + i_c + i_e = 0, \tag{A8.1}$$

$$v_{bc} + v_{ce} + v_{eb} = 0. \tag{A8.2}$$

For the CB connection

$$v_{eb} = h_{ib} i_e + h_{rb} v_{cb}, \tag{A8.3}$$

$$i_c = h_{fb} i_e + h_{ob} v_{cb}. \tag{A8.4}$$

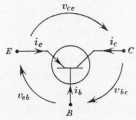

FIG. A8.1. Schematic diagram applicable to all transistor connections.

The determinant of the coefficients of (A8.3) and (A8.4) is called the CB h-parameter circuit determinant. Its value is

$$\Delta_{hb} = h_{ib} h_{ob} - h_{fb} h_{rb}. \tag{A8.5}$$

For the CE connection

$$v_{be} = h_{ie} i_b + h_{re} v_{ce}, \tag{A8.6}$$

$$i_c = h_{fe} i_b + h_{oe} v_{ce}, \tag{A8.7}$$

$$\Delta_{he} = h_{ie} h_{oe} - h_{fe} h_{re}. \tag{A8.8}$$

To express the CE h-parameters in terms of CB h-parameters we must determine v_{be} and i_c in terms of v_{ce} and i_b using equations (A8.1) to (A8.4). From these equations, treating v_{ce} and i_b as known quantities, we obtain

$$i_e + i_c + 0 \quad + 0 = -i_b, \tag{A8.9}$$

$$0 \quad + 0 + v_{be} \quad + v_{cb} = v_{ce}, \tag{A8.10}$$

$$h_{ib} i_e + 0 + v_{be} + h_{rb} v_{cb} = 0, \tag{A8.11}$$

$$h_{fb} i_e - i_c + 0 + h_{ob} v_{cb} = 0. \tag{A8.12}$$

The determinant of this is

$$\Delta_1 = \begin{vmatrix} 1 & 1 & 0 & 0 \\ 0 & 0 & 1 & 1 \\ h_{ib} & 0 & 1 & h_{rb} \\ h_{fb} & -1 & 0 & h_{ob} \end{vmatrix} = \begin{vmatrix} 1 & 0 & 0 & 0 \\ 0 & 0 & 1 & 1 \\ h_{ib} & -h_{ib} & 1 & h_{rb} \\ h_{fb} & -(1+h_{fb}) & 0 & h_{ob} \end{vmatrix}$$

$$= \begin{vmatrix} 0 & 0 & 1 \\ -h_{ib} & (1-h_{rb}) & h_{rb} \\ -(1+h_{fb}) & -h_{ob} & h_{ob} \end{vmatrix} = h_{ib}h_{ob}+(1-h_{rb})(1+h_{fb}), \tag{A8.13}$$

where the rules for the reduction of determinants have been applied. Using equation (A8.5),

$$\Delta_1 = \Delta_{hb}+1+h_{fb}-h_{rb}. \tag{A8.14}$$

By the rule of Appendix VII,

$$v_{be} = \frac{1}{\Delta_1} \begin{vmatrix} 1 & 1 & -i_b & 0 \\ 0 & 0 & v_{ce} & 1 \\ h_{ib} & 0 & 0 & h_{rb} \\ h_{fb} & -1 & 0 & h_{ob} \end{vmatrix} = \frac{1}{\Delta_1} \begin{vmatrix} 1 & 1 & -i_b & 0 \\ 0 & 0 & v_{ce} & 1 \\ h_{ib} & 0 & 0 & h_{rb} \\ (1+h_{fb}) & 0 & -i_b & h_{ob} \end{vmatrix}$$

$$= -\frac{1}{\Delta_1} \begin{vmatrix} 0 & v_{ce} & 1 \\ h_{ib} & 0 & h_{rb} \\ (1+h_{fb}) & -i_b & h_{ob} \end{vmatrix}$$

$$= \frac{1}{\Delta_1}\{h_{ib}i_b+v_{ce}[h_{ib}h_{ob}-h_{rb}(1+h_{fb})]\}, \tag{A8.15}$$

or
$$v_{be} = \frac{1}{\Delta_1}[h_{ib}i_b+(\Delta_{hb}-h_{rb})v_{ce}]. \tag{A8.16}$$

In a similar manner we obtain

$$i_c = \frac{1}{\Delta_1}[-(\Delta_{hb}+h_{fb})i_b+h_{ob}v_{ce}]. \tag{A8.17}$$

A comparison of (A8.16) and (A8.17) with (A8.6) and (A8.7) gives

$$h_{ie} = \frac{h_{ib}}{\Delta_1}, \tag{A8.18}$$

$$h_{re} = \frac{\Delta_{hb}-h_{rb}}{\Delta_1}, \tag{A8.19}$$

$$h_{fe} = \frac{-(\Delta_{hb}+h_{fb})}{\Delta_1}, \tag{A8.20}$$

$$h_{oe} = \frac{h_{ob}}{\Delta_1}. \tag{A8.21}$$

Using (A8.8) the CE h-parameter circuit determinant is found to be

$$\Delta_{he} = \frac{\Delta_{hb}}{\Delta_1}. \tag{A8.22}$$

Other relations between the h-parameters of the three connections may be obtained by a similar procedure. The relations that are most generally useful, and approximations to them discussed in Chapter V, are contained in Table A8.1.

TABLE A8.1

Summary of Relations between h-Parameters

$$\Delta_h = h_i\,h_o - h_f\,h_r, \quad \text{i.e.} \quad \Delta_{hb} = h_{ib}\,h_{ob} - h_{fb}\,h_{rb}, \text{ etc.}$$

$$\Delta_1 = 1 + h_{fb} + \Delta_{hb} - h_{rb}, \qquad \Delta_2 = 1 + h_{fe} + \Delta_{he} - h_{re}$$

CE parameters	CB exact equivalent	CB approximate equivalent
$h_{ie} = h_{11e}$	h_{ib}/Δ_1	$h_{ib}/(1+h_{fb})$
$h_{re} = h_{12e}$	$(\Delta_{hb}-h_{rb})/\Delta_1$	$(\Delta_{hb}-h_{rb})/(1+h_{fb})$
$h_{fe} = h_{21e}$	$-(\Delta_{hb}+h_{fb})/\Delta_1$	$-h_{fb}/(1+h_{fb})$
$h_{oe} = h_{22e}$	h_{ob}/Δ_1	$h_{ob}/(1+h_{fb})$
Δ_{he}	Δ_{hb}/Δ_1	$\Delta_{hb}/(1+h_{fb})$

CB parameters	CE exact equivalent	CE approximate equivalent
$h_{ib} = h_{11b}$	h_{ie}/Δ_2	$h_{ie}/(1+h_{fe})$
$h_{rb} = h_{12b}$	$(\Delta_{he}-h_{re})/\Delta_2$	$(\Delta_{he}-h_{re})/(1+h_{fe})$
$h_{fb} = h_{21b}$	$-(\Delta_{he}+h_{fe})/\Delta_2$	$-h_{fe}/(1+h_{fe})$
$h_{ob} = h_{22b}$	h_{oe}/Δ_2	$h_{oe}/(1+h_{fe})$
Δ_{hb}	Δ_{he}/Δ_2	$\Delta_{he}/(1+h_{fe})$

CC parameters	CB exact equivalent	CB approximate equivalent	CE exact equivalent	CE approximate equivalent
$h_{ic} = h_{11c}$	h_{ib}/Δ_1	$h_{ib}/(1+h_{fb})$	h_{ie}	h_{ie}
$h_{rc} = h_{12c}$	$(1+h_{fb})/\Delta_1$	1	$(1-h_{re})$	1
$h_{fc} = h_{21c}$	$-(1-h_{rb})/\Delta_1$	$-1/(1+h_{fb})$	$-(1+h_{fe})$	$-(1+h_{fe})$
$h_{oc} = h_{22c}$	h_{ob}/Δ_1	$h_{ob}/(1+h_{fb})$	h_{oe}	h_{oe}
Δ_{hc}	$1/\Delta_1$	$1/(1+h_{fb})$	Δ_2	$1+h_{fe}$

APPENDIX IX

TABLE A9.1

T-circuit parameters in terms of h-parameters
(For definitions of symbols see Appendix VIII)

T-circuit parameter	CB	CE	CC
r_e	$\dfrac{\Delta_{hb}-h_{rb}}{h_{ob}}$	$\dfrac{h_{re}}{h_{oe}}$	$\dfrac{1-h_{rc}}{h_{oc}}$
r_b	$\dfrac{h_{rb}}{h_{ob}}$	$\dfrac{\Delta_{he}-h_{re}}{h_{oe}}$	$\dfrac{\Delta_{hc}+h_{fc}}{h_{oc}}$
r_c	$\dfrac{1-h_{rb}}{h_{ob}} \simeq \dfrac{1}{h_{ob}}$	$\dfrac{1+h_{fe}}{h_{oe}}$	$\dfrac{-h_{fc}}{h_{oc}}$
r_m	$-\dfrac{h_{rb}+h_{fb}}{h_{ob}} \simeq \dfrac{-h_{fb}}{h_{ob}}$	$\dfrac{h_{re}+h_{fe}}{h_{oe}} \simeq \dfrac{h_{fe}}{h_{oe}}$	$-\dfrac{h_{rc}+h_{fc}}{h_{oc}} \simeq \dfrac{1+h_{fc}}{h_{oc}}$
a	$-\dfrac{h_{rb}+h_{fb}}{1-h_{rb}} \simeq -h_{fb}$	$\dfrac{h_{re}+h_{fe}}{1+h_{fe}} \simeq \dfrac{h_{fe}}{1+h_{fe}}$	$\dfrac{h_{rc}+h_{fc}}{h_{fc}} \simeq \dfrac{1+h_{fc}}{h_{fc}}$
α	$-h_{fb}$	$\dfrac{\Delta_{he}+h_{fe}}{1-h_{re}+h_{fe}+\Delta_{he}} \simeq \dfrac{h_{fe}}{1+h_{fe}}$	$\dfrac{\Delta_{hc}-h_{rc}}{\Delta_{hc}} \simeq \dfrac{1+h_{fc}}{h_{fc}}$

TABLE A9.2

h-parameters in terms of T-circuit parameters

h-parameters	CB	CE	CC
h_i	$r_e+r_b\dfrac{r_c-r_m}{r_c+r_b}$	$r_b+r_e\dfrac{r_c}{r_c-r_m+r_e}$	$r_b+r_e\dfrac{r_c}{r_c-r_m+r_e}$
h_r	$\dfrac{r_b}{r_c+r_b}$	$\dfrac{r_e}{r_c-r_m+r_e}$	$\dfrac{r_c-r_m}{r_c-r_m+r_e}$
h_f	$-\dfrac{r_m+r_b}{r_c+r_b}$	$\dfrac{r_m-r_e}{r_c-r_m+r_e}$	$\dfrac{r_c}{r_c-r_m+r_e}$
h_o	$\dfrac{1}{r_c+r_b}$	$\dfrac{1}{r_c-r_m+r_e}$	$\dfrac{1}{r_c-r_m+r_e}$

APPENDIX X

CIRCUIT PROPERTIES OF THE TWO-PORT DEVICE

THE following table gives the circuit properties of a transistor or other two-port device in terms of the z-, y-, and h-parameters when there is external impedance in series with the common electrode. This impedance (e.g. Z_e in the CE connection) is called Z_t.

Circuit property	h	z	y
		Matrix equivalent circuit	
Z_i	$\dfrac{h_i + \Delta_h(Z_l + Z_t) + Z_t(1 + h_f - h_r + h_o Z_l)}{1 + h_o(Z_l + Z_t)}$	$\dfrac{\Delta_z + z_{11} Z_l + Z_t(z_{11} + z_{22} - z_{12} - z_{21} + Z_l)}{z_{22} + Z_l + Z_t}$	$\dfrac{1 + y_{22} Z_l + Z_t(y_{11} + y_{12} + y_{21} + y_{22} + Z_l\,\Delta_y)}{y_{11} + (Z_l + Z_t)\Delta_y}$
Z_o	$\dfrac{(h_i + Z_g)(1 + h_o Z_t) + Z_t(1 - h_r)(1 + h_f)}{\Delta_h + h_o(Z_g + Z_t)}$	$\dfrac{\Delta_z + z_{22} Z_g + Z_t(z_{11} + z_{22} - z_{12} - z_{21} + Z_g)}{z_{11} + Z_g + Z_t}$	$\dfrac{1 + y_{11} Z_g + Z_t(y_{11} + y_{12} + y_{21} + y_{22} + Z_g\,\Delta_y)}{y_{22} + (Z_g + Z_t)\Delta_y}$
A_i	$\dfrac{h_f - h_o Z_t}{1 + h_o(Z_l + Z_t)}$	$\dfrac{-(z_{21} + Z_t)}{z_{22} + Z_l + Z_t}$	$\dfrac{y_{21} - Z_t\,\Delta_y}{y_{11} + (Z_l + Z_t)\Delta_y}$
A_v	$\dfrac{-Z_l(h_f - h_o Z_t)}{h_i + \Delta_h(Z_l + Z_t) + Z_t(1 + h_f - h_r + h_o Z_l)}$	$\dfrac{Z_l(z_{21} + Z_t)}{\Delta_z + z_{11} Z_l + Z_t(z_{11} + z_{22} - z_{12} - z_{21} + Z_l)}$	$\dfrac{-Z_l(y_{21} - Z_t\,\Delta_y)}{1 + y_{22} Z_l + Z_t(y_{11} + y_{12} + y_{21} + y_{22} + Z_l\,\Delta_y)}$

APPENDIX XI

MANUFACTURERS' DATA AND CHARACTERISTIC CURVES FOR THE 2N369 p-n-p ALLOY-JUNCTION TRANSISTOR

THE following information is taken from Texas Instruments Bulletin No. DL–S 873 dated March 1958:

Absolute Maximum Ratings at 25° C Ambient Temperature

Collector voltage referred to base . . . . -30 V
Emitter voltage referred to base . . . . -10 V
Collector current . . . . . . -50 mA
Emitter current . . . . 50 mA
Device dissipation (free air) . . . . 100 mW
Junction temperature rise (free air) . . . $0.5°$ C/mW
Device dissipation (infinite heat sink) . . 150 mW
Junction temperature rise (infinite heat sink) . $0.33°$ C/mW
Storage temperature . . . . . $-55°$ C to $+75°$ C

TABLE A11.1

Common base design characteristics at $T_j = 25°$ C

				Design centre	Max.	Unit
I_{co}	Collector cutoff current	$V_{CB} = -30$ V	$I_E = 0$	7	20	μA
I_{co}	Collector cutoff current	$V_{CB} = -5$ V	$I_E = 0$	5	..	μA
C_{ob}	Output capacitance	$f = 10$ kc	..	33	50	$\mu\mu$F

TABLE A11.2

Common base design characteristics at $T_j = 25°$ C

Bias conditions for the following characteristics are $V_{CB} = -5$ volts, $I_E = 1$ mA.

		Min.	Design centre	Max.	Unit
h_{ib}	Input impedance	25	30	50	ohm
h_{ob}	Output admittance	0.15	0.35	1.5	μmho
h_{rb}	Feedback voltage ratio	100	250	1,500	$\times 10^{-6}$
h_{fb}	Current transfer ratio	0.980	0.982	0.993	..
β	Beta†	49	55	142	..
NF	Noise figure†‡	..	7	..	db
$F_{\alpha b}$	Frequency cutoff	0.5	1.3	..	Mc

† Common emitter.   ‡ Conventional
noise—compared to 1,000-ohm resistor, 1,000 c.p.s., and 1 cycle band-width.

TABLE A11.3

Design centre h-parameters for the 2N369

Bias conditions: $V_{CB} = -5$ volts, $I_E = 1$ mA.

Parameter	CB	CE	CC
h_i (ohms)	30	1,670	1,670
h_r	250×10^{-6}	330×10^{-6}	1
h_f	-0.982	55	-56
h_o (μmhos)	0.35	19.4	19.4
Δ_h	256×10^{-6}	14.4×10^{-3}	56

Output and input characteristics for the *CB* and *CE* connections are shown in Figs. A11.1 to A11.5 inclusive. These were taken on a Tektronix Inc. Type 575 Transistor Curve Tracer. The curves apply to a unit whose characteristics were approximately the means of those of several units tested. The curves are unretouched with the exception of Figs. A11.4

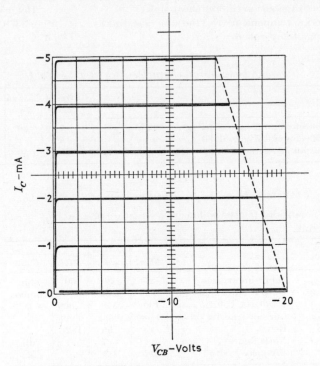

FIG. A11.1. 2N369. Common base output characteristics. The running parameter I_E has values of 0, 1, 2, 3, 4, and 5 mA.

and A11.5 on which the vertical lines and dots on the Curve Tracer figures have been removed.

Curves showing the effect of bias parameters and temperature on the CB and CE characteristics are shown in Figs. A11.6 to A11.11 inclusive. These were taken from the above-mentioned bulletin.

Additional curves showing the circuit properties R_i, A_i, A_v, and G as functions of load resistance and R_0 as a function of generator resistance are shown in Figs. A11.12 to A11.16 inclusive. These were calculated from the design centre values of Table A11.2 with the help of Appendixes VIII and X.

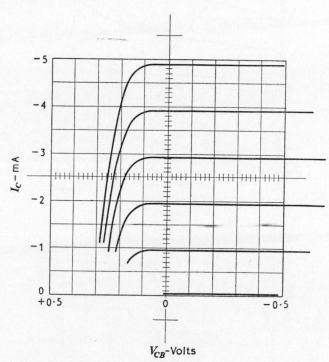

Fig. A11.2. Expanded portion of 2N369 CB output characteristics. The running parameter I_E has values of 0, 1, 2, 3, 4, and 5 mA.

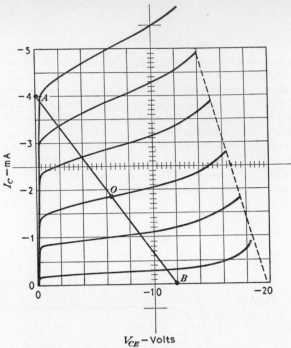

FIG. A11.3. 2N369. Common emitter output characteristics. The running parameter I_B has values of 0, 10, 20, 30, 40, and 50 μA.

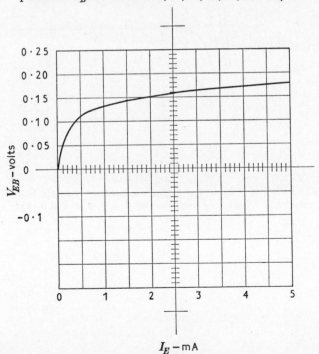

FIG. A11.4. 2N369. Common base input characteristic, taken at $V_{CB} = -5$ volts.

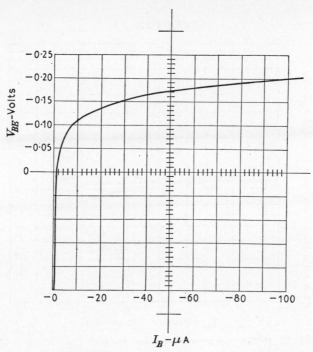

FIG. A11.5. 2N369. Common emitter input characteristic, taken at $V_{CE} = -5$ volts.

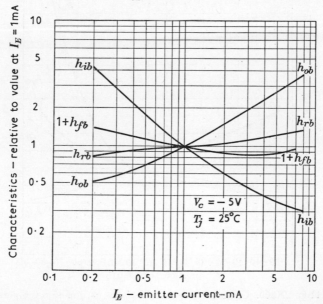

FIG. A11.6. 2N369. Common base characteristics vs. emitter current.

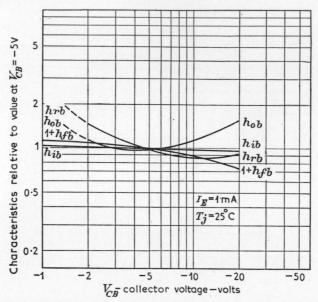

FIG. A11.7. 2N369. Common base characteristics vs. collector voltage.

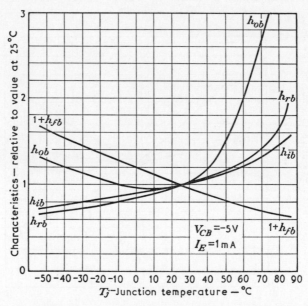

FIG. A11.8. 2N369. Common base characteristics vs. junction temperature.

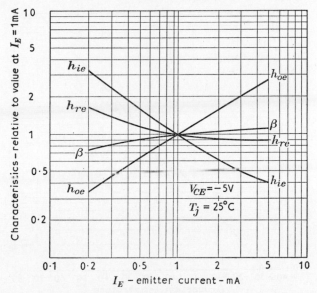

FIG. A11.9. 2N369. Common emitter characteristics vs. emitter current.

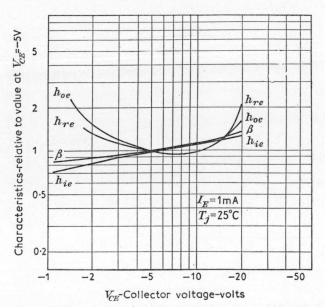

FIG. A11.10. 2N369. Common emitter characteristics vs. collector voltage.

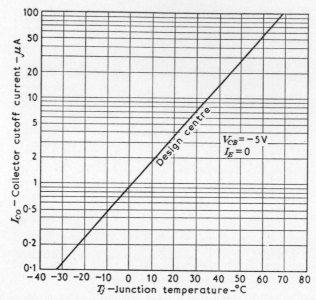

FIG. A11.11. 2N369. Collector cutoff current vs. junction temperature.

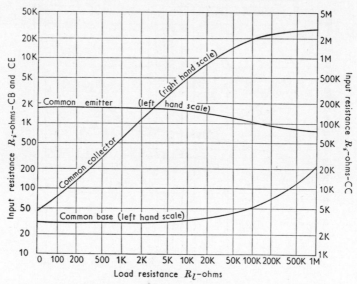

FIG. A11.12. 2N369. Input resistance vs. load resistance.

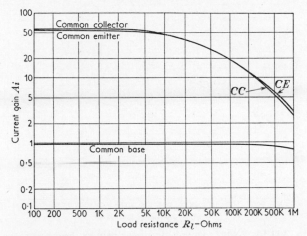

FIG. A11.13. 2N369. Current gain vs. load resistance.

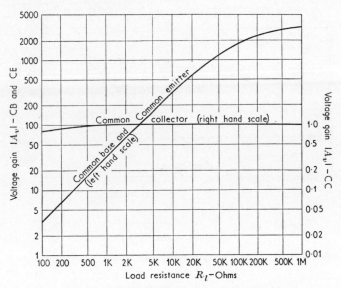

FIG. A11.14. 2N369. Voltage gain vs. load resistance.

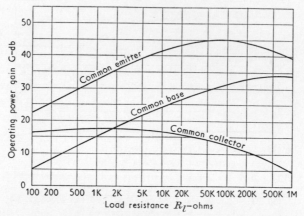

FIG. A11.15. 2N369. Operating power gain vs. load resistance.

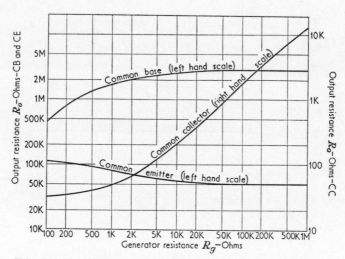

FIG. A11.16. 2N369. Output resistance vs. generator resistance.

APPENDIX XII

THE RESISTANCE-CAPACITANCE COUPLED CLASS A AMPLIFIER

IN this appendix we shall derive the expressions given in Chapter XII for the amounts of power dissipated in the transistor, in the load resistor, and in the collector bias resistor of an ideal RC-coupled Class A amplifier.

The following assumptions are made:

1. The collector can be driven to cutoff,
2. The saturation voltage drop is negligible.
3. External resistance in the emitter lead is adequately by-passed to earth, and the battery voltage may be suitably changed to enable the static voltage drop to be ignored.

In Fig. A12.1 two load lines are shown: one, AOB, of slope $-1/R_c$ drawn through the effective battery voltage V_{cc} at zero current represents the

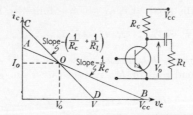

FIG. A.12.1. Load lines of RC-coupled amplifier.

collector bias resistor, R_c; the other, COD, whose slope is $-(1/R_c+1/R_l)$, represents the a.c. collector load consisting of R_c and R_l in parallel. It intersects the voltage axis at some value V.

The equations representing these lines are

$$i_c = \frac{1}{R_c}(V_{cc}-v_c), \qquad i_c = \left(\frac{1}{R_c}+\frac{1}{R_l}\right)(V-v_c).$$

These lines intersect at the operating point, O, whose coordinates (V_0, I_0) are found by simultaneous solution of these equations to be

$$V_0 = V + \frac{R_l}{R_c}(V-V_{cc}), \tag{A12.1}$$

$$I_0 = (V_{cc}-V)\frac{R_c+R_l}{R_c^2}. \tag{A12.2}$$

The transistor can develop the maximum voltage across R_l when V_0 is half-way between the origin and V, i.e. when $V = 2V_0$. If the base bias is adjusted so that this condition is satisfied an overdrive will cause the output waveform to be clipped symmetrically. The coordinates (V_0', I_0') of the optimum operating point are found by putting $V = 2V_0$ in equations (A12.1) and (A12.2):

$$V_0' = \frac{R_l}{R_c + 2R_l} V_{cc}, \tag{A12.3}$$

$$I_0' = \frac{1}{R_c} \frac{R_c + R_l}{R_c + 2R_l} V_{cc}. \tag{A12.4}$$

The effect of a sinusoidal base current is to cause the operating point to move along the line COD about O as centre. Hence we may put

$$i_c = I_0(1 + K\sin\omega t), \quad \text{where } 0 \leqslant K \leqslant 1.$$

Both signal and bias currents flow in R_c, but only signal current can flow in R_l. The signal-current component, $KI_0\sin\omega t$, is divided between R_c and R_l. Therefore, while the static value of the collector voltage is V_0, where $V_0 = V_{cc} - I_0 R_c$, the instantaneous value v_c is given by

$$v_c = V_{cc} - I_0 R_c - I_0 \frac{R_c R_l}{R_c + R_l} K\sin\omega t.$$

The power P_c dissipated by the transistor is the average value, taken over one cycle, of the product $v_c i_c$, which is found to be

$$P_c = V_{cc} I_0 - R_c I_0^2 - \tfrac{1}{2} K^2 I_0^2 \frac{R_c R_l}{R_c + R_l}.$$

Of the signal current, $KI_0\sin\omega t$, a fraction $R_c/(R_c + R_l)$ flows in R_l. The power in the load resistor R_l, averaged over one cycle, is therefore P_0, where

$$P_0 = \tfrac{1}{2} K^2 I_0^2 \left(\frac{R_c}{R_c + R_l}\right)^2 R_l.$$

The remainder of the signal current flows in R_c which also carries the d.c. bias current I_0. Hence the total power P in R_c is given by

$$P = I_0^2 R_c \left[1 + \tfrac{1}{2} K^2 \left(\frac{R_l}{R_c + R_l}\right)^2\right].$$

It is easily verified that

$$P_c + P_0 + P = V_{cc} I_0.$$

Assuming that the bias is chosen to give the optimum operating point defined by equations (A12.3) and (A12.4) we may replace I_0 in the expressions for P_c and P_0 to yield the equations stated without proof in Chapter XII:

$$P_0 = \tfrac{1}{2} K^2 V_{cc}^2 \frac{R_l}{(R_c + 2R_l)^2}, \tag{12.13}$$

$$P_c = (1 - \tfrac{1}{2}K^2) V_{cc}^2 \frac{R_l}{R_c} \frac{R_c + R_l}{(R_c + 2R_l)^2}. \tag{12.14}$$

The collector efficiency η is the ratio $P_0/(P_0 + P_0 + P)$ which is given by

$$\eta = \tfrac{1}{2} K^2 \frac{R_c R_l}{(R_c + R_l)(R_c + 2R_l)}. \tag{12.15}$$

Differentiating η with respect to R_c or R_l and equating the derivative to zero shows that the efficiency is at a maximum when R_c is equal to $R_l\sqrt{2}$. Under this condition, at full drive ($K = 1$), we find that the value of η is 0·086. The condition of maximum efficiency is also the condition for maximum power output if V_{cc} and I_0 are fixed and we are free to choose R_c and R_l. However, if V_{cc} and R_c are fixed and we are free to choose a value of R_l, it is seen by setting dP_0/dR_l equal to zero that we should make R_l equal to $\frac{1}{2}R_c$.

APPENDIX XIII

VOLTAGE-REGULATOR ANALYSIS

VOLTAGE and current regulators have been discussed in the literature for many years. The following is intended to serve as an introduction to some of the more detailed papers [1, 2, 3].

We consider a voltage regulator whose input voltage V_i and output voltage and current V_0 and I_0 are connected by the equation

$$V_0 = f(V_i, I_0). \tag{A13.1}$$

Since $V_0 = I_0 R_l$, where R_l is the external load resistance, we may also write

$$V_0 = g(V_i, R_l) \tag{A13.2}$$

and other equations of similar type.

Differentiating equation (A13.1):

$$dV_0 = \left(\frac{\partial V_0}{\partial V_i}\right)_{I_0} dV_i + \left(\frac{\partial V_0}{\partial I_0}\right)_{V_i} dI_0$$

$$= p\, dV_i - r\, dI_0. \tag{A13.3}$$

Here p is the 'regulation factor' measured at a constant output current and r is the 'effective output resistance' when the input voltage is constant.

By differentiating equation (A13.2) we have

$$dV_0 = \left(\frac{\partial V_0}{\partial V_i}\right)_{R_l} dV_i + \left(\frac{\partial V_0}{\partial R_l}\right)_{V_i} dR_l$$

$$= q\, dV_i + i\, dR_l. \tag{A13.4}$$

The regulation factor q is measured with a constant load resistance and differs from p. However, if the regulator is a good one, this difference is small.

Other derivatives may be obtained as needed (e.g. the load conductance $G_l = 1/R_l$ could have been used to derive an expression of the same type as equation (A13.4)) and relations may be found connecting them as is done in thermodynamics.

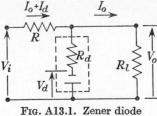

FIG. A13.1. Zener diode regulator circuit.

As an illustration consider the circuit of Fig. A13.1, which represents a regulating (Zener) diode in series with a resistor R, feeding an output voltage V_0 to a load resistor R_l. The input voltage is V_i and the value of the resistor R is assumed to include the internal resistance of the source. The output current is I_0, and a current I_d flows in the diode. The diode is assumed to have an equivalent circuit consisting of a source of voltage V_d in series with an internal resistance R_d.

The circuit equations are

$$V_i = I_0(R+R_l)+I_d R,$$
$$V_0 = I_d R_d + V_d,$$
$$V_0 = I_0 R_l.$$

To find the regulation factor p we eliminate I_d and express V_0 in terms of V_i and I_0. Thus,

$$V_0 = V_d + V_i \frac{R_d}{R} - I_0 \frac{R_d}{R}(R+R_l),$$
$$p = \left(\frac{\partial V_0}{\partial V_i}\right)_{I_0} = \frac{R_d}{R}.$$

To find q we express V_0 in terms of V_i and R_l. Thus,

$$V_0 = \frac{V_d + V_i(R_d/R)}{1+(R_d/R_l)+(R_d/R)}, \tag{A13.5}$$
$$q = \left(\frac{\partial V_0}{\partial V_i}\right)_{R_l} = \frac{1}{1+R\{1/R_d+1/R_l\}}.$$

The internal resistance r is found by eliminating R_l and expressing V_0 in terms of V_i and I_0:

$$V_0\left(1+\frac{R_d}{R}\right) = V_d + V_i \frac{R_d}{R} - R_d I_0,$$
$$r = -\left(\frac{\partial V_0}{\partial I_0}\right)_{V_i} = \frac{R R_d}{R+R_d},$$

i.e. the resistance of R and R_d in parallel, as is evident from the figure.

Typically when $V_d \simeq 10$ volts, $R_d \simeq 10$ ohms. Then if $R = R_l = 1\,\mathrm{k}\,\Omega$ the regulation factors p and q are: $p = 1/100$, $q = 1/102$.

REFERENCES

1. HUNT, F. V., and HICKMAN, R. W. (1939). *Rev. Sci. Inst.* **10**, 6–21.
2. HILL, W. R. (1945). *Proc. I.R.E.* **33**, 38–45.
3. —— (1945). Ibid. 785–92.

REFERENCES

CHAPTER I

1. BARDEEN, J., and BRATTAIN, W. H. (1948). *Phys. Rev.* **74**, 230–1.
   —— —— (1949). Ibid. **75**, 1208–25.
2. SHOCKLEY, W. (1949). *Bell Syst. Tech. J.* **28**, 435–89.
3. —— (1950). *Electrons and Holes in Semiconductors*, Van Nostrand, New York.
4. KITTEL, C. (1956). *Introduction to Solid State Physics*, 2nd ed., John Wiley & Sons, New York.
5. —— (1954). *Physica* **20**, 829–33.

CHAPTER II

1. SHOCKLEY, W. (1950). *Electrons and Holes in Semiconductors*, p. 58, Van Nostrand, New York.
2. HAYNES, J. R., and SHOCKLEY, W. (1949). *Phys. Rev.* **75**, 691.
3. PRINCE, M. B. (1953). Ibid. **91**, 271–2.
4. MOTT, N. F., and GURNEY, R. W. (1948). *Electronic Processes in Ionic Crystals*, p. 63, Clarendon Press, Oxford.
5. HALL, R. N. (1951). *Phys. Rev.* **87**, 387.
6. SHOCKLEY, W., and READ, W. T., Jr. (1952). Ibid. 835–42.

CHAPTER III

1. SHEPHERD, A. A. (1958). *An Introduction to the Theory and Practice of Semiconductors*, Constable, London.
2. PFANN, W. G. (1952). *Trans. Amer. Inst. Min. Metall. Engrs.* **194**, 747–53.
3. KECK, P. H., and GOLAY, M. J. E. (1953). *Phys. Rev.* **89**, 1297.
4. PFANN, W. G. (1958). *Zone Melting*, Wiley, New York; Chapman & Hall, London.
5. CZOCHRALSKI, J. (1918). *Zeit. f. phys. Chemie*, **92**, 219–21.
6. TEAL, G. K., and LITTLE, J. B. (1950). *Phys. Rev.* **78**, 647.
7. CRESSELL, I. G., and POWELL, J. A. (1957). *Progress in Semiconductors*, **2**, 139–64, Heywood, London.
8. BARDEEN, J. (1947). *Phys. Rev.* **71**, 717–27.
9. HENISCH, H. K. (1949). *Metal Rectifiers*, Clarendon Press, Oxford.
10. SHOCKLEY, W. (1949). *Bell Syst. Tech. J.* **28**, 435–89.
11. BOCCIARELLI, C. V. (1954). *Physica*, **20**, 1020–5.
12. TANENBAUM, M., and THOMAS, D. E. (1956). *Bell Syst. Tech. J.* **35**, 1–22.
13. HALL, R. N. (1952). *Phys. Rev.* **88**, 139.
14. PANKOVE, J. I. (1956). *Proc. I.R.E.* **44**, 185–8.

15. ANON. (1956). *Electronics*, **29**, August 1956, pp. 190, 192, 194.
16. LAW, R. R., MUELLER, C. W., PANKOVE, J. I., and ARMSTRONG, L. D. (1952). *Proc. I.R.E.* **40**, 1352–7.
17. GIACOLETTO, L. J. (1954). *R.C.A. Rev.* **15**, 506–62.
18. SMITS, F. M. (1958). *Proc. I.R.E.* **46**, 1049–61.
19. LEE, C. A. (1956). *Bell Syst. Tech. J.* **35**, 23–34.
20. PEARSON, G. L., and FULLER, C. S. (1954). *Proc. I.R.E.* **42**, 760.

CHAPTER IV

1. SHOCKLEY, W. (1949). *Bell Syst. Tech. J.* **28**, 435–89.
2. HALL, R. N. (1952). *Proc. I.R.E.* **40**, 1512–18.
3. GOUDET, G., and MEULEAU, C. (1957). *Semiconductors*, English translation by G. King. MacDonald & Evans, London.
4. SABY, J. S. (1956). *Report of the Physical Society Meeting on Semiconductors, Rugby, England*, pp. 39–48.
5. ABRAHAM, M., and BECKER, R. (1932). *Electricity and Magnetism*, Blackie, London.
6. HENDERSON, J. C., and TILLMAN, J. R. (1957). *Proc. I.E.E.* **104B**, 318–33.
7. PIETENPOL, W. J. (1958). *Bell Labs. Record*, **36**, 202–6.
8. PELL, E. M. (1955). *J. Appl. Phys.* **26**, 658–65.
9. —— and ROE, G. M. (1956). Ibid. **27**, 768–72.
10. CHYNOWETH, A. G. (1960). *Progress in Semiconductors*, **4**, 95–123, Heywood, London.
11. REDIKER, R. H., and SAWYER, D. E. (1957). *Proc. I.R.E.* **45**, 944–53.
12. HENISCH, H. K. (1949). *Metal Rectifiers*, Clarendon Press, Oxford.
13. PEARSON, G. L. (1957). *Am. J. Phys.* **25**, 591–8.
14. PRINCE, M. B., and WOLF, M. (1958). *J. Brit. I.R.E.* **18**, 583–95.
15. RAPPAPORT, P., LOFERSKI, J. J., and LINDER, E. G. (1956). *R.C.A. Rev.* **17**, 100–28.
16. ANON. (1957). *Industrial Laboratories*, **8**, No. 4, 82–83.

CHAPTER V

1. *I.R.E. Standards* (1957). *Proc. I.R.E.* **45**, 1612–17.
2. PIPES, L. A. (1940). *Phil. Mag.* **30**, 370–95.
3. *I.R.E. Standards* (1956). *Proc. I.R.E.* **44**, 934–7.
4. SHEA, R. F., *et al.* (1953). *Principles of Transistor Circuits*, Wiley, New York.
5. RYDER, R. M., and KIRCHER, R. J. (1949). *Bell Syst. Tech. J.* **28**, 367–400.
6. WALLACE, R. L., Jr., and PIETENPOL, W. J. (1951). *Proc. I.R.E.* **39**, 753–67.

CHAPTER VI

1. SHOCKLEY, W., SPARKS, M., and TEAL, G. K. (1951). *Phys. Rev.* **83**, 151–62.
2. EARLY, J. M. (1953). *Bell Syst. Tech. J.* **32**, 1271–1312.
3. MIDDLEBROOK, R. D. (1957). *An Introduction to Junction Transistor Theory*, Wiley, New York.
4. WEBSTER, W. M. (1954). *Proc. I.R.E.* **42**, 914–20.

CHAPTER VII

1. EARLY, J. M. (1953). *Bell Syst. Tech. J.* **32**, 1271–1312.
2. PRITCHARD, R. L. (1952). *Proc. I.R.E.* **40**, 1476–81.
3. GIACOLETTO, L. J. (1954). *R.C.A. Rev.* **15**, 506–62.
4. JANSSON, L. E. (1957). *Mullard Tech. Comm.* **3**, 151–60.
——— and WOLFENDALE, E. (1958). Chapter 3 of *The Junction Transistor and its Applications*, E. Wolfendale, editor, Heywood, London.
5. ——— (1957). *Mullard Tech. Comm.* **3**, 174–87.
6. WEBSTER, R. R. (Nov. 1956). *Electronics Industries and Tele-Tech.* 62–64, 124, 126, 128.
7. MIDDLEBROOK, R. D. (1957). *An Introduction to Junction Transistor Theory*, Wiley, New York.
8. EARHART, C., and BROWER, W. (1958). *Semiconductor Products*, **1**, No. 2, 14–21.
9. EBERS, J. J., and MOLL, J. L. (1954). *Proc. I.R.E.* **42**, 1761–72.
10. MOLL, J. L. (1954). *Ibid.* **42**, 1773–84.
11. DEUITCH, D. E. (1956). *Transistors,* I. 609–39, R.C.A. Laboratories, Princeton, N.J.
12. Cooke-Yarborough, E. H. (1957). *An Introduction to Transistor Circuits*, Oliver & Boyd, London.
13. LESK, I. A., and SURAN, J. J. (1960). *Electrical Engineering*, **79**, 270–7.

CHAPTER VIII

1. GIACOLETTO, L. J. (1954). *R.C.A. Rev.* **15**, 506–62.
2. EARLY, J. M. (1958). *Proc. I.R.E.* **46**, 1924–7.
3. PRITCHARD, R. L. (1955). *Ibid.* **43**, 1075–85.
4. MUELLER, C. W., and PANKOVE, J. I. (1953). *R.C.A. Rev.* **14**, 586–97. Reprinted in *Transistors*, I. R.C.A. Laboratories, 1956.
5. HEROLD, E. W. (1954). *Brit. J. Appl. Phys.* **5**, 115–26.
6. BRADLEY, W. E. (1953). *Proc. I.R.E.* **41**, 1702–6.
TILEY, J. W., and WILLIAMS, R. A. (1953). *Ibid.* 1706–8.
7. WALLACE, R. L., Jr., SCHIMPF, L. G., and DICKTON, E. (1952). *Ibid.* **40**, 1395–1400.
8. MOLL, J. L., and ROSS, I. M. (1956). *Ibid.* **44**, 72–78.
9. SMITS, F. M. (1958). *Ibid.* **46**, 1049–61.

10. KROEMER, H. (1953). *Naturwissenschaften*, **40**, 578–9.
11. —— (1954). *Arch. elekt. Übertragung*, **8**, 223–8, 363–9, 499–504.
12. —— (1956). *Transistors*, I. 202–20, R.C.A. Laboratories, Princeton, N.J.
13. KESTENBAUM, A. L., and DITRICK, N. H. (1957). *R.C.A. Rev.* **18**, 12–23.
14. EARLY, J. M. (1954). *Bell Syst. Tech. J.* **33**, 517–33.
15. NELSON, J. T., IWERSEN, J. E., and KEYWELL, F. (1958). *Proc. I.R.E.* **46**, 1209–15.
16. LEE, C. A. (1956). *Bell Syst. Tech. J.* **35**, 23–34.
17. KNOWLES, C. H. (1958). *Electronic Industries*, 55–60, August 1958.
18. THORNTON, C. G., and ANGELL, J. B. (1958). *Proc. I.R.F.* **46**, 1166–76.
19. EARHART, C., and BROWER, W. (1958). *Semiconductor Products*, **1**, Mar./April 1958, pp. 14–21.
20. SHOCKLEY, W. (1952). *Proc. I.R.E.* **40**, 1289–1313.
21. —— (1952). Ibid. 1365–76.
22. DACEY, G. C., and ROSS, I. M. (1953). Ibid. **41**, 970–9.
23. —— —— (1955). *Bell Syst. Tech. J.* **34**, 1149–89.
24. TESZNER, S. (1958). *C.R. Acad. Sci. Paris*, **246**, 72–73.
25. —— (1958). Centre National d'Études des Télécommunications. Royal Aircraft Establishment (Farnborough) Translation No. 777.
26. GÄRTNER, W. W. (1957). *Proc. I.R.E.* **45**, 1392–1400.
27. STATZ, H., PUCEL, R. A., and LANZA, C. (1957). Ibid. 1475–83.
28. ESAKI, L. (1958). *Phys. Rev.* **109**, 603–4.
29. SOMMERS, H. S. (1959). *Proc. I.R.E.* **47**, 1201–6.
30. BARDEEN, J., and BRATTAIN, W. H. (1948). *Phys. Rev.* **74**, 230–1.
31. SHOCKLEY, W. (1949). *Bell Syst. Tech. J.* **28**, 435–89.
32. GUNN, J. B. (1958). *J. Electronics and Control*, **4**, 17–50.
33. RYDER, R. M., and KIRCHER, R. J. (1949). *Bell Syst. Tech. J.* **28**, 367–400.
34. MILLER, S. L. (1955). *Phys. Rev.* **99**, 1234–41.
35. SHOCKLEY, W., SPARKS, M., and TEAL, G. K. (1951). *Phys. Rev.* **83**, 151–62.
36. MUELLER, C. W., and HILIBRAND, J. (1958). *I.R.E. Trans. on Electron Devices*, **5**, 2–5 (1/58).
37. PHILIPS, J., and CHANG, H. C. (1958). Ibid. 13–18 (1/58).
38. MOLL, J. L., TANENBAUM, M., GOLDEY, J. M., and HOLONYAK, N. (1956). *Proc. I.R.E.* **44**, 1174–82.
39. SHOCKLEY, W., and GIBBONS, J. F. (1958). *Semiconductor Products*, **1**, 9–13.
40. MILLER, S. L., and EBERS, J. J. (1955). *Bell Syst. Tech. J.* **34**, 883–902.
41. MACKINTOSH, I. M. (1958). *Proc. I.R.E.* **46**, 1229–35.
42. ALDRICH, R. W., and HOLONYAK, N. (1958). Ibid. 1236–9.

43. BEALE, J. R. A., STEPHENSON, W. L., and WOLFENDALE, E. (1957). *Proc. I.E.E.* **104**B, 394–402.
44. LESK, I. A., and MATHIS, V. P. (1953). *I.R.E. Convention Record*, **1**, Part 6, 2–8.
45. CLARK, M. A. (1958). *Proc. I.R.E.* **46**, 1185–1204.
46. MAUPIN, J. T. (1957). *I.R.E. Trans. on Electron Devices*, **4**, 1–5.
47. MARSHALL, J. F. (1956). *Characteristics and Circuit Applications for a Tetrode Power Transistor*. 1956 Transistor Circuits Conference, Univ. of Pennsylvania, Feb. 1956. Minneapolis–Honeywell Publication, 79–9010.

CHAPTER IX

1. JOHNSON, L. B., and VERMES, P. (1957). *Mullard Tech. Comm.* **3**, 68–96.
2. —— (1958). Chapter 4 of *The Junction Transistor and its Applications* (edited by E. Wolfendale), Heywood, London.
3. GOTTLIEB, E., *et al.* (1959). (U.S.) *General Electric Transistor Manual* (4th ed.), Semiconductor Products Dept., General Electric Company, Liverpool, New York.
4. DEWITT, D., and ROSSOFF, A. L. (1957). *Transistor Electronics*, McGraw-Hill, N.Y.
5. DARLINGTON, S. (1953). U.S. Patent No. 2,663,806.
6. SHEA, R. F., *et al.* (1957). *Transistor Circuit Engineering*, Wiley, N.Y.
7. LIN, H. C., and BARCO, A. A. (1956). *Transistors*, I. 369–402. R.C.A. Laboratories, Princeton, N.J.
8. —— (1958). *Semiconductor Products*, **1**, No. 1, 21–24.
9. THARMA, P. (1957). *Mullard Tech. Comm.* **3**, No. 24, 106–9.

CHAPTER X

1. JOHNSON, J. B. (1928). *Phys. Rev.* **32**, 97–109.
2. NYQUIST, H. (1928). Ibid. 110–13.
3. VAN DER ZIEL, A. (1954). *Noise*, Prentice-Hall, New York.
4. VAN VLIET, K. M. (1958). *Proc. I.R.E.* **46**, 1004–19.
5. VAN DER ZIEL, A. (1958). Ibid. 1019–38.
6. FONGER, W. H. (1956). *Transistors*, I. 239–95, R.C.A. Laboratories, Princeton, N.J.
7. GUGGENBUEHL, W., and STRUTT, M. J. O. (1957). *Proc. I.R.E.* **45**, 839–57.
8. NIELSEN, E. G. (1957). Ibid. 957–63.
9. FRIIS, H. T. (1944). Ibid. **32**, 419–22, 729.
10. MONTGOMERY, H. C., and CLARK, M. A. (1953). *J. Appl. Phys.* **24**, 1337–8.

CHAPTER XI

1. TRENT, R. L. (1955). *I.R.E. Trans. on Audio*, AU–3, No. 5, 143–61.

2. DE SAUTELS, A. N. (1956). *A.I.E.E. Trans. Pt. I (Communications and Electronics)*, **75**, 17–25.

3. VALLESE, L. M. (1956). Ibid. 391–5.

4. VALLEY, G. E., and WALLMAN, H. (1948). *Vacuum Tube Amplifiers*, McGraw-Hill, New York.

CHAPTER XII

1. EDWARDS, O. J. (1957). *Mullard Tech. Comm.* **3**, No. 22, 59–61.
—— (1958). Ibid., No, 29, 258–64.

2. SIMMONS, C. D. (1958). *Semiconductor Products*, Jan./Feb. 1958, 31–33.

3. LIN, H. C. (1958). Ibid. 21–24.

4. THARMA, P. (1957). *Mullard Tech. Comm.* **3**, No. 24, 106–9.

5. STURLEY, K. R. (1945). *Radio Receiver Design*, vol. 2, p. 84, Chapman & Hall, London.

6. HILLBOURN, R. A., and JONES, D. D. (1955). *Proc. I.E.E.* **102**B, 763–74.

7. EDWARDS, O. J., and LIGHT, L. M. (1957). *Mullard Tech. Comm.* **3**, No. 26, 188–94.

8. THARMA, P. (1958). Ibid., No. 29, 265–77.

9. SZIKLAI, G. C. (1953). *Proc. I.R.E.* **41**, 717–24.

10. MILNES, A. G. (1957). *Proc. I.E.E.* **104**B, 565–80.

11. BENTON, B. M. (1956). *Electronics*, **29**, Sept. 1956, 153–5.

12. BERESKIN, A. B. (1957). *Proc. Nat. Electronics Conf.* **13**, 189–97.

13. FILIPPOV, A. G. (1957). *Radiotekhnika*, **12**, No. 8, 21–27 (English translation, Pergamon Press, London, **12**, No. 8, 24–33).

14. PETERSON, A., and SINCLAIR, D. B. (1952). *Proc. I.R.E.* **40**, 7–11.

15. CHAI YEH (1953). Ibid. **41**, 743–7.

16. LIGHT, L. M. (1957). *Mullard Tech. Comm.* **3**, No. 24, 98–101.

17. LOHMAN, R. D. (1953), *Electronics*, **26**, Sept. 1953, 140–3.

18. McKINLEY, D. W. R., and RICHARDS, R. S. (1957). *Electronics*, **30**, Aug. 1957, 161–3.

CHAPTER XIII

1. BODE, H. W. (1945). *Network Analysis and Feedback Amplifier Design*, Van Nostrand, New York.

2. THOMASON, J. G. (1955). *Linear Feedback Analysis*, Pergamon Press, London.

3. WILLIAMS, F. C. (1946). *Journal of I.E.E.* **93**, Part IIIA, 289–308.

4. STEWART, J. L. (1956). *Circuit Theory and Design*, 92–97, John Wiley & Sons, New York; Chapman & Hall, London.

5. NYQUIST, H. (1932). *Bell Syst. Tech. J.* **11**, 126–47.

6. KOENIG, L. A. (1959). *Electrical Engineering*, 653–8.

7. ALMOND, J., and BOOTHROYD, A. R. (1956). *Proc. I.E.E.* **103**B, 93–101.

8. WILLIAMS, F. C., RITSON, F. J., and KILBURN, T. (1946). *Journal of I.E.E.* **93**, Part IIIA, 1275–1300.
9. HEGGS, P. (1956). *Electronic Engineering*, **28**, 168–70 and 212–15.
10. BLECHER, F. H. (1955). *Proc. Nat. Electronics Conference*, **11**, 415–30.
—— (1956). *Bell Syst. Tech. J.* **35**, 295–332.
11. KONIGSBERG, R. L. (1959). *Advances in Electronics and Electron Physics*, Academic Press, New York and London, **11**, 225–83.
12. GOLDBERG, E. A. (1950). *R.C.A. Review*, **11**, 296–300.
13. CHAPLIN, G. B. B., and OWENS, A. R. (1958). *Proc. I.E.E.* **105B**, 258–66.
14. STAMPFL, R. A., and HANEL, R. A. (1955). *Proc. Nat. Electronics Conference*, **11**, 67–73.
15. MIDDLEBROOK, R. D., and MEAD, C. A. (1959). *Semiconductor Products*, **2**, 26–35.
16. EKISS, J. A. (1960). *J. Audio Eng. Soc.* **8**, No. 1, 18–22.
17. DAVIDSON, J. J. (1960). *Semiconductor Products*, **3**, 42–50.
18. SLAUGHTER, D. W. (1955). *Electronics*, **28**, May 1955, 174–5.
—— (1956). *I.R.E. Trans. on Circuit Theory*, CT–3, 51–53.
19. CHAPLIN, G. B. B., and OWENS, A. R. (1958). *Proc. I.E.E.* **105B**, 249–57.
20. KELLER, J. W. (1956). *Electronics*, **29**, Nov. 1956, 168–72.
21. SPENCER, R. H., and GRAY, T. S. (1956). *A.I.E.E. Trans. Pt. I (Communications and Electronics)*, **75**, 15–17.
22. MIDDLEBROOK, R. D. (1957). *Proc. I.R.E.* **45**, 1502–9.
23. BROWN, T. H., and STEPHENSON, W. L. (1957). *Electronic Engineering*, **29**, 425–8.
24. ASPINALL, D. (1957). Ibid. 450–4.
25. BALDRINGER, E., and CZALA, W. (1959). *Electronics*, **32**, No. 39, 70–73.
26. THIELE, A. N. (1956). *Electronic Engineering*, **28**, 31–36 and 80–82.
27. O'CONNOR, D. J. (1956). Ibid. 536–9.

CHAPTER XIV

1. VALLEY, G. E., and WALLMAN, H. (1948). *Vacuum Tube Amplifiers*, McGraw-Hill, New York.
2. —— (1955). *Mullard Ferroxcube*. Issued by the Components Division, Mullard Ltd., London.
3. STURLEY, K. R. (1943). *Radio Receiver Design*, vol. i, Chapman & Hall, London.
4. LORD RAYLEIGH (1894). *The Theory of Sound*, vol. i (2nd ed.), Dover, New York.
5. MORSE, P. M. (1948). *Vibration and Sound* (2nd ed.), McGraw-Hill, New York.

6. RAND, R. C., and OAKES, J. B. (1955). *Proc. Nat. Electronics Conference*, **11**, 52–66.
7. TERMAN, F. E. (1943). *Radio Engineers' Handbook*, McGraw-Hill, New York.
8. JANSSON, L. E. (1957). *Mullard Tech. Comm.* **3**, 174–87.
—— (1958). Chapter 5 of *The Junction Transistor and its Applications*, E. Wolfendale, editor, Heywood, London.
9. PENISTEN, G. E., and HALL, D. B. (1960). *Semi-Conductor Products*, **3**, No. 1, 20–24.
10. BOOTH, G. H. (1959). *A High Frequency Transistor Design Procedure*, Defence Research Board of Canada (Ottawa) D.R.T.E. Report No. 1016.
11. CHOW, W. P., and STERN, A. P. (1955). *Proc. I.R.E.* **43**, 1119–27.
12. HURTIG, C. R. (1955). *I.R.E. Transactions*, Professional Group on Circuit Theory, **CT-2**, 191–6.
13. ETTINGER, G. M. (1955). *Electronic Engineering*, **27**, 458–9.
14. JANSSON, L. E., RUMING, J. B., and TAPLEY, J. M. (1957). *Mullard Tech. Comm.* **3**, 198–208.

CHAPTER XV

1. BRUUN, G. (1956). *Proc. I.R.E.* **44**, 1561–72.
2. ANGELL, J. B., and KEIPER, F. P. (1953). Ibid. **41**, 1709–12.
3. HUNTER, L. P., *et al.* (1956). Section 12.2 of *Handbook of Semiconductor Electronics*, McGraw-Hill, New York.
4. SHEA, R. F., *et al.* (1957). Chapter 7 of *Transistor Circuit Engineering*, Wiley, New York; Chapman & Hall, London.
5. STEWART, J. L. (1956). *Circuit Theory and Design*, Wiley, New York.
6. COOKE-YARBOROUGH, E. H. (1957). *An Introduction to Transistor Circuits*, Oliver & Boyd, Edinburgh.

CHAPTER XVI

1. MATZEN, W. T., and BIARD, J. R. (1959). *Electronics*, **32**, No. 3, 60–62.
2. BUCKERFIELD, P. S. T. (1952). *Proc. I.E.E.* **99**, Part 2, 497–506.
3. BLECHER, F. H. (1956). *Bell Syst. Tech. J.* **35**, 295–332.
4. BURTON, P. L. (1957). *Electronic Eng.* **29**, 393–7.
CHAPLIN, G. B. B., and OWENS, A. R. (1958). *Proc. I.E.E.* **105B**, 249–57, 258–66.
5. BRIGHT, R. L. (1955). *Trans. A.I.E.E.* **74**, Part 1 (Communications and Electronics), 111–21.
KRUPER, A. P. (1955). Ibid. 141–4.
6. WILLIAMS, A. J., EYNON, J. U., and POLSTER, N. E. (1957). *Proc. Nat. Electronics Conference*, **13**, 40–54.

7. GOTTLIEB, E., *et al.* (1959). (U.S.) *General Electric Transistor Manual* (4th ed.), Semiconductor Products Dept., General Electric Company, Liverpool, N.Y.

8. BAKER, R. H. (1956). *M.I.T. Lincoln Lab. Tech. Rep.*, No. 110.

9. HENLE, R. A., and WALSH, J. L. (1958). *Proc. I.R.E.* **46**, 1240–54.

10. SURAN, J. J., and RIEBERT, F. A. (1958). *I.R.E. Trans. on Circuit Theory*, CT–3, No. 1, 26–38.

11. SHEA, R. F., *et al.* (1957). *Transistor Circuit Engineering*, Wiley, New York.

12. NEETESON, P. A. (1959). *Junction Transistors in Pulse Circuits*, Cleaver-Hume, London.

13. PEDERSON, D. O. (1955). *I.R.E. Trans. on Circuit Theory*, CT–3, No. 1, 26–38.

14. LINVILL, J. G. (1955). *Proc. I.R.E.* **43**, 826–34.

15. WILLIAMS, F. C. (1946). *Journal of I.E.E.* **93**, Part IIIA, 289–308.

16. HAMILTON, D. J. (1958). *I.R.E. Trans. on Circuit Theory*, CT–5, No. 1, 69–73.

17. LINVILL, J. G., and MATTSON, R. H. (1955). *Proc. I.R.E.* **43**, 1632–9.

18. NARUD, J. A., and AARON, M. R. (1959). *Bell Syst. Tech. J.* **38**, 785–852.

19. LIGHT, L. H. (1956). *Mullard Tech. Comm.* **2**, No. 17, 157–204.

—— (1958). Chapter 10 of *The Junction Transistor and its Applications*, edited by E. Wolfendale, Heywood, London.

20. —— and HOOKER, P. M. (1955). *Proc. I.E.E.* **102**B, 775–86.

21. —— (1955). *Wireless World*, **61**, No. 12, 582–6.

CHAPTER XVII

1. BRAINERD, J. G., KOEHLER, G., REICH, H. J., and WOODRUFF, L. F. (1942). *Ultra High Frequency Techniques*, Van Nostrand, New York.

2. CLAPP, J. K. (1943). *Proc. I.R.E.* **36**, 356–8.

3. GOURIET, G. G. (1950). *Wireless Engineer*, **27**, No. 319, 105–12.

4. CADY, W. G. (1946). *Piezoelectricity*, McGraw-Hill, New York.

5. WITT, S. N. (1955). *Proc. Nat. Electronics Conference*, **11**, 431–40.

6. ROACH, W. E. (1960). *Electronics*, **33**, No. 2, 52–55.

7. NAMBIAR, K. P. P., and BOOTHROYD, A. R. (1957). *Proc. I.E.E.* **104**B, 293–306.

8. —— (1958). *Electronic Engineering*, **30**, 61–65.

9. MORGAN, L. P., and STEPHENSON, W. L. (1958). Chapter 9 of *The Junction Transistor and its Applications*, edited by E. Wolfendale, Heywood, London.

10. RIORDON, J. S. (1959). *Trans. Eng. Inst. of Canada*, **3**, No. 4, 113–18.

CHAPTER XVIII

1. TERMAN, F. E. (1955). *Electronic and Radio Engineering* (4th ed.), McGraw-Hill, New York.
2. STURLEY, K. R. (1943). *Radio Receiver Design* (2 vols.), Chapman & Hall, London.
3. WOOD, P. W. (1959). *Electronics*, **32**, No. 5, 64.
4. THEURER, H. C., KLEIMACK, J. J., LOARD, H. H., and CHRISTENSEN, H. (1960). *Proc. I.R.E.* **48**, 1642–3.
5. DE WOLF, N. (1960). *Electronic Industries*, **19**, No. 8, 84–87.

INDEX

PRINTED IN GREAT BRITAIN
AT THE UNIVERSITY PRESS, OXFORD
BY VIVIAN RIDLER
PRINTER TO THE UNIVERSITY